MENTAL HYGIENE

THE PSYCHOLOGY OF PERSONAL ADJUSTMENT

D. B. KLEIN
PROFESSOR OF PSYCHOLOGY, THE UNIVERSITY OF TEXAS

NEW YORK
HENRY HOLT AND COMPANY

TO

A MARYLAND MOTHER
AND HER TEXAS TRIO

Preface . . .

IN WRITING THIS GENERAL INTRODUCTION TO THE FIELD OF MENTAL hygiene I found that exhaustive and detailed treatment of the subject could not be undertaken if the book was to be kept within reasonable limits. The problem of selection was thus inescapable. My reasons for including some topics and omitting others will become evident from a reading of the book. I might say here that the relative emphasis given to a few of the themes introduced into the discussion is to be construed as a reflection of more than fifteen years of effort devoted to helping troubled people learn to cope with their difficulties. This is another way of stating that clinical experience as well as routine delving into the relevant literature served to influence the selection and rejection of many items.

Although a major objective of the present survey of the mental hygiene movement is to orient the student of psychiatry or clinical psychology who is just embarking on his professional studies, the needs and interests of the non-professional, but intellectually eager, general reader are given equal consideration. As a result almost no technical term is taken for granted. Even the elementary ones are explained or elaborated by means of simple and usually concrete examples. Furthermore, a glossary of the technical vocabulary has been appended to the text in order to facilitate its understanding by an educated person with no previous training in any of the fields of academic psychology or in the fundamentals of psychiatry.

The devotee of a particular specialty is apt to have a distorted perspective regarding the relative importance and success of his specialty. To guard against this all too human tendency I have made a deliberate attempt to appraise the success of the mental hygiene movement in terms of the ordinary canons of scientific procedure. I have tried to substitute the critical attitude of the conscientious laboratory worker for the zeal of the evangelist or promoter. My one hope is that in my endeavor to be loyal to the

gods of scientific method I have not erred on the side of underestimating the actual successes of mental hygiene specialists.

An examination of the Table of Contents will show that I have
divided the total field of mental hygiene into two broad spheres of
activity: (1) mental disease and its prevention, discussed in Parts
II and III of the book, and (2) the promotion of mental health, the
chief concern of Part IV. Justification for this division is to be
found in the first chapter (Part I). After familiarizing himself with
the latter chapter the reader can either proceed with the remaining
fifteen chapters in the order of presentation or else he may take up
Part IV and then go back to Parts II and III. These two middle
Parts are likely to prove difficult for uninitiated readers because
they deal with rather technical aspects of medical psychology;
hence it might be preferable for them to read the book in this
order: Parts I, IV, II, and III. The book has been so written that
there will be a minimum of overlap in case one prefers to deviate
from the given sequence in the manner suggested. To render this
possible it was necessary to treat a few of the concepts mentioned
in Part IV as if they had not already been discussed in the earlier
parts. Such minor duplication was deemed preferable, even at the
risk of slight repetition, to the interpolation of back references.

I might add that the order of Parts as arranged in the text makes
for a more systematic organization of the field of mental hygiene
and, in my opinion, is the order to be followed by the serious student whose eventual goal is professional orientation in the field.
The reader who is primarily interested in mental hygiene as a possible source of help in connection with personal problems of a non-
pathological sort will find Part IV more helpful than the other
Parts. In fact, if lack of time prevents one from reading the entire
book, I believe it would be more profitable to concentrate on the
portion dealing with the promotion of mental health (Part IV) and
to omit or slur over the sections devoted to mental diseases (Parts
II and III).

For the benefit of the professional reader I might explain that
the nomenclature used in describing mental diseases is that of the
"Official Classification of Mental Disorders, as Revised and
Adopted by the Committee on Statistics and Approved by the
American Psychiatric Association at its 1934 Annual Meeting."
Although the precise suitability of some of the terminology is to be

questioned, I have refrained from introducing changes in this "Official Classification" and have not encumbered the discussion with debates about such matters. My chief purpose was to give the student an elementary, working notion of the nature of each of the disorders listed and then to supply him with the present status of knowledge regarding their prevention. Because of this primary concern with problems of prophylaxis, very little space could be devoted to questions of therapy. In other words, I tried to restrict myself to the confines of mental hygiene territory without wandering too far afield.

For the privilege of availing myself of excerpts quoted from their publications I am gratefully indebted to the following publishers and organizations: American Psychological Association, Inc., The Commonwealth Fund, Farrar & Rinehart, Harper & Brothers, Henry Holt and Company, The Macmillan Company, The National Committee for Mental Hygiene, The New York Academy of Medicine, W. W. Norton & Company, Inc., Pan American Airways System, Princeton University Press, Charles Scribner's Sons, Charles C. Thomas, Publisher, The University of Chicago Press, D. Van Nostrand Company, Inc., John Wiley & Sons, Inc., and The Williams & Wilkins Company.

In addition, I wish to thank my friend, Dr. T. H. Howells, for his kindness in permitting me to quote from one of his publications. A large portion of Chapter II appeared originally under the title of "The Psychology of Conscience" in the *International Journal of Ethics*, 1930, Volume XL. Both the editor of the latter journal as well as the publisher, The University of Chicago Press, have been kind enough to permit me to reprint the larger part of this article.

In preparing the manuscript I received generous and appreciated assistance in the typing of many of the early chapters from Lt. Jerry H. Clark. I am also grateful to my daughter, Mrs. Henry E. Jameson, and to Miss Jary Geyer for their cooperation in the unwelcome task of reading proof.

D. B. K.

Austin, Texas
January, 1944

Contents...

CHAPTER 16

EDUCATING FOR MENTAL HYGIENE

PART ONE

GENERAL INTRODUCTION

1... THE NATURE AND SCOPE OF MENTAL HYGIENE

ENTAL HYGIENE IS A BROAD FIELD WITH ILL-DEFINED CONTOURS.
As its name suggests, it is concerned with the realization and
maintenance of the mind's health and efficiency. The factors militating against mental health are varied and often complex. They include not only those producing disease of the brain tissues, but also
those which warp the developing personality. They include not only
head wounds and bacteria and poor heredity, but also a nagging
mother, a dictatorial father, acute poverty, pangs of conscience, social disgrace, persistent jealousy, religious conflicts, lover's quarrels, and the businessman's worries. Mental hygiene is thus not exclusively a purely medical subject. It goes beyond the confines of
the laboratory and invades the precincts of the home, the school,
the church, the court, the factory, and any other institution which
influences human conduct.

PRELIMINARY ORIENTATION

Many fields of study are thus bound up with the field of mental
hygiene. Psychiatry, neurology, genetics, economics, ethics, religion, psychology, sociology, anthropology, and several others contribute to the total background necessary for adequate appreciation
of the ramifications of mental hygiene. It is really a composite of
many fields just as general medicine is a composite of anatomy,
physics, bacteriology, and other separate subjects.

The very complexity of the field renders it necessary to study
mental hygiene from different points of view. Each shift in point of
view will change one's perspective and result in a different impression of the field. Thus one may adopt the outlook of the professional
sociologist and consider the influence of slums, idleness, lack of recreational facilities, and poorly organized family life on the mental
efficiency of populations subjected to such living conditions. On the
other hand one may pursue the subject from the point of view of the
psychologist interested in the mental efficiency of the individual. It

is not at all unusual for a discouraged child to be brought to a school psychologist who finds that the youngster's discouragement is bound up with impending failure in Latin. To cite another example: a college boy may be a victim of acute feelings of inferiority because of a blemished complexion or because he has failed to receive a bid from a given fraternity. It would be easy to multiply such examples; but there is no need to do so at this point. For the time being it suffices to point out that a revealing way to be introduced to the subject of mental hygiene is to take the everyday troubles of everyday people as a convenient point of departure.

Mental hygiene endeavors to aid people to ward off trouble as well as to furnish ways of handling trouble in intelligent fashion when it cannot be warded off. What people call their " troubles " can be classified into a series of such conventional categories as illness, religion, finances, sex, social position, economic security, safety from accident, old age, fire, and inadequate shelter. The range and variety of these categories are further evidence of the fact already mentioned to the effect that many separate fields converge to contribute to mental hygiene.

Although it is desirable to keep this wide horizon of the sweep of mental hygiene factors before us, it is also desirable to bear in mind that the locus of any specific mental hygiene problem is always a given individual or family living in a given locality under given cultural conditions. Trouble or distress never takes place in the abstract. It is always a troubled or distressed individual with whom the mental hygienist has to deal. It is always a particular mother who is worried about the delinquency of a particular child. Thoughts of suicide occur to very-much alive but depressed or frantic or pain-racked individuals. Impulses of revenge well up within the breasts of specific people for whom to be jilted means to be consumed by jealousy. As a consequence, the mental hygienist cannot rest content with a mere discussion of delinquency, or suicide or jealousy as isolated and detached phenomena. No matter how abstruse his reflections on such phenomena chance to become, he must, if his reflections are to have vital significance, return to the flesh-and-blood victims of such phenomena and apply the fruits of his reflections to their individual problems in their individual uniqueness.

Despite its broad perspectives and diverse ramifications, the focus of mental hygiene thinking is consequently the troubled individual. Because of this fact, there is an inevitably close relationship between the field of mental hygiene and the field of psychology, particularly that branch of psychology which devotes itself to the systematic study of personality. A moment's thought will show that what people call a morbid personality is one which might be presumed to reveal violation of sound principles of mental hygiene; contrariwise, what people call a wholesome personality ought to be revelatory of the successful functioning of such principles.

Terms like morbid and wholesome are synonyms for sick and healthy, respectively. The meaning of the preceding sentence would be practically unchanged if the reference had been to sick and healthy personalities. What the sentence implied is that a given personality is sick because of failure to observe mental hygiene principles and that another personality is healthy because of loyalty to such principles. It ought to follow then that a good way to learn the nature of such principles is to study clear-cut cases of morbid and wholesome personalities, just as a good way to learn the nature of principles of ordinary hygiene is to study cases of people who are very sick and some who are very well. The use of the word *very* suggests that there are degrees of sickness and of health. Even in ordinary speech we talk of being " pretty well " or " fairly well " or " wonderfully well." On the other hand we sometimes talk as if there were no variations in the concept of health. This is exemplified by the common question: " Is he sick *or* well? " Such a formulation indicates a sharp line of demarcation between the concepts of sickness and health. As employed this way, the concepts are mutually exclusive. They leave no room for the possibility of being well in some respects and sick in other respects. There is evidently some ambiguity involved in the meaning of words like healthy, wholesome, sick, diseased, and morbid. Before much headway can be achieved in the task of understanding the field of mental hygiene, it will be advisable to clear up this ambiguity.

DIFFERENTIATING MENTAL HEALTH FROM MENTAL DISEASE

Raising questions about the meaning of ordinary words strikes many people as an irritating, school-teacherish proceeding. In the present context they are apt to say: " This entire question is just stupid pedantry. Everybody knows that to be healthy means to be well, to be normal." Unfortunately, the term *normal* is just as ambiguous as the word wholesome. It may mean " not abnormal " or it may mean " average " or it may mean " conforming to an ideal standard." Is it " normal " to wear glasses? Is it " normal " to have corns or occasional headaches? Is it " normal " for an adult to have a *perfect* set of teeth — no discoloration, no cavities, no malocclusion and not even the vestige of a defect? Here there is a clear instance of the ambiguity under discussion; for the question can be answered correctly by yes or no depending on the interpretation of the key word " normal." In the sense of an *ideal* dental standard it would be " normal " to possess a perfect set of teeth, but in the sense of the kind of teeth the *average* adult possesses a perfect set would not be " normal." There are thus at least two divergent meanings of the word *normal:* that of the statistical and that of the ideal standard. The former refers to that which is characteristic of the average and near-average, while the latter refers to some standard of perfection.

The norm for physical health in terms of the ideal is a bodily system altogether devoid of any blemish or defect. The norm in the statistical sense would allow for a large number of deviations from the ideal standard. As a matter of fact it is very difficult if not impossible to find a single person whose body would conform to such an ideal standard of physical perfection. It is more of an imaginary model than an experienced reality. It represents a goal to be approached rather than attained. In this respect it is like the concept of a mathematical limit, which is also an imaginary point to be approximated by increasing degrees of success but with final success indefinitely postponed.

The foregoing considerations may now be applied to the immediate problem of deciding the meaning of the phrase a healthy or wholesome personality. It ought to be obvious that the decision will vary depending on whether the statistical or the ideal meaning is to be elaborated. In terms of the statistical meaning one might readily classify a personality as normal or wholesome even though there were a record of minor fears, some tendency to be envious of wealthier people, occasional outburst of temper, a habit of smoking cigarettes rather furiously when nervous, and rather infrequent periods of mild discouragement. However, in terms of the ideal standard of normality such a personality would have to be classified as unwholesome; for depression, nervousness, envy, loss of emotional control, timidity, nail-biting, all constitute departures from such an ideal.

To clarify the statistical approach to the concept of the normal psychologists often have recourse to a graphic method of demonstration. They point out that measurable characteristics can be arranged in the form of a curve to bring out the relative frequency of particular measures. Such a curve for variations in the height of a large number of men would have the following form:

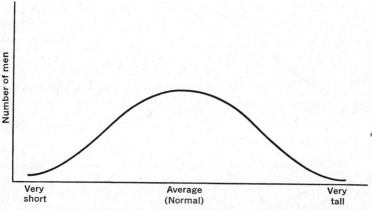

FIG. 1. Normal Distribution Curve for Height.

Examination of this curve shows that the majority of the measures cluster around the average. It also shows that midgets are as infrequent as giants. Furthermore, it demonstrates that there is no sharp line of separation between adjacent heights. The total population merges very gradually by smooth transitions from one extreme to the other. In technical language the measures are said to be *continuous*. This type of curve, called a *normal distribution curve,* is sometimes regarded as typical of the way in which phenomena are distributed in a state of nature. Support for this opinion is furnished by the fact that many measurements of natural objects conform to a curve of this general shape. For example, if 10,000 potatoes were weighed individually and the measures plotted in systematic fashion, the resulting curve would be like the one under discussion. A similar result would be secured by measuring the widths of 10,000 oak leaves or the intelligence quotients of 10,000 school children. In all these cases one is presumably dealing with a *continuum* of variation. To say where the normal ends and the abnormal begins would consequently require a rather arbitrary verdict. As a matter of fact this statistical usage implies two fields of abnormality, one at either end of the distribution curve. As applied to the concept of stature both the dwarf and the giant are abnormal. Only those around the man of average stature may be deemed to be of normal height. These relationships are illustrated in Figure 2.

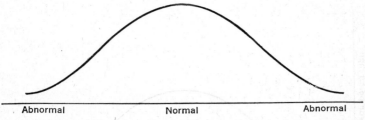

Abnormal   Normal   Abnormal

Fig. 2. Showing the Statistical Approach to the Concept of Abnormality as a Quantitative Deviation from the Normal or Average.

One consequence of this emphasis on the continuous character of many measurable objects and events is that it has aroused doubt of the validity of many popular types of judgment. We classify people as tall *or* short, bright *or* stupid, healthy *or* diseased, fat *or* lean, good *or* bad, religious *or* irreligious, attractive *or* repulsive, and loyal *or* traitorous. Each such mutually exclusive classification, involving sharply sundered opposites, is known as a *dichotomy*. The normal distribution curve represents one way of thinking about differences existing among people. Thinking in terms of dichotomous categories represents another way. The latter way assumes that the differences are *discontinuous,* so that each separate case can be neatly pigeonholed in a given category. However, if differences merge into one another by smooth, imperceptible gradations, as symbolized by normal distribution curves, then such pigeonholing is arbitrary, unwarranted, and contrary to fact. This is particularly true of transitional cases and not so true of extreme cases.

One might be justified in pigeonholing a man of six feet as tall and one of five feet as short, but shall the man of five feet and five inches be described as a " tall-small " man or as a " small-tall " man? To facilitate consideration of this question it might be well to assume that the figures apply to some tribe of Africans whose heights are so distributed that the tallest man of the tribe is a six-footer, the smallest man a four-footer and those of " medium " height exactly five feet tall — or short, as the case may be. This very uncertainty of description demonstrates the difficulty involved in trying to apply a dichotomous concept to a continuous variable. The transitional case, in this hypothetical example the five-footer, may be called either five feet tall or five feet short, depending on which end of the curve or which extreme of the dichotomy is taken as the reference point. As a consequence, contradictory descriptions or classifications may come to be applied to a particular case. Of course in daily usage we endeavor to circumvent the contradiction by adding a third category variously labelled the average or the normal; but this merely serves to reduce the range of contradiction and does not eliminate it. To understand this fact, one has merely to venture to pigeonhole another specific case such as a man whose position on the distribution curve is midway between the average and the " tall " end of the curve. It ought to be obvious that where continuous variables are involved, greater accuracy of description is achieved by describing the individual case as a point on the curve rather than as a representative of a given category. This is the reason that psychologists so frequently have recourse to the distribution curve in their descriptions of individual differences.

So many measures conform to a normal distribution curve that some students, upon being introduced to the existence of the curve, hastily conclude that *all* the facts of human nature of necessity conform to such a curve. They neglect to note that the curve is not applicable to facts which are *discontinuous* in distribution. Variations in the weight of the human eyeball would conform to the curve, but variations in number of eyes would not. Although this example is somewhat fantastic, it demonstrates the kind of issue such students overlook. People may legitimately be described as one-eyed or two-eyed. There may even be a few people who have had both eyeballs removed. There are many more who have lost one eye, but the vast majority of people have two eyes. Since fractional eyes do not exist, it would be impossible to find cases of people having one and three-fifths eyes. Differences here are discontinuous and not continuous. All the people in the country could be classified by means of a three-compartment scheme: one very small one to pigeonhole the rare cases of people without eyes, a larger one for the one-eyed people, and a very large one for the two-eyed people. There would be no problem of transitional cases and no need for a pigeonhole labelled " miscellaneous." In fact, the chances are that one could get along very satisfactorily with a two-compartment scheme involving the dichotomy of one-eyed *or* two-eyed. Under these circumstances thinking in terms of a dichotomy would be entirely relevant and valid, while thinking in terms of a normal distribution curve would be irrelevant and invalid.

After this detour into the field of the logic of statistics, the journey through the field of mental hygiene may be resumed. An immediate problem is that of deciding whether the facts of mental hygiene are to be handled in terms of a scheme which regards the difference between the normal and abnormal just a matter of degree, or whether the scheme should allow for the possible existence of lines of cleavage between the normal and abnormal, the shift being discontinuous and qualitative rather than continuous and quantitative. As has already been suggested, the popular view is to dispose of the problem by means of a normal-abnormal dichotomy as contrasted with what many psychologists regard as the more " scientific " distribution curve approach. For these psychologists the abnormal is just an extreme form of the normal. There is no difference in kind; there is only a difference in amount, like the difference between a small and large loaf of bread. According to this conception the abnormal is merely an exaggeration or quantitative distortion of the normal. This implies that facts learned by studying abnormal cases are applicable to normal ones and, contrariwise, the facts of normal psychology are applicable to abnormal cases provided due allowance is made for the variations in quantity.

Stated more concretely, this view conceives of the fear-obsessed personality as one in which the " normal " attitudes of caution or mild panic of an occasional sort have been stepped up in intensity and frequency. The frantically jealous personality is thus thought of as an enlarged version of the modest amount of jealousy attributable to the average person under appropriate conditions of provocation. Even the existence of hallucinations may be brought into line with this approach; for at the time it occurs an ordinary dream is experienced as a reality by the dreamer. Furthermore, even during waking states ordinary people sometimes mistakenly believe they heard the telephone bell ring or that the stranger in the crowd ahead is an old friend. Both illusions and hallucinations may thus take place within normal portions of the curve. Furthermore, under certain circumstances even delusions may be discovered as " normal " phenomena. This is illustrated by the not uncommon cases of errors of belief regarding prejudice. Children sometimes are convinced that a given teacher has a grudge against them only to discover eventually that they were altogether mistaken in the conviction. Adults are by no means immune from such delusional beliefs about others. Although these are not " insane " delusions, they are, so the advocates of the quantitative approach would say, the psychological stuff out of which the insane ones are manufactured. In general, they would contend, there is no abnormal phenomenon which is not explicable as a quantitative outgrowth of a normal phenomenon. Such a contention is also reflected in everyday beliefs that " everybody is a little crazy " or that " we all have our abnormal moments " or " nobody is perfectly sane all of the time."

There can be no question regarding the usefulness of the distribution curve as a convenient instrument with which to symbolize the quantitative relationships between many normal and abnormal events. But whether it can be used to symbolize *all* such relationships is another question. It may be that the view which conceives of this relationship in terms of a dichotomy may also have facts in its favor. To appreciate this possibility it might be well to indulge in another intellectual detour and ask whether the facts of physical health and bodily disease can be subsumed in the graphic symbol of a distribution curve. With respect to such measurable indices of health as pulse rate, temperature, and respiration, it is easy to apply such a concept. If the point of normal temperature be selected as the center, then subnormal temperatures may be plotted on the left and degrees of fever on the right. In analogous fashion excessive and diminished rates of heart ac-

tion or breathing may be plotted, with their respective normal
rates taken as convenient central reference points. From this point
of view it might seem quite in order to conceive of disease symptoms as merely quantitative fluctuations from a normal condition.
There ought to be no genuine and decisive dichotomy between the
sick and the well. Still, this hardly is a tenable position. There is
no gradual transition between no malaria and malaria or between
no tumor of the brain and such a tumor. This is not to deny that
once a disease process is established there are quantitative variations in the severity of symptoms to be observed: all pneumonia
patients are sick, but some are sicker than others. What is more,
if suitable means of measuring the extent and acuteness of each
case were available, the relative positions of 1000 pneumonia cases
with respect to the concept of *degree* of illness could doubtless be
ordered in the form of a frequency distribution. However, such a
distribution would not have its terminal points established by the
opposition between very healthy lungs at one extreme and very
diseased ones at the other. The opposition would be between the
very slightly diseased and the almost dead. Stated differently, we
have to ask whether the facts of respiratory efficiency are to be
disposed of by means of a single or a double distribution curve.
Would the curve representing the entire gamut of possible cases
be unimodal like the familiar normal distribution curve or would
it be bimodal? These theoretic possibilities are presented in the
following diagram:

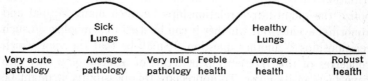

FIG. 3. Showing Hypothetical Bimodal Distribution to Illustrate the Dichotomy between Sick and Healthy Lungs.

It is quite evident that the bimodal curve represents the juxta-
positon of two normal distribution curves. In the present instance
it symbolizes the state of affairs which would prevail if the hypothesis of a dichotomy between healthy and diseased lungs were
a reality. A dichotomy of this kind implies not only quantitative
differences, but also qualitative ones. With respect to quality it

maintains that lungs can be divided into the sick and healthy or the pathological and the " normal " or non-pathological. In addition it maintains that quantitative variations can be established within these two categories. Thus it would be possible to apply the distribution curve idea to the non-pathological group by noting that a few are superb, unusually well-developed lungs, a few rather puny, poorly developed but still healthy lungs with intermediate gradations falling between these extremes. An analogous distribution would apply to the pathological group.

Support for this analysis is furnished by the work of Landis [1] and his associates in their study of the general adjustment of two groups of women, one normal and the other abnormal. Their 295 subjects were evaluated by trained judges in terms of " an evaluation scale ranging from extremely good adjustment to extremely poor adjustment." The findings revealed " a distribution that was definitely bimodal, normal individuals clustering at one end of the scale and the abnormal individuals at the other end, with a small number of cases from each group in the middle."

Additional evidence in favor of this analysis is to be found in the work of psychologists engaged in studying abnormal behavior in animals. Maier,[2] for example, has stated explicitly that his well-known experimentally induced abnormalities in the rat are to be regarded as " qualitative " deviations from " the normal pattern of activity " and that " normal and abnormal behavior *do not form a continuum* such as is suggested by the normal distribution curve."

There is consequently a genuine possibility of successfully contending that the facts of mental health belong in one category and those of mental disease in another and that the quantitative gradations of the normal curve apply to each of these categories separately. This contention presupposes a dichotomy between health and pathology and argues for a bimodal distribution if the extremes of the dichotomy were made the end-points of a curve. This is not the fashionable contention among psychiatrists and specialists in abnormal psychology. The conventional view suggests a unimodal distribution; but the view may be so constricted

[1] Landis, C., and Co-authors, *Sex in Development*, New York, Paul B. Hoeber, Inc., 1940, pp. 82–83.
[2] Maier, N. R. F., *Studies of Abnormal Behavior in the Rat*, New York, Harper & Brothers, 1939, pp. 58–59. (Italics not in the original.)

as to be blind to contrary considerations. Although we have already alluded to a few of these considerations, it might be well to make them more explicit by availing ourselves of Gordon Allport's [3] trenchant formulation:

Is the normal personality simply an undistinguished edition of the mentally diseased? We do not hold this view in reference to *organic* conditions. There is no continuum of states from cancer to no-cancer. The patient either has a malignant growth or else he hasn't; there are no intermediate conditions. Similarly a diseased mind is in many respects functionally quite different from (and not merely an exaggeration of) the normal mind.

The belief in the perfect continuity of the normal and the abnormal . . . has resulted in the rapid multiplication of studies of disordered people, partly because, confined as they are to institutions, they are easily accessible, and partly because the extreme nature of their disorders makes them more interesting and more spectacular. Actually the number of studies of neurotic and psychotic personalities far exceeds the number devoted to normal personality, although, of course, the ratio in the world at large is precisely the opposite. The uncritical carrying over of the point of view of the mental hospital into the world outside has made . . . for serious one-sidedness in the psychological study of *normal* personality. This charge is justified, even though occasionally the discoveries of psychopathology may be of indirect aid to the psychology of normality.

PROPHYLACTIC *versus* MELIORATIVE MENTAL HYGIENE

In the light of the preceding analysis it is convenient to block out two broad spheres of mental hygiene usefulness. These spheres, although related and interpenetrating in many respects, may be called the *psychopathic* and the *normal,* respectively. Despite their mutual interrelationships they ought to be considered as, in the main, separate and distinct. In other words, with all due respect to the fetish of the normal distribution curve, it is our belief that both a quantitative and a qualitative dichotomy between the wholesome and the pathological is justified. If this belief is sound, then the kind of mental hygiene to be prescribed for psychopathic personalities might conceivably be very different from the kind to be placed at the disposal of ordinary, non-psychopathic personalities.

[3] Allport, G. W., *Personality,* New York, Henry Holt & Company, 1937, p. 76.

To render this bifurcation of spheres of influence understandable, it will be necessary to enlarge on the common meaning of the term *hygiene.*

Any act or measure which prevents illness or promotes well-being may be classified as hygienic. In the field of medicine methods introduced for the purpose of warding off disease are called *prophylactic.* Bacteriologists have furnished a number of such prophylactic techniques which the physician employs whenever he endeavors to *prevent* diphtheria, typhoid fever, or lockjaw from developing. To the extent that he urges his patients to include particular vitamin-containing foods in their diets in order to prevent such diseases as pellagra or scurvy or rickets, he may be said to be practicing prophylactic or preventive medicine. He may also recommend regular daily sessions of physical exercise, plenty of sleep, fresh air and exposure to sunshine for the purpose of building up the body's " resistance " to disease. In terms of this purpose such recommendations may also be classified as prophylactic ; but this is not their sole purpose. The critical physician realizes that apart from increasing " resistance " to disease his recommendations are calculated to make the strong, healthy body still stronger and healthier : to make it a more efficient biological instrument. To promote bodily well-being is just as much sound hygiene as to prevent disease. One is the positive and the other the negative aspect of the medical recommendations. They are akin to a football coach's double set of recommendations to his team : those having to do with playing an offensive game and those pertaining to a defensive game. The latter are analogous to the prophylactic aspect of hygiene while the former are analogous to what may be called the *meliorative* aspect of hygiene. (To meliorate means to improve, to grow or make better.)

The prophylactic side of hygiene is oriented toward the prevention of disease, breakdown, weakness, disaster, death. It stresses the pathological. The meliorative side of hygiene is oriented toward the acquisition of buoyant health, more energy, and abundant life. It stresses the normal and the ideal as opposed to the abnormal and the pathological. Prophylactic hygiene is associated with hypodermic syringes, antitoxins, disinfectants, sanitary engineers, isolation wards and quarantine regulations. Meliorative hygiene is associated with golf links, baseball diamonds, football gridirons, tennis courts, summer vacations, recreations, hobbies, camping trips, keen appetites and the joy of living.

In the realm of mental hygiene a parallel division of purposes to be accomplished may now be outlined. What might be designated as prophylactic mental hygiene is intended to prevent the development of mental disease or the loss of mental efficiency. Its orientation is psychopathic in that it is concerned with warding off insanity and other mental disturbances. In theory at least this aspect of the subject is concerned with enlightening the public regarding the causes of mental breakdown so that appropriate prophylactic measures may be instituted. Meliorative mental hygiene, on the other hand, is concerned less with actual disease and more with improving mental efficiency, learning how to cope with mental difficulties, injecting more zest in one's daily living, teaching people how to get along with one another and with their work. It is definitely non-psychopathic in its orientation and emphasis. Its task is that of working out techniques of better living for all of us and not merely those who are potentially threatened by the specter of mental disease. This phase of mental hygiene is consequently interested in such varied questions as: the relationship of discipline to a child's life at home, in the school, and on the playground; the influence of religious beliefs in meeting bereavement; the effect of monotony and bleak routine on housewife or factory worker; friction between parents and its effect on the distressed children; the relationship between ethical ideals and moral or immoral urges; the place of such emotionalized attitudes as jealousy, envy, and bitter competition in a well-ordered mental household.

We thus have a tremendously wide field of legitimate mental hygiene issues. It ought to be obvious, accordingly, that mental hygiene is by no means restricted to the job of safeguarding people from actual mental disease. Its more positive task is that of the meliorative branch of the subject: to render the worried serene, the efficient more efficient, and the good better. The scope of this branch goes beyond the individual and includes the family, the factory, the farm, the school, the church, welfare organizations, the judiciary, the police, and all who contribute to the life of the modern community; for modern man cannot live by himself alone. His life is too bound up with the society of which he is a member.

THE GOAL OF MELIORATIVE MENTAL HYGIENE

Traditionally, the goal of mental hygiene used to be disposed of by the ancient Latin aphorism: a sound mind in a sound body. More recent insight into the complexities of this goal has brought about a change in this maxim so that in its modern form it reads: a sound mind in a sound body in a sound society. Although this maxim constitutes a dramatic slogan, its figurative language ought to be emphasized. It is positively misleading if it causes one to think of mental hygiene as having to do with three independent *entities* labelled mind, body, and society. It is more accurate to regard these terms as referring to varying aspects of a complex array of dynamic processes each one of which involves and implies the other just as a catcher in baseball implies a pitcher. It is foolish to think of society as existing independently of individual people and of an individual's mind as existing in detached grandeur from his body. Such independent existence is attainable only by an act of abstraction like thinking of a laugh as separated from the laugher. In reality, as we all know, without moving muscles there can be no laughter. Furthermore, under ordinary circumstances there is no laughter without something to laugh *at*. Here too, in other words, three aspects of a dynamic process can be distinguished *conceptually* despite the fact that the process is basically a unitary affair. As a consequence, for purposes of analysis one may consider humor as if it were made of a combination of a funny external situation, appreciation of the joke, and the physiological process we call laughing. Analysis of this kind is necessary and useful in the interests of scientific understanding of the subject, but fraught with intellectual danger if the products of analysis are then regarded as possessing an independent existence of their own. This danger can be avoided, or at least minimized, if we keep reminding ourselves that the analysis was applied to an active, dynamic interaction and not to a static object. Terms like mind, body, and society refer to such an interaction or to such a functional relationship. They no more refer to static objects than the idea of laughing at a genuinely funny joke involves static objects in the way of the action described in the joke, appreciation of the ludicrousness of this action, and the consequent facial distortion. In both situations analysis merely stresses three aspects of a complex, unitary, dynamic whole. Aspective analysis of this kind is not to be confused with substantive analysis by means of enumeration of removable objects or parts.

Even though the figurative nature of the mental hygiene slogan under discussion has been grasped, the meaning of the slogan itself may require additional discussion. To speak of a " sound mind in a sound body in a sound society " may have an eloquent ring, but just what does it mean? Does it mean that a person with a broken leg also has a fractured mind? Does it mean that whenever the body is damaged, the mind is also damaged? Does it mean that every case of mental illness must be accompanied by some demonstrable injury to the body? Does it mean that the jilted lover brooding over his frustration and thinking of suicide or murder is sick not only in mind, but also in terms of organic pathology? Does it mean that a society whose political officials are corrupt, must inevitably contain mentally disturbed citizens? Does it mean that a society many of whose citizens are unable to find work is to be labelled an unsound society? And will these jobless citizens consequently be unsound of mind? And if they are, will they as a further consequence also be of unsound body? There is no immediate need for us to answer these questions in detail here. They are intended to provoke reflection on the implications of this mental hygiene slogan in order to anticipate its complexities and its ramifications.

To regard the goal of mental hygiene as achieving a " sound mind in a sound body in a sound society " is thus not only figurative but also somewhat vague. Its vagueness is due to the absence of any explanation of how these three aspects of the slogan are related to one another. Another source of vagueness is the difficulty of deciding just what is meant by the word *sound* in this context. The chief usefulness of the slogan for our purposes is that it does emphasize the need for the mental hygienist to consider these three aspects and not to limit his attention to one and neglect the others. It helps, in other words, to drive home the basic idea with which we started; namely, that mental hygiene is a broad field with ill-defined contours. It helps to suggest the very vastness of the field. If we are not to lose ourselves in this vastness, however, we ought to find a less figurative and more definite goal in terms of which the field of mental hygiene can be envisaged.

MORALE AND MENTAL HYGIENE

If one were forced to furnish a one-word definition of mental hygiene, possibly the most adequate and revealing would be the word *morale*. What the mental hygienist is actually striving to accomplish is to promote morale. Anything which influences morale interests the mental hygienist. But just what is meant by the concept of morale? It is an enduring master attitude by virtue of which difficulties, dangers, or crises are faced hopefully, efficiently, and courageously. Morale is opposed to despair, panic, and funk. Whatever lends zest to one's work, significance to one's duties, and meaningfulness to one's routine contributes to morale. When morale is good there is a determined intention to fight on and not give up despite hardship and distress. When morale is low the future looks bleak and hopeless and further struggle seems futile. As a result there is a close relationship between learning brave and intelligent ways of dealing with trouble and acquiring morale. This is why the mental hygienist is so concerned about having children learn satisfactory ways of coping with frustrations. Whining, indulging in temper tantrums, sulking, pretending to be sick, foisting the blame on others, and nursing attitudes of self-pity represent some of the *unsatisfactory* ways we find prevalent among children — and childish adults. To handle difficulties by means of such techniques is to demonstrate poor mental hygiene or poor morale.

The concept of morale is by no means restricted to individuals. As everybody knows, commanding officers are concerned with the morale of their regiments. Enlightened business executives are mindful of the morale of factory workers, office personnel, and field representatives. School administrators, provided they too are enlightened, are watchful of the morale of the class. Wherever people are assembled to work together or play together the question of morale asserts itself. In the army it is closely allied to the concept of *esprit de corps,* in schools it has been dubbed *school spirit,* and in the world of industry it has been called *company loyalty.* Morale thus makes for enthusiastic cooperation, a willingness to do one's job joyfully, and a consciousness of doing something that counts or is important or significant or worthwhile. Whatever adds *to* the joy of living aids morale; hence, in the last analysis, whatever adds to the joy of living is a contribution to the cause of mental hygiene.

PERSONAL CONFLICTS AND MORAL ABSOLUTES

It was previously pointed out that meliorative mental hygiene is interested in making the bad good and the good better. Nothing was said about making the better the best. This silence about perfection was not accidental, but deliberate; for as yet we do not know enough to draw a set of blueprints for an ideal mind. Possibly a more revealing way to put this is to say that we know enough about human nature not to talk about a generalized ideal personality to hold up as model for all to copy. Successful mental hygiene cannot traffic with absolutes. Just as a competent architect can suggest how a given house might be made better even though he is unable to describe a " best " house, so the mental hygienist may indicate how a given personality might be improved and yet find himself nonplussed if asked to specify the characteristics of an absolutely ideal personality.

Mental hygiene is not to be mastered by memorizing copybook maxims extolling honesty, self-control, purity, and service. The problem of conjuring up an image of an ideal personality is not to be disposed of by conceiving of all such traditional virtues associated together in the same person. Furthermore, mental hygiene has to do with the dynamics of everyday living, and such abstractions as loyalty and self-sacrifice are too static to furnish a stimulating picture of a personality in action. Even if this were not the case, the approach would not lead to an understanding of the mental hygiene ideal because of its failure to supply a means of resolving inevitable deadlocks when such abstract ideals conflict. The child who has been taught to be both loyal and honest may suffer an agony of indecision if asked by his teacher to testify against his classmate. To tell the truth would involve disloyalty to his friend, while loyalty to the friend would necessitate lying to the teacher. Similarly, the virtue of obeying the law may conflict with the conscientious objector's allegiance to the ideal of non-resistance. For him there is a conflict between the draft law and his ideal of the virtue of peace. Merely pitting one virtue against the other will not suffice to resolve the conflict.

MENTAL HYGIENE AND ETHICS

The foregoing considerations should not be interpreted to mean that mental hygiene can afford to ignore such ethical issues. Quite the contrary. In fact, much of the grist poured into the mental hygiene mill is composed of such ethical ingredients. Conflicts between duty and the pleasure-seeking impulse can usually be counted on to arouse the mental hygienist's professional interest. How people stand up to such conflicts, and the ways in which they strive to handle them, tell him a great deal about the mental hygiene of the persons concerned. Although his notes on a given case may not be couched in the language of academic ethics, the basic ethical factors responsible for the conflict can usually be detected as implicit in his observations.

Consider, for the sake of illustration, the case of a woman who complained of a loss of ability to concentrate, marked irritability, and loss of interest in pursuits that she formerly found more or less fascinating. More specifically, she reported that these symptoms seemed to develop some weeks after her first child was born. Her first clear-cut observation of the problem dated back to her experiences at the bridge table when the baby was two months old. It was the first time she had resumed her old custom of playing bridge every Tuesday afternoon. She had left the baby in care of her mother. In the course of her recital of the history of her difficulties she remarked rather casually, " Mother is kind of old-fashioned and never did like the idea of my playing cards." The notion of possible mental trouble appeared when she experienced difficulty in keeping her mind on the bridge game. She became annoyed with herself because of the frequency with which she had to have the bidding reviewed. This annoyance persisted even after she arrived home and she found herself rather irritated by the baby's crying. Even after the baby stopped crying she was still " jumpy and jittery," as she put it. There is no need to pile up more details. For our purposes there are enough items in these fragments of the case history to detect the ethical issues around which the symptoms seemed to cluster. There was quite evidently a conflict between desire for an afternoon of card playing by way of social diversion and the desire to be a " good mother." The fact that her own mother frowned upon such diversion only served to intensify the ethical conflict. Feelings of guilt are a frequent consequence of such failure to abide by inner standards of conduct. Irritability and trouble in concentrating on the cards are understandable in the light of such guilty feelings.

There is thus a close relationship between mental symptoms and ethical factors. For more adequate insight into the nature of mental hygiene problems it is therefore desirable to study these factors beyond the superficial level of pious repetition of honesty-is-the-best-policy type of moralistic proverb. A child armed with such a collection of precepts is by no means necessarily equipped to handle his personal conflicts in efficient fashion. It is even conceivable that his uncritical application of the proverbs to given situations might increase rather than decrease both the number and the severity of his conflicts. " Go to the ant, thou sluggard . . ." will have to be squared with the invitation to loaf, as he thinks of what " all work and no play " threatens to do to Jack.

PHILOSOPHY AND MENTAL HYGIENE

The fact that mental hygiene can be discussed in terms of ethical problems suggests that in many respects it is concerned with age-old problems. As a self-conscious movement with a novel name of its own, mental hygiene is only about thirty-odd years old. But in terms of its larger objectives it may be regarded as new name for some very old ways of dealing with life's problems. It often aids our grasp of the seemingly novel to envisage it as a variation of the old and familiar. As a consequence, it might prove helpful to realize that what our grandfathers and their forefathers called a *philosophy of life* was not altogether different from what we describe as sound mental hygiene. It is the same old quest for a wise, satisfying way of life. It is the same old quest for ways of meeting adversity without going to smash. It is the same old quest for enduring values that will enable us to be brave and steadfast when the going gets tough. It is the same old quest for a type of training and education that will equip the child to make the business of living synonymous with the joy of living. A big difference between the old approach and the new is that mental hygiene is making a specialty of the quest instead of permitting it to be an incidental part of other activities as it used to be in the old days. Another difference is that in many respects we have a better grasp of the factors involved than our ancestors had. But even if our diagnostic tools may be better and our psychological insights more profound, our goals are not so radically different. As mental hygienists we too are trying to help people, children as well as adults, work out individual philosophies that will make their pursuit of happiness less futile, less blundering, and less unenlightened.

CONCLUDING COMMENTS

The vast scope of mental hygiene interests has now been outlined. We have furnished some preliminary insight into the complexity of factors to be incorporated in a complete program of mental hygiene and the ramifications of such a program. No single book and no single course and no single author can do justice to the full implications of so ambitious a program. Furthermore, there are still so many gaps in our knowledge that many mental hygiene suggestions have to be made cautiously and tentatively.

In many respects the practice of mental hygiene is more of an art than a science. A vast portion of this art rests on the foundation of critical common sense, thoughtful clinical observation, and much preoccupation with the troubles of perturbed people. The clinical psychiatrist, the practising psychoanalyst, and the clinical psychologist have all contributed to the mental hygiene movement. However, specialists of this sort do the bulk of their professional work in the consulting room and not in the laboratory. As the product of this work we get a case history rather than an experiment. This means that experimental support for mental hygiene teachings is available for only a limited number of such teachings.

Taken by and large, in other words, the kind of science underlying the doctrines and theories of mental hygiene is still at the descriptive and empirical level. By this is meant that it is based on a more or less systematic ordering of the fruits of clinical observation. It is rooted in experience, but not the *controlled* experience of the laboratory. Even that phase of it which we have called prophylactic mental hygiene — the phase concerned with *preventing* mental breakdown — does not rest on secure experimental foundations.

Mental breakdown is the subject of special study both of the psychiatrist and the abnormal psychologist. But neither psychiatry nor abnormal psychology, the foundation subjects for a program of prophylactic mental hygiene, are predominantly experimental subjects. This was brought out a few years ago by a survey made by Hunt and Landis.[4] They tabulated the percentage of space devoted to experimental studies in standard textbooks of abnormal psychology and of psychiatry. On the average less than 1% of the pages of the representative texts in the two fields had to do with experimental work. In fact, the authors were prompted to conclude that " this neglect of the experimental approach (only .8 per cent) seems the most glaring shortcoming in our texts." [5] Whether this " shortcoming " is inevitable because of the nature of the problems being studied is a consideration we cannot elaborate upon here. For our purposes it is sufficient to use this finding as a means of warning the student at the very beginning of his study of mental hygiene not to expect too much in the way of firmly established, experimentally grounded principles from such study. We believe it is better to have this understood and freely granted before presenting these principles in order to safeguard the student from subsequent disappointment.

The student of mental hygiene must consequently be prepared for a body of suggestions, recommendations, and somewhat loosely formulated general principles. In our opinion it would be a misuse of language to dignify such general principles as " laws " of mental hygiene. They constitute plausible generalizations based more on clinical judgment and clinical experience than on the rigorous proof we expect of well-conducted laboratory experiments. It would constitute a violation of these very principles to mislead the student by claiming too much for them. To raise false hopes is poor mental hygiene.

With this matter disposed of, we are ready to embark on our mental hygiene journey. As inspection of the table of contents showed, we shall be making two trips : one to the territory of prophylactic mental hygiene and the other to the territory of meliorative mental hygiene. The scenery will overlap, but the ports of call will be different.

---

[4] Hunt, W. A., & Landis, C., " The Present Status of Abnormal Psychology," *Psychol. Rev.*, 1935, *42*, pp. 78–90.
[5] *Ibid.*, p. 83.

PART TWO

THE NATURE OF MENTAL DISEASE

2ₒₒₒ MENTAL DISEASE AND SCIENTIFIC UNDERSTANDING

IN THE PRECEDING CHAPTER THE PROPHYLACTIC AND MELIORATIVE functions of mental hygiene work were pointed out. The latter function, it will be recalled, has to do with efforts to *improve* personal efficiency, family relations, and the morale of individuals and groups. Later chapters will be devoted to more detailed discussion of this aspect of the work. The chapters that follow will be concerned chiefly with the prophylactic or preventive aspects of the mental hygiene program.

How can we prevent mental breakdown? To what extent and by what means can society ward off and reduce the incidence of mental disease? Specific answers to questions like these cannot be given with the same confident assurance with which a public health official can tell us how to ward off a typhoid or a diphtheria epidemic. The factors involved are much more complex. In addition, the organized, systematic attack on problems of this kind is a very recent development in man's medical history. Consideration of a very restricted phase of this history will enhance appreciation of the difficulties involved and will make us more tolerant of the shortcomings of psychiatry as well as more respectful and enthusiastic as we note its hard-won successes.

A BRIEF HISTORY OF MENTAL HYGIENE

Mention has already been made of the fact that mental hygiene is, as a formal movement, less than 40 years old. The chief impetus to the movement's launching was furnished by Clifford W. Beers in 1908. Mr. Beers was neither a professional psychologist nor a psychiatrist. His interest in the work was an outgrowth of his own experiences as a victim of mental breakdown. He told of these experiences with courageous candor in his influential book entitled *A Mind That Found Itself*. It furnished an account of the events which compelled his family to have him institutionalized after he became so acutely depressed that he attempted to commit suicide.

It also described the nature of the patient's reaction to the institutional management prevalent in the first decade of this century. There seemed to be a deplorable lack of understanding of the psychology of the mentally sick. Beers was so impressed by this lack that he decided to devote his energies to bettering the situation once his own recovery was attained.

In those days a straitjacket was the routine technique for " quieting " excited patients. Beers not only experienced this treatment, but also supplied vivid descriptions of what such painful immobilization of the arms means to the overwrought patient. He called attention to the intensification of inner excitement produced by such crude means of restraint. Instead of inducing an attitude of voluntary cooperation the straitjacket aroused rebellious, if impotent, rage. This, as Beers realized, was a deplorable outcome; for it magnified the patient's emotional distress and made it harder for him to view attending physicians as understanding, friendly healers. Instead he tended to regard them as hostile jailers or uncomprehending blunderers. There was a manifest failure to establish a therapeutically wholesome physician-patient relationship.

Under the circumstances, Beers realized someone ought to intervene and explain that this was no way to handle sick people — especially mentally sick people. Beers resolved to make himself the agent of intervention. He aroused the interest and aid of such outstanding men as William James, the eminent psychologist, and Adolf Meyer, the distinguished psychiatrist. It was the latter who suggested the term *mental hygiene* as an apt designation for the movement about to be launched. At its inception, in other words, the mental hygiene movement was primarily concerned with improving the treatment and status of the mentally ill. It was concerned with changing the attitude of the public toward the " insane " in the direction of understanding sympathy and away from the " mad dog " attitude. For generations people had regarded mental disturbances as radically different from ordinary illnesses. A " crazy " person was thought of as " possessed " or " in league with the devil." Contempt, abuse, and punishment rather than pity, solicitude, and kindness were the consequences of such superstitious teachings.

Accordingly, one of the first tasks undertaken by the new movement was to eliminate this superstitious setting by educating the public to regard mental illness as an *illness* and not as a demonic invasion. People had to be taught that " insanity " like appendicitis was a misfortune and not a disgrace. They had to be induced to view mental disease in the light of twentieth-century science as opposed to seventeenth-century witchcraft. This effort to enlighten the public is among the finest educational goals of the program envisioned by Beers.

Relatively rapid progress was made by the psychiatrists and other public-spirited citizens who cooperated with Beers in formulating his program and getting it under way. The first Society for Mental Hygiene was founded May 6, 1908 in Connecticut. This local society became part of a national movement in 1909 when the National Committee for Mental Hygiene was established. Ten years later this organized movement attained international status when the International Committee for Mental Hygiene came into being, and in the following years more and more foreign countries were brought within the scope of the movement. Men like Toulouse in France, von Ley in Belgium, Sir Maurice Craig in England, Ferrari in Italy, Sommer in Germany, and Stransky in Austria were among the leading European organizers. By 1930 when the First International Congress on Mental Hygiene was held in Washington, D. C., representatives of 53 countries were in attendance, so that in a little over two decades the movement started by Beers had come to exercise some influence in every continent.[1]

THE NATURALISTIC APPROACH TO MENTAL DISEASE

As has already been suggested, one of the first objectives of the new movement was to divest the topic of mental disease of its traditional demonic or mystical associations by bringing it within the orbit of non-mystical, scientific thinking. To facilitate this task it was deemed necessary to educate both the professional and lay public in the use of more suitable descriptive terms. Older designations of medical specialists in the field of " insanity " included such names as " asylum doctor," " alienist," or " mad doctor." As

[1] For a more extended discussion of the history of the mental hygiene movement, see Cross, W. L., Editor, *Twenty-Five Years After: Sidelights on the Mental Hygiene Movement and Its Founder,* New York, Doubleday, Doran, 1934.

For the spread of the movement in Europe, see Stransky, E., Editor, *Leitfaden der psychischen Hygiene,* Vienna, Urban & Schwarzenberg, 1931, pp. 11–15 and 286–305.

the educational campaign progressed, the general public became increasingly familiar with the term *psychiatrist*. That this constitutes progress is evident as soon as we reflect upon the connotation of a word like *alienist*. The word suggests that the mentally sick are a strange species different from other sick people. The term is even reminiscent of the concept of demonic possession by implying that a foreign agent has taken possession of the victim's body. No such dubious connotation is linked up with a word like *psychiatrist*,[2] which is Greek for mind-healer. As the campaign of enlightenment spread, the term *asylum* with its original quasi-theological suggestion of a shrine to which criminals and paupers could turn for refuge gave way to the more medically oriented phrase *psychopathic hospital* or *psychiatric institute*. The very word *psychopathic* emphasized the new approach; for the suffix *pathos* means disease or illness.

By inducing people to conceive of mental disturbance as a matter of illness these pioneers of the mental hygiene movement initiated a commendable change in public opinion. Illness calls for scientific study, sympathetic understanding, and appropriate treatment, not for condemnation, punishment, and attitudes of reproach. There is thus no justification for placing the mentally ill in a unique category by sending them to a special institution called an " asylum " where strong-armed " guards " are ready to give unruly " inmates " the works. Like the physically ill they belong in hospitals and require nursing care. This need had been recognized by isolated leaders long before the time of Beers. Pinel, who lived at the time of the French revolution, was among the first to anticipate this need. However, for several generations, the general public as well as many physicians failed to adopt the implications of Pinel's teachings. As we have already indicated, one of the big accomplishments of the psychiatrists cooperating with Beers was their success in bringing about more adequate appreciation of these implications.

Unfortunately this educational objective is not yet completely

---

[2] More recently even the term *psychiatry* has been viewed askance as militating against acceptance of a naturalistic interpretation of mental disease. Rosanoff, for example, writes: " There is little to justify a continuance of the employment of this term, other than the inertia of general usage. Would not *cerebrology* be a more suitable and a more scientific form? " (Rosanoff, A. J., *Manual of Psychiatry and Mental Hygiene*, 7th Edition, New York, John Wiley & Sons, Inc., 1938, p. 1075.)

attained. The old attitude still persists in many circles. Many people still feel squeamish about acknowledging the existence of mental disease in the family. They prefer to resort to a euphemism like " nervous breakdown " or " nervous trouble." However, as the educational work of psychiatrists and mental hygienists continues, a more enlightened attitude ought to make such euphemistic evasions superfluous.

It is also part of this educational program to eliminate such terms as " crazy " or " insane " as suitable synonyms for the concept of mental illness. The latter is by no means identical with the concept of insanity. Taken strictly, insanity is neither a psychiatric nor a psychological term; but one that pertains to the field of law.[3] For the lawyer a person is to be adjudged insane when he can no longer differentiate between " right and wrong and know the nature and consequences of his acts." Another version of this forensic concept holds that an individual charged with the commission of a crime is to be called sane and must stand trial provided he " is capable of understanding the nature and object of the proceedings against him, and can conduct his defense in a rational manner." A little reflection will show that it is entirely possible for a person to be mentally sick and yet not be insane. The concept of mental disease is thus both broader than and different from the purely legal concept of insanity. As a consequence, psychiatrists are altogether justified in refusing to regard their professional work as restricted to the study of insanity. They are also correct in holding that in the interests of mental hygiene it would be well for the general public to realize and understand the difference between mental illness and insanity. It would serve to make it easier for many who might profit by consultation with a psychiatrist to overcome a reluctance to avail themselves of such aid — a reluctance due in large measure to a fear of being dubbed " crazy " by those ignorant of the fact that psychiatry is not synonymous with the treatment of the " insane."

As a matter of fact, large numbers of psychiatric patients never require institutional commitment. Their difficulties of adjustment are of the kind which the psychiatrist associates with the concept

---

[3] For an excellent introduction to the complex issues bound up with the clash of legal *versus* psychiatric approaches to mental disease, see McCarty, D. G., *Psychology for the Lawyer*, Prentice-Hall, Inc., New York, 1929, pp. 394–490.

of a *neurosis*. A neurosis is a relatively minor kind of abnormality. The term *psychosis* is usually applied to the more serious kinds. Most " insanities " are really psychoses; for a psychosis ordinarily involves a fairly drastic personality disturbance so as to render hospitalization desirable. In the case of a neurosis, however, although the patient may be considerably distressed, he does not require the safeguard of rigorous supervision afforded by segregation in a psychopathic hospital. Neuroticism is somewhat different from the common term *nervousness*. In general, a neurotic patient recognizes his " nervousness " as abnormal. In technical language he is said to possess *insight* because of such recognition. On the other hand, the psychotic patient lacks such clear-cut insight. As a consequence, he is apt to injure himself or others; hence the need for institutionalization. It should thus be quite clear that not everybody who has need of a psychiatrist's services is to be viewed as " crazy " or " insane," even in the loose sense in which such words are employed in colloquial speech.

STRUCTURAL *versus* FUNCTIONAL INTERPRETATIONS

In the endeavor to understand mental diseases as natural rather than supernatural events, specialists have sought for some anatomic or bodily disturbance as the basis for specific abnormal phenomena. In many instances such disturbances could be found, but in others, despite diligent search, no relevant pathology could be demonstrated. This led to the introduction of a distinction between structural psychoses on the one hand and functional psychoses on the other. The result is that many psychiatrists and clinical psychologists conceive of mental disturbance in terms of this distinction. For example, they classify mental symptoms attributable to brain injury as structural or organic. An actual lesion of the brain substance caused by the passage of a bullet through the head would constitute such an injury. A consequent mental difficulty might be revealed by the patient's disturbed memory or speech or perception. Another example of such structural interpretation is that of the delirium incident to a toxic condition accompanied by high fever as in typhoid cases. The mental disturbance of the intoxicated patient is another familiar instance of this relationship between a toxin and disordered mental states. Analogous relationships have been established between such states and damage to blood vessels resulting in cerebral hemorrhage. The damage caused by syphilitic infection of the brain would also furnish an example of what is meant by an organic or structural cause of an abnormal mental state. In brief, any kind of demonstrable pathology of the nervous system, its supporting tissues, or its blood supply would justify application of the concept of structural damage.

Unfortunately, in the interests of simplicity of exposition, not all mental difficulties can be associated with such demonstrable pathology. There may be mental illness, in other words, despite the absence of either brain lesions or biochemical irregularities. Such an illness would be called *functional*. What this concept implies is that, although structures may be intact, their dependent functions may nevertheless exhibit a loss of efficiency. To those who restrict the idea of disease to such conventional causative factors as bacterial invasion, tissue damage, chemical imbalance, and kindred items of organic pathology this concept of a purely *functional* disease is, at best, a convenient label for medical ignorance. For them the concept of a functional disease is basically untenable. If *all* the relevant facts were available, so they believe, these so-called functional cases could be merged with the structural ones. They consequently prefer to let the term *functional disease* stand for those illnesses whose presumed underlying bodily causes are so minute or obscure as to defy present powers of detection.

There are other thinkers, however, who regard the concept of functional disease as more than a label for our ignorance. They refuse to regard the dichotomy between structural and functional interpretations of disease as spurious. This dichotomy as applied to mental diseases, so they contend, makes for a valid and useful distinction. They base their contention on the empirical fact that some mental diseases reveal organic causative factors while others are free from such factors. To assume that the latter *must* nevertheless be dependent on such factors is to disregard existing contrary evidence.

But how, it may be asked, is one to make use of this dichotomy? Just what does the concept of a functional disease imply? Is it not as ridiculous to introduce such a concept in a scientific discussion as it would be for a group of automotive engineers engaged in discussing their branch of applied science to argue that some cars which are structurally perfect may nevertheless function poorly? To answer questions of this kind the more thoughtful psychiatrists have sometimes taken the dichotomy to indicate two different approaches to an understanding or interpretation of mental diseases. Many years ago, for instance, a distinguished psychiatrist suggested that the structuralistic approach is based on what he called the " brain spot hypothesis." He also introduced the phrase " mind twist hypothesis " to designate the functional approach.

What he meant by these phrases might merit a little elaboration. The structural approach stresses some " spot " in the sense of a blemish on the integrity of neural architectonics as the basis for disturbed mental integrity. On the other hand to conceive of such disturbance in terms of a "twisted mind " is to emphasize the more extreme implications of the functional approach. Common sense terms like " eccentric personality," " warped thinking," or " mental quirks " are all in line with this " mind twist " approach. It does not presuppose an underlying injury to the tissues of the nervous system to account for the vagaries of abnormal behavior. Instead it allies such vagaries with the loss of control one ordinarily associates with emotional difficulties.

A convenient example of such an emotional difficulty is furnished by the victim of stage fright. His pounding heart, trembling knees, and perspiring hands are all symptoms of an " abnormal " condition; but the abnormality is *functional* rather than structural. No pathology of the sort described in text books of pathology is involved. Nevertheless the disturbed muscles and glands behave *as if* something were damaged. This *as if* character does not mean that functional disturbances are unreal or imaginary. They are as real as the visceral distress of a conscience-stricken person, as real as the loss of appetite experienced during grief, and as real as the sudden muscular weakness of the frightened victim of a hold-up. The foregoing are all familiar instances of mild functional disabilities. Furthermore, the intimate participation of emotional factors is clearly evident in each of these instances.

Emotion, it will be recalled, is bound up with factors which *move* us because of their direct or indirect bearing on personal welfare. We are emotionally aroused by being threatened with loss of employment, by being jilted, by serious illness in the family, by sincere praise of those whose opinions we respect — in short, by whatever has a bearing on our security or self-esteem. If we find ourselves moving closer to the realization of some personal goal, we experience exhilarating emotional changes. Contrariwise, to be frustrated in our striving precipitates unpleasantly toned changes. There is thus a close relationship between the dynamics of emotion and the dynamics of our wishes and strivings. That is why so many mental experts venture to account for functional disturbances in terms of emotional disturbances, especially those associated with frustrated ambition, balked desire, and ungratified or unrecognized wishes. They interpret the bodily symptoms — the digestive ills, poor heart action, or the chronic fatigue — as expressions of poorly handled disappointments, humiliations, or fears or resentments. The pathology is not the pathology of the cadaver on the dissecting table, but the pathology of personal grievances, wounded vanity, persistent anxiety, protesting conscience, and injured self-respect. No post-mortem technique can be expected to reveal the latter kind of pathology.

" Mind twist " and " brain spot " interpretations should not be regarded as necessarily mutually exclusive. In other words, this dichotomy should not be taken to mean that in a given patient the diseased condition must inexorably be classified as either structural *or* functional. Even the most obvious of structural cases may be accompanied by symptoms of functional disturbance and there is no reason why signs of organic pathology might not develop in what started as a " purely functional " case. As an illustration of the latter possibility mention might be made of the contention of some gastroenterologists that gastric ulcer may develop as a result of years of digestive upset incident to acute and prolonged worries or anxieties.[4] With respect to the former possibility, it ought to be easy to perceive what the relationship might be. Almost any organic condition might be either directly or remotely influenced by the patient's emotionalized attitude toward his illness. For a person with a heart lesion to *worry* about his heart is to add a possible functional difficulty to an existing structural one. These possibilities merely serve to emphasize that what we call

4 For a recent study of this relationship, see Mittelmann, B., Wolff, H. G., & Scharf, M. P., " Emotions and Gastroduodenal Function: Experimental Studies on Patients with Gastritis, Duodenitis and Peptic Ulcer," *Psychosomatic Medicine*, 1942, 4, pp. 5–61.

mind is a unified manifold — a *unitas multiplex* — of which that which we call *body* is but a convenient abstraction. To put this a little differently: in the living, human being there is a constant interplay of functional and structural factors. The dichotomy we have been discussing should not blind us to the essential unity underlying this interplay.

UNDERSTANDING ABNORMAL BEHAVIOR

There have been some students of mental diseases who have taken a one-sided view of the interplay we just mentioned. For them the only way to achieve " scientific " understanding of mental illness was to ferret out some evidence of organic pathology in the way of disordered endocrine glands, ruptured blood vessels in the brain, poorly developed cells in the cerebral cortex, or some other kind of deviation from the norm of healthy tissue structure. Their concept of pathology was thus restricted to morbid tissue changes. As Adolf Meyer has worded it, " Pathology has been, and to this day is, limited largely to the sphere of the owner of the corpse and of the microscope." [5] Meyer protests against this limitation; for it hamstrings the psychiatrist in his efforts to understand the dynamics of abnormal behavior. Orthodox medical tradition has made this laboratory concept of pathology part and parcel of " scientific medicine " and it doubtless plays a necessary role in helping the physician to understand the nature of such diseases as diabetes, leprosy, pneumonia, and endocarditis. But to insist that this is the only approach to an understanding of human ills — especially mental ills — may be a stumbling block to medical understanding. This is what the famous Heidelberg specialist, Jaspers,[6] was referring to some years ago when he said that to require the psychiatrist to translate all of his psychiatric concepts into the language of morbid, anatomic pathology is tantamount to forcing him " to stop thinking " altogether about his professional problems.

As a matter of fact there is no justification for confining " scientific " explanations to the world of mechanics or to what lends itself to representation by diagram or chemical formula. Scien-

[5] Meyer, A., " Preparation for Psychiatry," *Arch. Neurol. and Psychiatry,* 1933, *30,* p. 1111. (Quoted by Rosanoff in his *Manual of Psychiatry.*)
[6] Jaspers, K., *Allgemeine Psychopathologie,* 3rd Ed., Berlin, Julius Spranger, 1923, pp. 13–14.

tific understanding cannot be compressed within such narrow limits. A survey of the kind of operations which the scientist introduces in his work will show at least four different kinds of procedures by means of which understanding is furthered. We may consider these in order:

1. **Understanding in terms of continuity of structure.** This type of understanding is exemplified by such everyday situations as the broken filament in a light globe, a fractured arm, or a severed artery. We understand the result in each of the foregoing cases in terms of the " pathology " of the structures involved. For a light to glow the filament must be intact, and to lift a heavy weight the bones of the arm have to move like a lever. A broken arm is like a broken lever. Similarly, an artery is like a pipe so that a rupture of arterial walls " *causes* " an escape of blood. The concepts of mechanics suffice to give us the requisite understanding. When we attribute a particular patient's blindness to atrophy of the optic nerve and go on to say we " understand why he can't see," then this structural-continuity type of understanding is being invoked. In the field of abnormal behavior this kind of understanding has a legitimate, if not exclusive, place. Thus we can understand the ineducability of an idiot in terms of demonstrable maldevelopment of his brain cortex. The bizarre and often unpredictable action of some paretic patients is also understandable in the light of damage to the brain caused by the invading spirochete. As should be obvious, this is the kind of understanding already described in our discussion of structural mental disease.

2. **Understanding in terms of functional relationships.** Even within the field of physics there are numerous situations which are not explicable by means of mechanical analogies. What the physicist calls *action at a distance* involves this kind of situation. The relationship between the moon and tidal changes is not one of material continuity. There are no strings or rods or levers connecting moon and ocean. In fact, the simple experiment of releasing a ball from the top of a vacuum jar and noting its fall will serve to demonstrate the meaning of action at a distance despite the absence of a structural linkage. All gravitational phenomena, in other words, are understandable only in terms of functional relationships. The same holds true for magnetic and electrical ones. To understand the transmission of light through a vacuum tube is

to appeal to such a relationship. It may even be that understanding of the concept of a neural impulse calls for more of an appeal to functional than to structural factors. And if one goes beyond the naïve descriptive level with respect to the concept of matter by having recourse to the language of electronic physics, then even what we call a " nerve " or a " brain " loses its fixed, substantial, static characteristics and gives way to the dynamism of electrical equilibria. This is another way of saying that for the modern physicist understanding of the " material world " is achieved by converting its hard " materiality " into the fluidity of fields of force. Mechanical models of the nineteenth-century physicist no longer suffice to picture such dynamic changes. His twentieth-century descendant has to picture such changes in terms of functional relationships amenable to mathematical description.

3. **Understanding in terms of logical implication.** The physicist using mathematical tools is trying to understand his problem by means of the logic of numbers applied to such concepts as space, energy, and time. Scientific understanding is thus not merely a consequence of working out structural continuities. It also involves grasping logical relationships. The very fact that traditional accounts of scientific method speak of inductive and deductive methods suggests this. But what should be stressed in the present context is the meaning of logical understanding. Let us take some familiar examples of purely logical relationships. If all men are mortal, then John Doe, an individual man, is bound to die. If the sum of the angles of a triangle must always equal 180°, then a triangle drawn by prehistoric man must have had angles which added up to 180°. If football will always be played, then people living a thousand years from today will still have a chance to see a football game. These three logical propositions refer to the present, the past, and the future. In each instance we can *understand* that what is stated as a conclusion is true provided the hypothetical generalization is assumed to be true. This logical type of understanding enables us to extend our immediate experience and project ourselves either into the past or the future. We can even determine the truth or falsity of purely imaginary constructs. When the mathematics teacher asks his pupil, " How much is minus four multiplied by minus four ? " and the child says, " minus sixteen," then those of us who remember the manipulation of nega-

tive numbers can *understand* why the teacher calls the answer " false."

Our understanding of the world as described by physics and chemistry is dependent on these three kinds of understanding. Sometimes we need to emphasize structural continuity, sometimes a functional relationship, sometimes a logical implication and often all three categories taken together. In one sense it results in an impersonal type of understanding; for it omits references to personal aspirations, individual purposes, and the joys and sorrows of particular people. It describes the world as it would be with human experience left out of consideration. It is a world of shifting light waves, whirling electrons, twitching muscles, chemical reactions, and mathematical equations. It is the world of natural as opposed to social science.

Questions concerning human institutions, human rights, and human schemes are alien to this natural science account of the world. It ignores such issues as the tariff, the plottings of an international spy, the martyrdom of a Joan of Arc, the tribal customs of Australian aborigines, the functions of the House of Lords, and the troubles of delinquent boys. To understand issues of this kind we have to consider the world as it is with man as the chief actor. We have to study man as a creature of motive and purpose who is influenced by what he has been taught and by what he has read and experienced. We have to study the effect of social tradition and historical precedent on the lives of men. We have to consider the influence of law, religion, language, commerce, custom, recreation, and esthetics is shaping their lives and guiding their choices. All of the social sciences such as anthropology, government, sociology, history, jurisprudence, etc., have something to contribute to this sort of understanding. It constitutes the fourth type to be listed here and, since it is so obviously bound up with man's mental life, we shall call it the psychological type.

4. Understanding in terms of psychological or experiential factors. As was just mentioned, the natural sciences like physics and chemistry differ from the social sciences in their lack of concern with the individual as a person. To understand the individual organism as a going physiological mechanism it suffices to limit ourselves to the methods and concepts of the natural sciences. However, to understand him as a person — as one cherishing ambitions, striving after power and success, endeavoring to master a new language or a new machine, trying to win a military or a business or an academic promotion — we have to invoke the methods and concepts of the social sciences.

There has been considerable debate as to whether psychology is to be classified as a natural or as a social science. Actually, so it seems to us, it belongs to both groups. When a psychologist studies the process of vision in the abstract he tends to work as a natural scientist as he notes the characteristics of the anatomy of the eye, the neurology of the optic tract, and the physics of light. But when his interest turns to particular men choosing to employ their visual processes in individually unique ways he becomes more of a social scientist. Why some people look at musical scores rather than at baseball scores and why others prefer comic books to textbooks are questions physiological psychology cannot answer. Nor can it tell us why some people pray in one way, others according to a different ritual, and still others pray not at all. These are legitimate questions, but to answer them in scientific fashion the investigator must turn away from the impersonal world of the physicist to the methods and concepts of the students of human culture. For him to do otherwise would be akin to seeking the explanation for the greatness of Shakespeare's plays by means of a chemical analysis of the ink with which they were written.

There are a host of human problems the understanding of which demands familiarity with man as a social being. The social sciences rather than the natural sciences can furnish the requisite bases for such understanding. Under the circumstances it is idle to debate which of the groups of sciences is the more scientific. Of course physics and chemistry, having fewer variables to control, are more rigorously precise than economics or sociology. In this sense they are more scientific. In the same sense and for the same reason they are more scientific than such other natural sciences as physiology or bacteriology. But precision is always relative to magnitude of the problem being studied. The essence of the scientific approach has to do with the *verifiability* of the conclusions reached. Each science has to develop methods and to introduce concepts relevant to the problems with which it is dealing if its results are to be verifiable. Intrinsically the concept of specific gravity is no more scientific than the concept of a protective tariff. The first is relevant to the field of physics and the second to the field of economics. It would be fatuous for an economist, anxious to make his work " more scientific," to try to describe a protective tariff in terms of valence, kindling temperature, density, chemical composition and similar ideas germane to the natural sciences. Technical language taken by itself does not make a report scientific. If it did, the publicity literature of certain popular patent medicines would have to be adjudged scientific. What does endow a report with scientific respectability is the cogency of the evidence presented, the relative completeness of this evidence, and the extent to which the conclusions drawn square with the evidence submitted. But it should be stressed once again that the evidence has to be of a kind which lends itself to verification by competent observers. Within this framework of restrictions the anthropologist, the social psychologist, the economist, the historian, the student of comparative religion, and other social scientists can avail themselves of the methodology of science even though their data have to be gathered from Indian villages, ancient manuscripts, government reports, or case histories. Even folklore may be grist to the mill of the social scientist.

How is this kind of understanding related to mental hygiene issues? A question of this sort can be answered by noting the extent to which human institutions — the broad field of social science study — are involved in personal problems. Consider, for the sake of illustration, the distress of a woman married to a chronic drunkard who finds it impossible to solve her problem by recourse to divorce, because her church refuses to sanction such solution. Laboratory tests of the woman's blood chemistry will not enable us to understand her loyalty to church doctrine. Neither will a sedulous probing of her body by means of X-rays, percussion, auscultation, electrocardiographs, ophthalmoscopes and kindred techniques. All these belong to the natural science type of investigatory procedures. But the church is a social institution, and to understand how its taboos and sanctions come to grip its devotees we must avail ourselves of social science concepts. This is what we mean by the psychological type of understanding. By its means we can hope to understand a wide range of mental hygiene issues that are refractory to the natural science mode of attack.

The conflict between the structural and functional explanations of mental disease discussed in the previous section can now be grasped as a conflict between natural and social science modes of explanation. Those who are enamored of " brain spot " hypotheses are limiting scientific understanding to the pattern of physico-chemical explanations: to the first three kinds of understanding as we have sketched them here. On the other hand, those who lean toward the " mind twist " hypotheses envisage man as more than a miniature chemical laboratory. They seek their explanations for his personality quirks in the social pattern of ethical teachings, economic standards, marriage customs, family prestige, religious doctrine, legislative statutes, and business institutions by which he is surrounded and in which he becomes enmeshed by sheer virtue of having been born into a given culture rather than another.

Now it ought to be clear why we stated earlier in this book that mental hygiene is a broad field with ill-defined contours. It has to borrow from all of the sciences, the social sciences as well as the natural sciences. It cannot do justice to the very concept of mental disease itself without such borrowing. Furthermore, although our understanding of such disease is still far from complete, we do know that for still more complete understanding we must divest ourselves of a tendency, still prevalent in some quarters, to cast aspersions on social science contributions as being less orthodox or less respectable than those of natural science. Because of this tendency far too many medical men continue to view psychiatry as a sort of stepchild in the family of medical specialties. Some extremists among them may even prefer to substitute the analogy of an illegitimate child for that of the step-child. Their failure to appreciate the scientific legitimacy of the psychiatrist's work may in part be due to exclusive preoccupation with man as an organism to the neglect of man as a person. The understanding psychiatrist has succeeded in emancipating himself from the confines of such one-sided medical thinking.

3... A SYNOPTIC VIEW
OF STRUCTURAL DISORDERS

TO APPRECIATE THE NATURE AND MAGNITUDE OF THE TASK OF THE mental hygienist interested in warding off the occurrence of mental disease, it is necessary to be at least superficially familiar with an elementary knowledge of such disease. This knowledge is usually supplied by courses in abnormal psychology or psychiatry. Since not all readers of this volume can be assumed to have had such courses, it will be advisable to devote this chapter and the following one to a hasty survey of some of the basic information supplied by such courses. Without a survey of this kind it will be impossible to understand the implications of a program of prophylactic mental hygiene.

AN ETIOLOGICAL CLASSIFICATION

There are various ways in which the many symptoms of mental disease might be grouped to facilitate learning about them. The problem of the most accurate and useful system of classification is a technical one which need not be elaborated here. It is mentioned merely to indicate that the system to be presented in this chapter should not be regarded as necessarily superior to other systems with which the student happens to be familiar. We shall select one which seems to be particularly adapted to the exposition of the mental hygiene problems under discussion. Since our immediate concern has to do with prophylaxis, a system based on the presumed causation of mental disease should prove more useful than some others; for a knowledge of relevant causes is usually helpful in planning a defence against the emergence of the effects of such causes. To prevent fires one controls their causes. This does not mean, however, that prophylaxis is impossible without complete knowledge of *etiology*, to use the medical man's technical designation for causation. Although the etiology of smallpox is unknown, a very effective prophylactic technique has been devised by the use of vaccination. Similarly, some people knew how to prevent scurvy before the cause of this disease had been worked out. Years before the concept of vitamins had been developed there were isolated observers who had noted that scorbutic symptoms were a function of the sailor's diet. But taken by and large it is nevertheless quite obvious that knowledge of specific causes makes for more certain and more intelligent control of given effects. As a consequence it seems wise procedure to consider the classification of mental disorders in terms of etiology.

A casual inventory of a textbook of psychiatry will show more than 100 conditions regarded as specific mental diseases. It would be both tedious and profitless to list them here. These 100-odd diseases can be grouped into a few etiological categories. In fact, in 1934 the *American Psychiatric Association* adopted as its official diagnostic system [1] a scheme of classification based on the following etiological outline:

A. Psychoses due to or associated with infection.
B. Psychoses due to intoxication.
C. Psychoses due to trauma (traumatic psychoses).
D. Psychoses due to disturbance of circulation.
E. Psychoses due to convulsive disorders (epilepsy).
F. Psychoses due to disturbances of metabolism, growth, nutrition or endocrine function.
G. Psychoses due to new growth.
H. Psychoses due to unknown or hereditary causes, but associated with organic changes.
I. Disorders of psychogenic origin or without clearly defined tangible cause or structural change.

This outline shows that all the psychoses listed from A to H inclusive are of the structural or organic variety. Only the last

[1] The system in question is taken from the "Official Classification of Mental Disorders, as Revised and Adopted by the Committee on Statistics and Approved by the American Psychiatric Association at its 1934 Annual Meeting." We have presented the original wording in the outline above, but have not included a few non-etiological categories such as "undiagnosed psychoses" and "primary behavior disorders." For the complete list in the original, see Rosanoff, A. J., *Manual of Psychiatry and Mental Hygiene*, 7th Edition, New York, John Wiley & Sons, Inc., 1938, pp. 967–985.

The nature of the non-etiological categories omitted from this list will be explained in Chapter IV under the caption of *Mixed Symptoms and Miscellaneous Groups*.

Familiarity with this system of classification is desirable because it is the one followed by the U. S. Bureau of the Census since 1935 in its annual reports on *Patients in Hospitals for Mental Disease*.

division, I, embraces the functional conditions. They are referred to here as being of *psychogenic* origin. This term means " of mental origin " and is to be contrasted with the correlative term *somatogenic*, meaning " of bodily origin." Such terms may be descriptively useful provided their dualistic implications do not lure one into fanciful, mystical speculations.

The fact that 8 of the 9 categories refer to somatogenic disorders should not be taken to mean that the overwhelming majority of cases are of the organic type. In fact, as will be shown in greater detail in the next chapter, more than one-half of the resident population of our large psychopathic hospitals is to be classified as suffering from one of the " disorders of psychogenic origin."

A more profitable immediate task is to give substance to the foregoing outline by considering each of the categories separately. Understanding of the scope and variety of mental disorders will be aided by brief elaboration of a few diseases characteristic of each of these 9 classes of psychoses. We shall be especially brief in discussing the first 8 since they are not so directly related to psychological factors and devote more space to consideration of the psychogenic disorders. However, even in the latter discussion no exhaustive presentation is to be expected. Our chief object is to furnish general orientation by way of a background for subsequent appraisal of the mental hygienist's prophylactic suggestions. Those desirous of supplementing our fragmentary review of diseases and symptoms should consult standard texts in psychiatry and in abnormal psychology.[2]

[2] In addition to the text in psychiatry by Rosanoff already mentioned, see also White, W. A., *Outlines of Psychiatry*, Washington, Nerv. & Ment. Dis., Pub., 1935; Strecker, E. A., and Ebaugh, F. G., *Practical Clinical Psychiatry for Students and Practitioners,* Philadelphia, P. Blakiston's Son & Co., 1935.
    For the psychological approach, see Conklin, E. S., *Principles of Abnormal Psychology,* 2nd Edition, New York, Henry Holt & Co., 1935; Dorcus, R. M., and Shaffer, G. W., *Textbook of Abnormal Psychology,* 2nd Edition, Baltimore, Williams & Wilkins, 1939; Maslow, A. H., and Mittelmann, B., *Principles of Abnormal Psychology,* New York, Harper & Brothers, 1941.
    For an excellent discussion of the neurological approach to mental disorders, see Wechsler, I. S., *A Text-book of Clinical Neurology,* 3rd Edition, Philadelphia, W. B. Saunders Co., 1935.
    For general orientation with respect to the general physiological background desirable for more direct appreciation of the structural approach, see Sections VII and VIII of Best, C. H., and Taylor, N. B., *The Physiological Basis of Medical Practice,* Baltimore, Williams & Wilkins Company, 2nd Edition, 1940.

INFECTIOUS PSYCHOSES

Some mental disturbances are caused by infection of the central nervous system. Thus the spirochetes responsible for syphilis may lodge in the tissues of the brain. This results in the disease variously known as general paralysis, paresis, or *dementia paralytica*. As the name suggests, one finds disturbances of thought and motor control in these cases. In addition there are emotional disturbances as well as changes in the patient's character. A previously tractable person, for example, becomes hard to get along with and increasingly irritable and selfish. He may show signs of disintegration by his inexplicable *forgetting* of his home address, important appointments, or the number of children in his family. *Confusion* of an extreme sort is another common symptom as if the patient had lost his bearings. He mistakes a neighbor's house for his own or takes a bath without removing his clothes. Later he may develop ridiculous ideas regarding his greatness or financial power. His capacity for motor coordination becomes more and more disrupted. Characteristic swaying movements will be noted as the patient tries to stand still with his eyes closed. Speech, handwriting, gait, and reflexes are all affected. Unless effective treatment is instituted, the patient becomes worse and worse as the disease progresses until at the final stages he is a helpless, vegetative hulk. Fortunately, for reasons not yet understood, only about 5% of syphilitic patients become paretic and present methods of treatment are very much more effective than those of a generation ago. However, it is more relevant in the present context to note the direct relationship between the disintegration of personality and the easily demonstrable underlying changes in the integrity of the brain tissues. Paresis constitutes a dramatic example of what is meant by a structural psychosis.

Other examples of mental disturbances following infectious invasion of the central nervous system are those associated with *meningitis* and *encephalitis*. The former term refers to inflammation of the *meninges* or membranes covering the brain. Various bacterial agents are responsible for such involvement: the meningococcus itself, of course, as well as the tubercle bacillus and a few others. Of particular mental hygiene significance is the fact that feeblemindedness may sometimes be a consequence of meningitis in early childhood. Approximately 2% of the cases of mental deficiency in our public institutions are there because of this disease. *Encephalitis*, meaning inflammation of the brain, and popularly known as sleeping sickness, is caused by a *filterable virus* and not a bacterial agent. All sorts of physical and mental sequelae are associated with this type of infection. The list is a long one and includes disturbances of muscular coordination, heart action, breathing, and sleeping. It is important to realize that changes in personality may be among such sequels. In fact some cases of juvenile delinquency as well as what the clinical psychologist calls *behavior difficulties* of children are sometimes manifestations of such changes.

PSYCHOSES DUE TO INTOXICATION

The intimate relationship between drugs and mental efficiency is too well known to require special emphasis. Everybody is familiar with the fact that alcohol, carbon monoxide, opium, heroin, etc., may produce changes in thinking, feeling, and action. The detailed description of the precise nature of these changes need not concern us here. It is sufficient to point out that the statistics issued by psychopathic hospitals usually include the caption *Alcoholic Psychoses*. The devastating consequences of chronic alcoholism have been widely publicized. There is no need to do more than mention the disturbances of vision, speech, memory, motor control, ethical judgment, and general intellectual competence associated with alcoholism. Even the technical term for one of the alcoholic psychoses, *delirium tremens,* is known to the general public. In this condition one finds the patient *confused* and often unable to state where he is or even to specify whether it is summer or winter. His confusion is also revealed by his absurd failure to recognize·people so that he may greet a stranger as his uncle or the attending physician as a priest. This confusion is also accompanied by the well-known symptom of *hallucinations.* The latter is predominantly visual and for some curious reason frequently takes the form of actively moving animals about to attack the patient. The " horrors " of the D.T. patient have become classic. They have to do with the *terror* and *agitation* precipitated by the hallucinations.

Chronic alcoholism may also give rise to the disorder known as

Korsakoff's psychosis. This disturbance is of particular psychological interest because of the prominence of the signs of distorted memory. The patient appears to be free from confusion as one talks to him; i.e., there is no *clouding of consciousness.* He comprehends simple questions and answers relevantly. However, he is unable to remember that which he had just experienced. The fact that his brother visited him this morning or that he had lunch an hour ago is beyond recall. His capacity for retention is obviously impaired. Because of this he invents stories by means of which to fill in the lacunae in his memory. *Retrospective falsification* is the technical name for this kind of fabrication. Furthermore, not all memory processes are disturbed; for if one quizzes the patient about events experienced before the illness started, normal memory for such events will be found to exist. The same patient who is unable to remember the make of car the family purchased last month can remember the make of car his uncle purchased twenty years ago.

In recent years it has become evident that all of the symptoms of alcoholic psychoses are not entirely due to a direct toxic action of alcohol on neural and other tissues. Many of them are products of a vitamin deficiency associated with the dubious eating habits of the heavy drinker. In particular, vitamins belonging to the B-complex are known to be necessary for healthy neural action. This has been demonstrated by animal experimentation as well as by clinical studies. A variety of factors are responsible for making chronic alcoholism the basis for a " central neuritis " of nutritional origin. Among such factors one might include poor choices of food on the part of alcoholics; their frequent attacks of vomiting; their not uncommon rejection of food in favor of drink; and their digestive disturbances which might conceivably interfere with the adequate absorption of ingested vitamins. At all events it seems clear that some of the psychotic symptoms prominent in advanced cases of alcoholism are comparable to those found in pellagra patients. The latter, as will be brought out later, are also victims of a vitamin deficiency. For the time being it must suffice to note the existence of an etiological relationship between some symptoms of mental disorder and disturbed body chemistry. Such chemical disturbance may be due to the presence of a toxic substance like alcohol or the absence of a necessary substance like vitamin B..

TRAUMATIC PSYCHOSES

Trauma is the Greek word for wound so that the phrase *traumatic psychoses* can be translated as mental disorders caused by wounds or injuries. The fact of a direct relationship between such disorders and severe blows to the head is common knowledge. A fall or the impact of a policeman's nightstick may result in unconsciousness, disorientation, visual disturbances, or semiconsciousness. These facts are so well known as to require no elaboration. It is also well known that the amount of brain injury can be roughly gauged by the magnitude and duration of the mental symptoms. Momentary unconsciousness indicates less severe trauma than days of unconsciousness. Usually the loss of consciousness is an immediate consequence of the blow. However, on occasion such loss may not supervene until a few hours after the injury. This is doubtless due to the fact that in these cases one is confronted with injury to the blood vessels of the brain and the delayed unconsciousness signifies the consequence of a slow trickle of blood from the damaged vessels. The victim of brain trauma may recover from his unconsciousness rather promptly and show no after-effects. Sometimes recovery may be very much delayed and permanent sequelae are by no means unknown. That memory disturbances and the confusion of delirium may be due to mechanical injury of the brain requires no special emphasis. In fact, the diagnostic term *traumatic delirium* is employed to describe this condition. Ordinarily patients recover from such delirious episodes, but in some instances there may be more or less permanent changes in emotional life and other phases of mental life; hence the use of such diagnostic captions as *traumatic neurosis, post-traumatic personality disorder,* and *post-traumatic mental deterioration.* However, only a very small percentage of the cases admitted to psychopathic institutions are there because of a traumatic psychosis.

PSYCHOSES DUE TO CIRCULATORY DISTURBANCES

It was just pointed out that damage to the brain's blood vessels or interference with its blood supply may be the cause of mental disorder. Such damage or interference is not always the result of a head injury. It may be caused by pathological changes involving the heart, blood vessels, and associated systems. For example, a clot may be carried by the blood stream to a cerebral artery and lodge there, thus blocking the circulation in that part of the brain. This condition would then be called a *cerebral embolism*. Sometimes poor heart action is associated with kidney disease and such *cardio-renal* involvement would constitute another example of the kind of pathology with which we are dealing here. Probably the most familiar example is that of the hardening of the arteries of the brain or *cerebral arteriosclerosis*. The psychotic symptoms resulting from these circulatory difficulties may vary from mild memory disturbances to serious impairment of judgment and thinking. Of course the memory disturbances may also be very severe and the errors of judgment may be a consequence of the inability to bring past experience to bear on present problems. Loss of the ability to persevere in simple tasks, another common symptom, may also be related to the memory disturbance. The patient has trouble adding a column of figures or writing a short business letter or engaging in other tasks calling for sustained action.

PSYCHOSES DUE TO CONVULSIVE DISORDERS (EPILEPSY)

This heading should not be taken to mean that all epileptics are psychotic. Many of them have been capable of first-rate achievement. Julius Caesar and Alexander the Great were epileptics. Lord Byron seems to have had mild attacks. Other famous writers like Flaubert, Swinburne, Dostoyevsky, and Guy de Maupassant were also subject to epileptic seizures. Despite the long list of eminent victims it is nevertheless true that psychotic manifestations are constituent features in the lives of many. Mental deterioration may be so severe as to necessitate permanent segregation in an epileptic colony.

The nature of the attacks themselves are not the same for all patients. Some exhibit what is called the *grand mal* attack. This is marked by actual convulsions. The latter are usually preceded by some special experience such as moodiness, a slight feeling of nausea, a muscular jerk or some other change which the patient and the members of his family come to recognize as a signal of the impending attack. This signal is called the *aura*. It is followed by *loss of consciousness* as the patient *falls*. Incidentally, many epileptics accumulate scars as a result of these falls, since the automatic protective reflexes do not function for the epileptic. He falls more like a sack of potatoes and not like the normal person does as he trips over a rug. In one sense this simile is misleading for the epileptic is not limp like a sack. As a matter of fact his musculature tightens in spasmodic fashion. Sometimes as the chest muscles contract suddenly there is an actual *cry* or other involuntary sound produced. The rigidity of the muscles as the patient lies on the floor marks the *tonic* stage of the seizure. Soon this tonic stage gives way to a stage marked by alternate contraction and relaxation of the muscles affected. The latter kind of jerking is known as the *clonic* stage. There may also be *loss of sphincter* control and consequent involuntary bladder and bowel action as part of this motor turmoil. Even the jaw muscles and tongue muscles may go on a rampage and lips and tongue may be bitten. This clonic stage may last about a minute and then the patient becomes more and more relaxed and falls into a *stupor* of heavy, motionless sleep.

Contrasted with the extremely startling nature of the symptoms of a full-fledged grand mal attack are those of another type of epilepsy known as *petit mal*. This " little illness " has no aura or falling or prolonged loss of consciousness. There is just a momentary loss sometimes accompanied by an involuntary jerking of some muscle group. It is over in a few seconds and the victim goes right on with his work or play. There does not seem to be any mental deterioration associated with petit mal attacks. The third type, known as *Jacksonian* epilepsy might also be mentioned here. This is exclusively a motor disturbance. There is no loss of consciousness, just a sudden convulsion of an arm or leg or one side of the face. It is entirely a reflex-like jerking beyond the patient's control and is now known to be due to some factor irritating the motor area of the brain.

In recent years there has been much progress in the understanding of epilepsy and associated conditions.[3] This progress has been very much facilitated by the study of electrical potentials in the

---

[3] For a splendid and clearly written account of this progress as well as of the entire subject of epilepsy, see Lennox, W. G., *Science and Seizures*, New York, Harper & Brothers, 1941. William Gordon Lennox is President of the *International League against Epilepsy*. See also Gray, G. W., " The Attack on Brainstorms," *Harper's Magazine*, 1941, *183*, pp. 366–376.

brain. By means of *electroencephalograms,* as the records of these
" brain waves " are called, it is now possible to diagnose the type
of epilepsy with which one is dealing as well as to detect the existence of a " predisposition " or an " inherent tendency " to convulsive seizures. The irregularity in rhythm of these " brain
waves " or the *cerebral dysrhythmia,* as it is labelled technically,
is now regarded as the immediate antecedent of epileptic attacks.
This is to be thought of as the necessary or fundamental cause
with other factors such as emotional upsets, dietary indiscretions,
dehydration, certain drugs, etc., functioning as accessory causes.
The latter are important for purposes of explaining and controlling the actual incidence of the seizures. Not every person whose
encephalograms reveal a cerebral dysrhythmia is a victim of epilepsy, for only one out of twenty of such persons is subject to
attacks. It is the combination of fundamental plus accessory
causes which results in the activation of the predisposition. Precisely what is responsible for the dysrhythmia cannot yet be described with detailed specificity. Lennox and his co-workers conceive of it as an inherited " electro-physico-chemical " peculiarity
of nerve cells in the brain. The emphasis on the chemical factor is
given considerable justification in the light of recent success in
preventing epileptic seizures by means of a new drug. In 1937 two
outstanding neurologists, Merritt and Putnam, revealed the results
of their experimentally controlled search for an effective remedy
with their announcement of the relative efficacy of a synthetic
drug called *dilantin.* This white powder containing sodium, oxygen, nitrogen, carbon, and hydrogen has since been employed,
often with spectacular success, in thousands of cases.

It may not prove to be too much of a digression to add a few
words regarding the so-called epileptoid character traits. Mental
hygiene is particularly concerned with problems of this kind; for
adequacy of personal adjustment is clearly in part dependent upon
the individual's habitual traits. According to traditional psychiatric teaching, there is a recognizable constellation of traits associated with epilepsy. For example, in their discussion of the " personality of the epileptic " Maslow and Mittelmann give expression
to this traditional teaching in these words: [4]

---

[4] Maslow and Mittelmann, *op. cit.,* p. 526.

The patient's general personality may be essentially normal, but in some cases characteristic alterations are observable. Sometimes these alterations appear before the attacks occur; in still other instances they develop only after repeated attacks. Irritability is very evident. The patient is angered easily, raises his voice, and becomes abusive. This is combined with destructiveness in younger age periods; for example, the adolescent child is inclined to attack his playmates rather violently on slight provocation and to tear up and break things. The patient grows extremely self-centered. He is selfish, inconsiderate, and preoccupied with his own person; everything pertaining to it is of prime importance, and he expects others to have the same attitude. He may grow especially susceptible to flattery and boast childishly. The patient has a shallow, at times sentimental and superficial, interest in his environment. This interest is often religious. As McCurdy says, " These patients are considerate without being kind, religious without zeal, and . . . they will work for praise, but not for love."

To what extent the foregoing characteristics are attributable to epileptics as a class has been questioned by Lennox, who has had direct contact with victims of all ages, levels of education, and diversity of social background. It is his contention that the alleged personality characteristics are not ingrained concomitants of the epileptic constitution. To put this in his own language: [5]

Doctors who emphasize these characteristics have been most familiar with institutionalized patients. Physicians who deal with patients in hospital clinics or private offices find that the majority of patients are no more peculiar than the " run " of the population. A minority of patients show the type of personality described. In some instances the peculiarities appeared after seizures began and may be ascribed to them or to the social-psychological insults suffered. Invalids from chronic heart or joint trouble may show the same characteristics. In some patients a peculiar personality may indeed be an essential background for seizures, just as mental impairment is. In these cases similar characteristics should be discoverable in blood relatives who are free of seizures.

METABOLIC PSYCHOSES

The heading *metabolic psychoses* is merely an abbreviation for those disorders previously listed as " psychoses due to disturbance

[5] Lennox, *op. cit.*, pp. 58–59.

of metabolism, growth, nutrition or endocrine function." Quite obviously a very broad diagnostic category is involved here. Any abnormality of mental life resulting from disturbance of the series of transitions by virtue of which the human organism moves from babyhood to senility could be classified with this group of mental troubles. Normal metabolism depends on an adequate supply of chemicals for the maintenance of healthy action of the body's cells. These chemicals come from the food ingested as well as from the glands of internal secretion. As a consequence, abnormal metabolism may be caused by failure to receive the right sort of food or by failure of one or more of the endocrine glands to furnish the blood with the correct kind or amount of *hormone,* as these glandular products are called.

Thyroxin, the hormone produced by the thyroid gland, is indispensably necessary for healthy maturation. A baby suffering from a thyroid deficiency and not treated for this deficiency will become maldeveloped in mind and body. The maldevelopment is called *cretinism,* a condition marked by stunted growth both physically and mentally. In mental deficiency of this kind we have an excellent example of the type of disorder to which the concept of metabolic disturbance applies. Incidentally, when an adult suffers from prolonged deficiency of thyroid secretion the resulting diseased condition is known as *myxedema.* The disease in question is marked by a dry and puffy skin, low basal metabolism, slow pulse, loss of hair, general apathy, sluggishness of action, and mental dullness. The administration of thyroid substance is standard treatment for myxedema.

Having just given an example of mental disturbance based on an endocrine insufficiency, it will be in order to furnish an illustration of one due to a dietary insufficiency. *Pellagra,* a disease already mentioned in our previous discussion of alcoholism, is a good case in point. In this country pellagra has been rather common in our southern and central states. Dogs as well as human beings may have the disease. In the dog the disease is called *blacktongue.* The symptoms of pellagra are associated with the skin and the digestive and nervous systems. There are characteristic symmetrically located patches of reddened hardening of the skin as well as nausea, abdominal pains, and vomiting. Of particular interest to us are the mental symptoms: confusion, delirium, melancholia, lack of energy, occasional convulsions, and a serious impairment of the thought processes so that in the very advanced cases of deterioration one may find the patient verging on idiocy. Not all of these symptoms need to appear in every case of pellagra. Often the skin lesions are all that one finds. However, the entire array of symptoms are now known to be the result of disturbed metabolism. Technically, pellagra is classified as one of the *avitaminoses,* as the diseases resulting from vitamin deficiency are called. In other words, pellagra is a consequence of a poor diet or more specifically a diet poor in vitamin G (or B_2), also known as *riboflavin.* Prevention and treatment of pellagra consequently involves control of the diet so that the missing vitamin will be supplied.

There are numerous other conditions to be classified as metabolic psychoses not all of which can be listed here. We shall mention just a few by way of indicating their range and diversity. There are mental consequences linked with some cases of *diabetes,* a condition of disturbed sugar metabolism involving the endocrine portion of the pancreas. *Addison's disease,* resulting from tuberculous infection of the adrenal gland, may also manifest mental symptoms in consequence of the metabolic upset occasioned by the absence of the gland's hormone. In addition to such direct endocrine causes, metabolic psychoses may be due to changes incident to aging as exemplified by the symptoms of a *senile psychosis.* These refer to the whole train of symptoms people have in mind when they describe someone as " being in his dotage." There are also mental changes associated with the middle years, especially the period of cessation of the menstrual cycle in women. This period of *involution* is sometimes marked by acute despondency, insomnia, feelings of inferiority and worthlessness; hence the name *involutional melancholia* given to this disorder. It is by no means exclusively bound up with the termination of childbearing functions as the reference to the menopause might have suggested; for involutional melancholia also occurs in men. In part the condition may be due to the patient's inability to cope with the bleak fact that his mature years are over — that his physical attractiveness is on the wane and that years of decline are stretching ahead. Learning to grow old gracefully and cheerfully is an important part of mental hygiene wisdom.

PSYCHOSES DUE TO NEW GROWTH

Symptoms of mental disturbance can be observed in many patients suffering from a brain tumor. These symptoms will vary from patient to patient depending on the precise localization of the tumor. One may find hallucinations of the olfactory, gustatory, visual, and more rarely of the auditory senses. Drowsiness, speech disturbances, irritability, and childish jocularity may also be found. Of course along with one or more of the foregoing mental symptoms there has to be additional evidence indicating that a tumor and not some other condition is responsible for the symptoms in question. The examining physician suspects the existence of such a tumor when his clinical notes show that the patient's vision has been getting progressively worse, that there has been forceful or "projectile" vomiting despite the absence of any intrinsic digestive pathology, that there have been headaches of an otherwise inexplicable kind, that the pulse is very slow, and that the pressure of the cerebrospinal fluid (intracranial pressure) is markedly increased. There may be still other symptoms noted, but the ones mentioned will suffice to give a general idea of the symptomatic consequences of this type of brain disturbance. The details belong to works on neurology and neuropsychiatry. All that need be added here is that sometimes, as the tumor grows larger and interferes more and more with the cerebral circulation, there may be diffuse mental changes such as confusion, stupor, and general intellectual deterioration. Since the etiology of brain tumors is unknown, there is little to be said regarding prophylaxis; furthermore, since brain surgery offers the only mode of treatment, there is practically nothing for the psychiatrist to do except to guide the patient to a competent brain surgeon.

ORGANIC PSYCHOSES OF UNKNOWN ORIGIN

The caption employed for this section refers to the group of disorders which the system of classification we are following describes as "psychoses due to unknown or hereditary causes, but associated with organic changes." This category is logically closely related to the preceding one pertaining to brain tumors, since the etiology of the latter is also obscure or unknown. However, the present category rules out new growths and all other causative factors mentioned in the previous seven groups of disorders. It provides a diagnostic pigeonhole in which one can file all other cases of neural pathology accompanied by psychotic manifestations. As instances of such cases mention might be made of *Huntington's chorea* and *paralysis agitans*. These diseases are *always* the result of the demonstrable impairment of neural structure, the former being due to hereditary factors and the latter to more obscure factors, although infection seems to play a part in many cases.

Huntington's chorea differs from other forms of chorea in being incurable, not very common in children, and in being due to germ-plasm inheritance. It is characterized by spasmodic and irregular muscular action involving either a few muscle groups or the entire musculature depending on the stage to which the disease has advanced; for the course of the disease is a progressive one once the initial symptoms appear. Mental changes are among these early symptoms and they take the form of disturbed judgment, increasing irritability, and difficulty in getting along with others. In some of the patients these changes actually precede the choreic symptoms. In general, the total clinical picture grows worse through the years as the patient becomes more and more deteriorated. Many of these patients come into conflict with the police, for their deterioration leads them into trouble. Sex misconduct, delinquency of various kinds, alcoholism, and criminal behavior are sometimes associated with Huntington's chorea.

Paralysis agitans, " the shaking palsy," is a disease of middle age and old age. In advanced stages there is a constant tremor of hands and feet. The affected limb shakes or trembles like a mass of loose jelly in a strong wind. This coarse tremor may also involve the head and trunk; but the characteristic mask-like expression of the face and the constant flexion of the joints making for an impression of mechanical rigidity is of more diagnostic value. Actually the voluntary muscles are kept in a state of rigidity because the portion of the brain affected has to do with regulating the *tonus* of the muscles. By the latter term one designates the state of tension to which muscles are subjected as a result of automatic, non-voluntary neural action. An excess of tension will produce a tremor. *Paralysis agitans* is not always accompanied by mental symptoms. However, in many cases there are personality changes in the direction of chronic dejection, morbid hopelessness, and acute irritability which in rare instances may become sufficiently serious to render institutional commitment necessary. It is altogether likely that these mental symptoms are not primarily induced by the brain pathology; they are secondary effects as the patient realizes his condition is growing worse and finds himself confronted with the prospect of being an incurable invalid the remaining years of his life. The precise cause of the disease is not known although post-mortem dissection has revealed damage to the group of brain cells called the *lenticular nucleus*. In other words, the nature of the brain pathology is known, but the cause of the pathology still remains to be determined. Since *paralysis agitans* symptoms sometimes develop in conjunction with epidemics of sleeping sickness (*encephalitis lethargica*), it is not unlikely that the pathology in question is of infectious origin.

CONCLUDING REMARKS

We have now outlined the types of mental diseases regarded as structural or organic in nature. In etiology they have all conformed to what has already been described as the physicochemical kind of understanding. Infections, drugs, poisons, tumors, and tissue damage have all been seen to play a part in their causation. Nor has poor heredity been left out of consideration as an etiological factor. The meaning of *somatogenic* disorders should consequently be fairly clear. Clarification of the meaning of *psychogenic* disorders will be our next task.

4... *A SYNOPTIC VIEW*
OF FUNCTIONAL DISORDERS

As has already been mentioned, this chapter will be concerned with an exposition of the " disorders of psychogenic origin " or those " without clearly defined tangible cause or structural change." These are the disorders to which the " mind twist " hypothesis has been applied. What we have described as the psychological or experiential type of scientific understanding, in contradistinction to the physicochemical, will have increasing relevance from now on. For the time being, however, we shall have to continue with a descriptive review of the salient characteristics of each disorder of the functional kind in somewhat more amplified fashion than was deemed necessary in the summary of organic disorders as presented in the previous chapter.

Functional disorders are like the prophets in being classified in two groups: the major disorders and the minor disorders. Reference was made to this division on an earlier page when the distinction between psychoses and neuroses was being discussed. The neuroses or *psychoneuroses,* to introduce an alternative technical name, constitute the minor functional disorders. They are minor in the sense that their victims as a rule do not require institutional commitment. A psychoneurosis is not synonymous with " insanity." We shall postpone further consideration of this group of minor functional disturbances until after disposing of the major ones, the ones constituting the functional psychoses.

For our purposes it will suffice to furnish only a generalized picture of these disorders and to disregard exceptions and debates concerning suitable nomenclature. There are three functional psychoses: manic-depressive psychosis, schizophrenia, and paranoia. Each of these will now be considered in order.

Manic-depressive psychosis

The mental disorder characterized by extreme shifts of mood from extreme despondency to equally extreme elation is called *manic-depressive psychosis.* As the name implies, it refers to disturbed affective processes so that the same patient may exhibit maniacal excitement today and become a victim of stuporous depression next week or next month or next year. In fact, there are so many gradations in intensity and variations in duration of such emotional shifts observed by students of this psychosis that for purposes of descriptive convenience many of them employ a sixfold scheme of classification. A sketch of each of these six varieties or types of manic-depressive patients will serve as an excellent means of reviewing the chief symptoms of the disease in question.

1. **Manic Type.** In the manic type the prevailing emotional trend is in the direction of excitement. This excitement may take the form of either joyous good spirits or embittered vindictiveness: the excitement of pleasure or the excitement of anger. In either event one finds the manic patient talking at a rapid rate as though his ideas were crowding one another for a vocal outlet and making it impossible to stick to one theme. The technical name for this high-pressure talkativeness coupled with a logically irrelevant switching from topic to topic is *flight of ideas*. As might be expected, such a patient keeps more than his speech muscles active. He may gesticulate energetically, pace up and down furiously, or give other evidence of an abnormal amount of energy spilling over into motor channels. For very brief periods the manic patient may seem to be depressed and the excitement appear to have subsided; but such evanescent changes should not interfere with recognition of his basically manic status.

2. **Depressive Type.** In contrast with the foregoing manic patient the *depressive* type, as the name implies, exhibits signs of despondency as the chief affective trend. A victim of emotional depression, as we all know, is apt to bestir himself reluctantly and to speak slowly. The heavy-hearted individual seems incapable of quick thinking and snappy, decisive action. His thoughts come laboriously at a slow tempo so that instead of a flight of ideas we have *retardation* of ideas. There is a lack of initiative and reduced self-confidence as though morale had gone to smash. Action as well as thought is retarded under the circumstances. The depressed patient seems to be licked by his problems and a " what's-the-use-nobody-can-help-me " attitude seems to dominate him. In his de-

spair suicide may impress him as the only means of relief and because of this danger he must be protected from his own morbid impulses by suitable precautions and supervision. Often this means hospitalization throughout the period of depression.

3. **Circular Type.** There are some manic-depressive patients whose affectivity shifts from the manic phase to the depressive phase or vice versa in direct fashion; i.e., without the interposition of a neutral or " normal " emotional phase. There is an oscillation from one condition to the other and because of this the patient is said to belong to the *circular* type. It is *as if* the patient were coping with his personal difficulties by emotional attacks and emotional retreats or now deciding to fight it out and then deciding to surrender. By assuming such changes in attitude one might account for the alternation between the elation of anticipated victory and the despair of imminent defeat.

4. **Mixed Type.** The efforts to classify psychiatric patients have a good deal in common with our efforts to classify ordinary personalities. In everyday life we find ourselves employing certain conventional ideas about people in the abstract. Conventionalized abstractions of this kind are exemplified by such stereotyped concepts as " typical Frenchmen," " typical labor leader," " typical corporation lawyer," " typical college professor," or " typical old maid." There is a long series of such *social stereotypes* in terms of which we endeavor to catalog people. Even if we have not yet met a concrete representative of our conventionalized abstraction, we have " a pretty good idea " of what he must be like. Thus our " typical corporation lawyer " would be expected to manifest such recognizable " symptoms " as the cartoonists have sketched in caricatures of this political type: a well dressed, tall man with a bulging vest, hanging jowls and an inevitable cigar. We also expect this man to be reactionary in his political philosophy, not too scrupulous in his professional practices, and opposed to labor unions, government ownership, and federal supervision of big business.

In other words, the most characteristic " symptoms " of " corporation lawyerhood " can be specified. But the question is: how accurately do they describe flesh and blood corporation lawyers? If we were to attend a convention of lawyers, could we pick out or " diagnose " the corporation lawyers? Might there not be some who would escape diagnosis because they happen to be hollow-cheeked, pipe-smoking, cadaverous little men? Might there not be some who advocate stricter control of banking practices or some who under no circumstances would countenance unethical or shady maneuvers? In fact, these departures from the " type " might actually be more numerous than those who conform. It might be hard for us to find an example of the " pure " type — a corporation lawyer who measured up to our expectations in every respect. A similar state of affairs would prevail if we set out to hunt for a " typical " college professor, communist, artist, poet, or old maid. In one or more respects the individuals being scrutinized would fail to possess the full quota of expected " symptoms."

A similar state of affairs is found as soon as we try to classify individual patients into rigid diagnostic pigeonholes. The " pure " case — the one showing *all* the symptoms the textbook describes — is hard to find. Instead we find those who *approximate* our concept of the " manic type " or the " circular type " or the other types yet to be described. It is not at all unusual to have a patient who fails to exhibit one or more of the symptoms belonging to a given syndrome or who manifests symptoms of two diseases so that the psychiatrist is not sure whether to call it a case of manic-depressive psychosis or of schizophrenia. Within the group of manic-depressive patients there can be such a contradictory complex of symptoms in a given patient that the case cannot be fitted into a neat diagnostic stereotype; hence the need for a label like *mixed type*.

The phrase *mixed type* is consequently employed to describe those patients whose symptoms of disturbed emotionality cannot be classified as being either manic or depressive. Instead one finds both manic and depressive components in the same patient at the same time. A familiar instance of such a combination of reactions is furnished by what the psychiatrists call an *agitated depression*. By this term one refers to patients who, although obviously dejected, keep on the move as if being driven by excitement. Worried excitement is a rough equivalent of the meaning involved.

And then there are cases in which, despite evidence of the patient's fundamentally manic status, the expected additional symptom of flight of ideas is absent. There is a heightening of mood and more action than one would regard as normal, but no production of a stream of ideas. Under the circumstances this would induce the examining psychiatrist to speak of an *unproductive mania*. As a final instance of a mixed type mention might be made of what is called *manic stupor*. This paradoxical term is applied to patients whose mood verges on elation or excitement and who manifest flight of ideas, but whose lack of motor responsiveness suggests the retardation ordinarily associated with the depressive type.

5. **Perplexed Type.** There are some manic-depressive patients whose chief symptom is not so much the disturbed affectivity as the bewilderment it seems to occasion. These patients are obviously *perplexed* as though unable to grasp what is happening to them and around them. In their perplexity they may act in somewhat bizarre fashion. Incidentally, this type is sometimes confused with one of the schizophrenic types to be mentioned later in our discussion of schizophrenia. However, the persistent bewilderment in a setting of sadness should serve as a useful distinguishing characteristic.

6. **Stuporous Type.** Another form of manic-depressive manifestation which might be confused with some cases of schizophrenia is called the *stuporous type*. Patients of this kind are so acutely depressed as to be indifferent to their surroundings. Instead of being perplexed they just don't care. It is hard to arouse their interest and they may refuse to eat, to converse, or participate in the life around them in any way. They may even fail to react to vigorous prodding so that the descriptive term *stuporous* is by no means inappropriate. The marked resemblance of this sort of behavior to that of some schizophrenic patients will be clear as soon as we outline the implications of the concept of schizophrenia.

SCHIZOPHRENIA

Approximately one-half of the patients resident in psychopathic institutions are diagnosed as suffering from *schizophrenia*. The wide prevalence of the disorder thus makes it of particular significance to the mental hygienist. Just what is to be included within the concept of schizophrenia is hard to compress within the limits of a simple declarative sentence. The word itself was introduced early in this century by the Swiss psychiatrist Bleuler as a sub-

stitute for the term *dementia praecox* which the German psychiatrist Kraeplin had introduced in 1898.[1] The latter term is Latin
for the phrase *adolescent insanity*. Kraeplin had been impressed
by the fact that the disease usually appears during adolescence
and that mental deterioration occurs very early in the course of
the disorder. On the other hand, Bleuler observed there was no
necessary association between this developmental period and the
onset of the disease. In addition, Bleuler emphasized that dementia
praecox or schizophrenia is not so much a single disease entity as
a group of disorders. He preferred to speak of the *schizophrenias*
rather than of schizophrenia.

Casual inspection of a large number of schizophrenic patients
is apt to perplex the untutored observer. The behavior and attitudes of the patients will be so different as to render it hard to
understand what they have in common to justify the use of a single
diagnostic label for all of them. To a certain extent such a naïve
observer will overcome his perplexity once he grasps Bleuler's
reason for coining a word like *schizophrenia,* a Greek compound
meaning " split mind." As Bleuler interpreted the symptoms, this
group of patients has divorced itself from effective contact with
the physical and social environment. This divorce constitutes one
sign of splitting.

Another such sign is furnished by examination of the patient's
ideational and emotional processes. Ordinarily, for the normal individual, there is a congruous relationship between his thoughts
and feelings. To think of bad news is to arouse feelings of sadness
and to think of good news is to arouse feelings of happiness. For
our physician to announce that we have to submit to a dangerous
and costly operation is to cause us to experience feelings of dread,
anxiety, and despair. Contrariwise, when he tells us the symptoms
we took to mean malignant cancer are of no consequence and that
we are actually in superb physical condition, we experience joyous
relief. There is thus a constant congruity or harmony between the
life of ideation and the life of emotion in the mentally healthy indi-

---

[1] It might be more accurate to say that Kraeplin's writings gave currency
to the term dementia praecox. The term itself was first employed by French
psychiatrists. The phrase *démence précoce* was used for the first time by Morel
about the year 1860. Some discussion of this point can be found in Zilboorg, G.,
and Henry, G. W., *A History of Medical Psychology,* W. W. Norton & Company,
New York, 1941, p. 458.

vidual. But what Bleuler noted was a split between these ideational and emotional aspects of mental life. There was a disharmony or an incongruity between the news imparted to the patient and his affective reaction to that news. The death of his son might leave him indifferent, but the sight of a folded handkerchief in the pocket of a fellow-patient might cause acute emotional upheaval. Apparently what we are dealing with in schizophrenia is a split between the mental life of the patient and the reality of the outer world as revealed by the incongruity between the events of that world and those of the patient's inner world of thought and feeling.

As was just pointed out, the schizophrenic patient is apt to remain unmoved when confronted with situations the average person would regard as interesting or exciting or important. This lack of interest, this *apathy*, is one of the clues for which the psychiatrist searches in sizing up the possible existence of a schizophrenic trend in one of his patients. Another clue to be considered has to do with the patient's willingness to mix with people, to be communicative, and to take an active part in the affairs of his little world. The schizophrenic patient shows no such willingness. He prefers to keep to himself, to be a spectator rather than a participant or, if we prefer, a dreamer rather than a doer. This is what is meant by saying that the schizophrenic personality is *seclusive* or what one psychiatrist rather aptly called the *shut-in* personality.

A shut-in, seclusive personality of this kind gives one the general impression of emotional aloofness. It is hard to get to know such a person and to find out just what he is thinking and feeling. The emotional aloofness has been interpreted to mean a disinclination to brave the uncertainties of active competition in the rough-and-tumble of ordinary business and social rivalry. According to this interpretation, the schizophrenic individual prefers to run away from such uncertainties to an inner world of imaginary success and congenial fantasy. All this adds up to a composite picture of a withdrawn, seclusive, rather shy, introvertive, unaggressive, and somewhat apathetic individual as the prototype of the schizophrenic personality make-up. This generalized picture may be given more definiteness by scrutiny of its various clinical manifestations. Orthodox psychiatry conventionally recognizes four clinical types: the simple, the hebephrenic, the catatonic, and the paranoid. We shall consider these in order.

1. **Simple Type.** Patients belonging to the diagnostic category of *simple* schizophrenia are not likely to impress the layman as mentally disturbed. The lay observer is more likely to indulge in moral condemnation, for this type of patient tends to induce comments indicative of disapproval such as " shiftless," " aimless loafer," " untidy bum," or " lazy idler." To the trained observer such character traits are all consequences of an underlying apathy. In turn the apathy may be a consequence of an underlying fear of failure. The patient lacks ambition and industriousness because, if this interpretation is sound, he is afraid to fail. By not trying he guards himself from the ignominy of failure. If we never tried to master the violin, nobody can accuse us of being a poor violinist. The apathy of the schizophrenic of this type may consequently be a defense mechanism. At all events through the years the apathy may become more pronounced and its effects more noticeable. It is commonly held that many chronic drifters, ne'er-do-wells, prostitutes, hermits, and hoboes are really victims of schizophrenia of this simple type. Occasionally initial contact with patients of this type will cause one to suspect feeblemindedness as a diagnostic possibility. However, more careful probing into the case history will enable one to make a differential diagnosis. The present mental dullness will be revealed as the outcome of years of *indifference* to opportunities for learning and mental growth.

2. **Hebephrenic Type.** In contrast with the simple type, the *hebephrenic* patient will strike the average observer as " positively crazy." The discrepancy between the hebephrenic's behavior and normal behavior is so conspicuous that anybody can recognize it. One does not have to be a mental expert to detect the silliness and absurdity of the patient's conduct. The silliness manifests itself in word, deed, and gesture. Often the patient talks unintelligible nonsense. Part of this unintelligibility is due to a tendency to invent new words and phrases. This coining of new words and phrases is what the psychiatrist calls the use of *neologisms,* just as he describes the constant repetition of meaningless phrases on the part of the hebephrenic patient as *verbigeration.* Sometimes the patient persists in saying the same phrase over and over again or in making the same ridiculous movement over and over again. This is technically known as *stereotypy.* Irrelevant laughter is another common symptom. There is no understandable relationship

between the laughter or the grimacing and what the patient happens to be saying or doing. Hallucinations are also common symptoms. The total picture is one of weird, bizarre disorganization as if an uninhibited amateur with little talent for clowning were trying to substitute for a professional clown.

3. **Catatonic Type.** Just as the hebephrenic type is apt to be fantastically active, so the catatonic type of schizophrenic patient is apt to veer to the opposite extreme of inactivity. The patient seems to be resistant to outside intrusion. He seems to have adopted a firm " leave-me-alone-and-don't-bother-me " attitude. He refuses to talk or to answer questions. Such *mutism* is usually accompanied by the correlative symptom of *negativism*. The latter term refers to the tendency to resist any suggestion by doing the opposite of what is suggested: to eat when told not to eat, to sit down when requested to stand, to stand when requested to sit, etc. By extension negativism is also taken to refer to any form of consistently uncooperative behavior carried to unreasonable extremes. It is often observed in the " contrariness " of young children whose negativistic set causes them to say " no " or " I don't want to " irrespective of what is proposed. They may even refuse candy or a proffered toy or some other object ordinarily desired.

Catatonia can often be recognized by the fact that the patient will hold a fixed bodily attitude of a queer sort for hours at a stretch. Absurd muscular postures often stand out in consequence as an obvious sign of catatonic schizophrenia. And sometimes there is a curiously passive condition of the musculature during these poses so that an attendant can mold the limbs in arbitrary fashion. The imposed posture will then be maintained until the attendant introduces another change. This symptom for obvious reasons is called *waxy flexibility* or *lead pipe flexibility*. By some psychiatrists it is interpreted as an expression of the patient's resigned *indifference* to external happenings or but another sign of apathetic withdrawal from the surrounding environment. In fact, should the indifference become very extreme as manifested by no reaction to external pushes and prods and yells, the psychiatrist would speak of the condition as an example of *catatonic stupor*. To some observers such a catatonic stupor has suggested a heavy sleeper lost in the land of dreams and most unwilling to be called back from his little land of private fantasy to the waking world of stern reality, hard work, and constant care. It seems so much easier and pleasanter to be a successful dreamer.

Catatonic postures are not always characterized by waxy flexibility; for, in some patients, the negativistic attitude governs the musculature. Under such circumstances when the attendant tries to move the patient's arm upward, he meets sturdy resistance in a downward direction. Continued efforts to push elicit continued counter-pressure so that, when the manipulator ceases to push, the arm comes down with a resilient snap. This sort of resilient counter-pressure is an example of what is technically called the phenomenon of *spring-resistance*.

In brief, the catatonic type reveals several of the following constellation of symptoms: negativism, mutism, waxy flexibility or spring-resistance, and often a seeming stupor. The latter symptom is qualified by the word " seeming " to allow for the possibility of descriptive error in calling the condition a stupor. At all events there is some doubt about the reality or completeness of the stupor in many cases because, when improvement sets in, the patient's recollections show that he was not entirely unaware of what was going on around him while he was supposed to have been unconscious.

4. **Paranoid Type.** Some schizophrenic patients seem to be preoccupied with the need of protecting themselves against imaginary enemies. There is much talk about schemes to poison, electrocute, or " to put a spell " on the patient. In other words, the paranoid type of schizophrenic patient is a victim of *delusions of persecution*. Often this type of patient also thinks of himself as a person of some importance so that delusions of *grandeur* may accompany those of persecution. These delusions are illogically and ridiculously elaborated. They lack coherence and plausibility, and this lack is one means of differentiating this form of schizophrenia from another rare form of functional disease known as paranoia. These paranoid patients are classified as schizophrenic because of an underlying apathy. Even the patient who regards himself as of royal blood or a great conqueror may often give the impression of being basically indifferent about his grandiose status. This apathy is apt to become more pronounced as the patient's mental condition deteriorates. Incidentally, there is some evidence which

suggests that difficulties of sex adjustment having to do with homo-sexual inclinations may play a prominent role in the causation of these paranoid trends.

PARANOIA

A rather rare form of functional psychosis is that of *paranoia*. This psychosis is not to be confused with the paranoid form of schizophrenia. As we have just indicated, the latter disorder mani-fests illogical thinking, blurred ideas, hallucinations, and loosely organized delusions of grandeur and persecution. The only symp-tom a victim of paranoia shares with the paranoid schizophrenic is the conviction of being a victim of persecution.

However, the precise form in which the delusion of persecution develops is not the same for the two classes of patients. In paranoia there is a logical, coherent, systematic, plausible elaboration of some misinterpreted actual event. Far from being indifferent or apathetic the paranoid individual takes these elaborations very seriously. He talks about them and worries about them constantly. They form the basis for his thinking about plots and counterplots. Unlike the schizophrenic, he keeps in firm touch with the real world in all respects except with reference to what bears on the theme of his delusional system. And even the latter is not with-drawn from contact with his environment. On the contrary his delusion of persecution, forming a central focus in his mental life, influences his daily routine in innumerable ways. Chance remarks of acquaintances are taken as subtle references to the schemes of his enemies. He may even succeed in persuading an innocent out-sider that the delusional interpretation is logically sound and en-tirely justified.

A paranoid patient behaves like an intelligent spy in a foreign country. He is constantly on the alert for evidence of the next move to be made by the " enemy." Nor does he remain passive when he thinks such evidence has come his way, for the paranoid personality is a fighting personality. He is even ready to defend himself by violent means if necessary. This is what makes para-noia a dangerous disorder.

Many paranoid patients are well read, educated, and intelligent, and their general behavior by no means conforms to the popular notion of insane behavior. There is no evidence of anything wrong with their general make-up as far as contact with reality and knowledge of everyday affairs are concerned. Those who are better acquainted with them might regard them as " cranks " on particular subjects. When carefully analyzed it is found that the " crankiness " in question involves a distortion of reality. The individual has *projected* his own fears and suspicions into the world and the distortion follows.

To render this more understandable it suffices to note what happens to a person when a gossip informs him that the new neighbor is a dope addict. The information may actually be altogether erroneous, but if it is accepted as true, then even innocent actions of the neighbor may be construed as indications of his addiction. Should a second telephone be installed in his home, it is interpreted as a means of enabling the supposed addict to keep in touch with his dope peddler from the privacy of his room while the unsuspecting members of his family are busy at the other telephone. If the new neighbor keeps to himself, it is taken to mean fear of discovery. On the other hand, if he seems sociable and friendly, that is regarded as a clever maneuver to throw people off the trail. In other words, once a wrong conviction grips us, it colors our judgment and distorts our interpretations. But the chief difference between such " normal " distortion and paranoid distortion is the impossibility of dislodging the wrong conviction in the latter case. Once the normal person gets to know his neighbor and finds no positive evidence to support the gossip's accusation and much contrary evidence, there is a tendency to question the truth of the original accusation. The accusation itself is finally dismissed as idle or malicious gossip or the result of mistaken identity. However, the delusion of a paranoid patient cannot be dislodged in this way by the accumulation of convincing facts. Such facts are always explained away, frequently in ingenious fashion, and the integrity of the delusion remains undisturbed. The paranoid patient continues to *project* the fears, hates, and suspicions clustering around his delusional system.

The dynamics of the projective mechanism in the case of some paranoid individuals can be regarded as personality quirks induced by illicit sex urges. According to this hypothesis, the patient may have been distressed to find himself prompted to indulge in some sinful act. He reacted to this impulse by feeling guilty and humiliated. To protect himself from such humiliation, he denies the desire as *his* desire and repudiates it by telling himself he abhors such misconduct. Other people may be low enough to cherish such vile longings, but not he. In fact other people do, and one ought to do something about it. Every self-respecting man ought to be on his guard against the machinations of such vile degenerates. By this time he has developed the beginnings of a delusional system to protect himself from the stress of his original self-accusations. Now instead of accusing himself, he can accuse others. To put this metaphorically, it is as if he rid himself of his illicit desires by throwing them out, or projecting them. As long as he keeps them projected he can be safe from the distress of self-condemnation.

Whether this hypothesis be accepted or not, it is nevertheless true that the mechanism of projection plays an important role in the paranoid's thinking. It makes him a suspicious individual. He is always on his guard and is apt to misinterpret what one says or does. He is the kind of person who becomes involved in a never-ending series of law suits or the kind of person who keeps writing warning and complaining letters to the newspapers. It is alto-gether likely that some fanatic reformers and vice crusaders of the belligerent variety are to be classified as paranoid personalities. As might be anticipated, the paranoid personality is a grim, some-what humorless, irritatingly suspicious personality. This suspi-ciousness shows itself by the existence of *ideas of reference* or the tendency to maintain others are talking about him or acting against him even though impartial investigation fails to substan-tiate such ideas. To sum up: paranoia is a functional psychosis characterized by *systematized* delusions of persecution and projec-tion of delusional ideas as revealed by suspiciousness, humorless aggressiveness, and ideas of reference.

THE PSYCHONEUROSES

The distinction between the concepts of a psychosis and a psy-choneurosis has already been introduced in our earlier reference to neuroses. It will be recalled that the latter term was used to designate the mild mental disturbances or those minor mental troubles which, although distressing, rarely call for institutional commitment. Now these functional neuroses may also be called *psychoneuroses.* There are some psychologists who endeavor to differentiate neuroses from psychoneuroses, but the resulting distinctions are so trivial that no useful purpose is served by the differentiation. (The situation is roughly comparable to the efforts of speech experts who try to maintain a rigid distinction between stuttering and stammering.) Accordingly, we shall regard the terms as essentially synonymous and, because of its brevity, the adjective *neurotic* will be used as a substitute for psychoneurotic.

Experts differ in their terminology and in their views regarding these functional disorders. Some divide the group into a rather long series of special disorders and others compress the symptoms into a relatively few diagnostic categories. For present purposes it will be enough to limit our exposition of the psychoneuroses to three representative disorders: hysteria, psychasthenia, and neurasthenia. Consideration of the variety of symptoms associated with these disorders will suffice to furnish an adequate grasp of the meaning of a neurotic disturbance.

HYSTERIA

Everybody has heard of hysteria, but its popular connotation is different from its technical meaning. As a technical diagnostic term *hysteria* is not limited to the exhibition of uncontrolled emotionality to accord with the journalistic phrase " attack of hysterics." In fact it is hard to set limits to the possible scope of hysterical reactions. Although the etymology of the word *hysteria* — from the Greek term for uterus — suggests a uniquely feminine disturbance, the condition in question need have nothing to do with such disturbance, for men as well as women suffer from hysteria. Furthermore, even in the case of women patients there need be no uterine factor involved.

A complete listing of possible symptoms of hysteria is an almost impossible task. In fact, there is no fixed hysterical syndrome as there is for most diseases. Because of this circumstance some experts refuse to classify hysteria as a disease entity and prefer to think of it more as a character defect. The reason for this is that in many respects the hysterical reaction is rooted in unconscious bluff or deception. In addition, those who have had extensive experience with hysterical patients have been impressed by their ethical shallowness. Their conduct is not motivated by high moral principles. On the contrary, they seem incapable of genuine solicitude for the rights of others. Selfish expediency and selfish prudence appear to dominate hysterical behavior. For the hysteric the crucial question is not, " Is this a decent, honorable thing for me to do? " but " Can I get away with this? " What he tries to get away with is a matter of gaining his ends by unconsciously pretending to be physically disabled.

Because of this basic mechanism, hysteria may resemble the symptoms of innumerable physical disorders. This is the mechanism which disposes the hysteric personality to take refuge in symptoms of illness as a way of escape from personal difficulties, the need for honest labor, or family responsibilities. The technical name for this mental mechanism is *flight into illness*. It furnishes a key to understanding the dynamics of the hysteric's motivation.

There is no single symptom invariably characteristic of hysteria. Any symptom of any disease which a skillful actor might simulate can become an hysterical symptom. Such symptoms, of course, are legion: blindness, deafness, lameness, nausea, tremors, stupors, etc. It is *as if* the hysteric were deliberately acting the role of sick man or cripple in order to outmaneuver the opposition like the small boy who gets excused from his school examinations by pretending to suffer from a " terrible headache." In the case of the small boy the simulation of illness is deliberate. Such *deliberate* simulation of a disease or a disease symptom is called *malingering*.[2] Some mental specialists refuse to regard the hysteric as a

[2] The psychological factors responsible for malingering or hysterical behavior may conceivably also induce some individuals to go beyond the mere *simulation* of disease or injury. To attain their ends they may resort to measures calculated to produce the real thing. For example, prisoners sometimes deliberately amputate a foot or a hand in order to be transferred from a convict labor gang to a hospital ward. Military surgeons are familiar with similar drastic measures undertaken by conscripts in the hope of dodging military service. Some conscripts have been known to insert sharp instruments into the external auditory canal with sufficient force to puncture the drum membrane. Others may act on the belief that a venereal disease will suffice to bar them from the armed forces and, in accord with this mistaken belief, they intentionally proceed to expose themselves to infection. Although, strictly speaking, acts of this sort involve a result which cannot be classified as malingering, the motivation is very likely the same as that of the malingerer. As a consequence it might be desirable to enlarge the customary definition of malingering to mean " one who feigns illness or who deliberately injures himself or who intentionally contracts a disease for the purpose of achieving a selfish goal by deceptive means." The latter qualification is necessary to differentiate the malingerer from the scientific investigator who may " deliberately injure himself " in order to study nerve regeneration, the therapeutic value of a new drug, or the efficacy of a new anesthetic. For a recent discus-

malingerer, because he is not aware of his simulation. The bluffing is an unconscious process over which the hysteric has no control.

However, in actual clinical practice it is by no means easy to maintain such a rigid distinction between malingering and hysterical behavior. One merges into the other. Possibly all hysterical behavior, genetically considered, starts as malingering and in the course of years develops into hysteria. At all events such an hypothesis is in line with the learning process in general. What we first attempt deliberately and consciously becomes automatic and habitual once we become expert at it. Learning a new dance step is a vividly conscious affair for the beginner. He has to attend to every step. Months later, though, he can execute the series of intricate steps while he carries on a conversation with his dancing partner. In the light of these considerations it is not too farfetched to regard every malingerer as a potential hysteric or every hysteric as an *habitual* malingerer. The hysteric, in other words, has made malingering his specialty; hence he can carry it out with the deftness of an expert.

We have already stated that there is no fixed array of symptoms to be found in hysteria. They vary from patient to patient. It is nevertheless possible to introduce a measure of order into the somewhat chaotic medley of symptoms by grouping them into so-called clinical forms. Description of these forms will aid in learning just what the concept of an hysterical reaction implies. Since avoidance of such reactions is important for effective mental hygiene, we shall not hesitate to introduce a rather tedious catalogue of common hysterical manifestations.

1. **Anxiety Hysteria.** There are neurotic patients whose outstanding symptom is an inexplicable anxiety or chronic sense of apprehension. Whether they are to be regarded as victims of hysteria is a moot question. Some specialists prefer to think of them as victims of a separate psychoneurosis to which they have given the name of *anxiety state*. There may be some justification for this contention; because the patients of this group seem to be somewhat more highly developed along ethical lines than the rank and file of hysterics. However, those who interpret the anxiety as an hysterical phenomenon are impressed by what they take to be a

sion of some aspects of this problem, see Flicker, D. J., " The Self-Inflicted Injury," *Amer. J. of Psychiatry,* 1942, *99,* pp. 168–173.

similarity in the mental processes responsible for the anxiety and those assumed to be responsible for the production of unambiguous hysterical symptoms. These mental processes are not directly accessible to the patient's direct observation. For the most part he is unable to recognize them. This lack of awareness on his part is what is meant by calling them *unconscious* processes. According to this interpretation, the anxiety in anxiety hysteria is an expression or a symptom of an unconscious conflict between rival impulses. An example of such a conflict would be the antagonism between the desire to honor one's father and the wish to inherit his money. Another example might take the form of a desire to earn an honest living competing with the unconscious desire to gamble with marked cards. Fear of yielding to the unconscious wish is then taken to be the explanation for the anxiety. In other words, the anxiety is regarded as an involuntary expression of an inner conflict with persistent temptation.

2. **Conversion Hysteria.** More clear-cut symptoms of hysteria are found in *conversion hysteria*. This name is given to those cases in which the underlying conflict or the unconscious desire expresses itself by means of a symptom of bodily disease or by some physical disability. It is as though the energy of the conflict becomes transformed or converted into some symbol of the conflict. To revert to our earlier example: the temptation to gamble with marked cards might result in a paralysis of the fingers of the right hand. Paralysis of this sort would protect the victim from yielding to his temptation. He might even be able to cash in on his paralysis by collecting disability insurance. By " cheating " the insurance company there is no need to take a chance on being caught cheating at cards. The hysterical paralysis is a safer way of getting " easy " money.

Conversion hysteria takes many forms. According to one conventional classification, six forms are recognized as variants of conversion hysteria. These are known as the anesthetic, the paralytic, the hyperkinetic, the paresthetic, the autonomic, and the amnesic types; to enrich our grasp of the concept of hysteria, we shall take these up in order.

a. *The Anesthetic Type.* In this form of hysteria absence of normal sensation stands out as the most conspicuous symptom. The functional blindness or deafness called *hysterical* blindness or deafness are stock illustrations of this form. Another example is furnished by the symptom of hysterical *anesthesia,* or a functional loss of sensitivity in some particular region of the skin surface. Incidentally, such anesthetic regions conform to popular rather than to technical ideas of neurology and anatomy. The patient will complain of numbness of the hand or leg. This is known as *glove anesthesia* and *stocking anesthesia,* respectively. Anesthesia due to injury to the cutaneous nerve is never restricted to the skin regions covered by gloves and stockings. The regions involved are always far more irregular in outline and the zones separating the anesthetic from the normal areas are never identical with the skin covering wrist, ankle, elbow, or knee joints. Familiarity with the precise distribution of each branch of the cutaneous nerve thus enables one to decide whether a given case is one of hysterical anesthesia or not.

b. *The Paralytic Type.* An hysterically disposed soldier whose unit is being moved to the scene of action may wake up one morning and discover that he can no longer move his right arm. Upon careful examination the army physicians fail to find any injury to the arm muscles, its motor nerves, or the relevant parts of the brain cortex. They would consequently designate the case as one of hysterical paralysis after ruling out the possibility of deliberate shamming or malingering. Under the circumstances the soldier would actually be unable to lift his arm just as all of us, when terror-stricken, may temporarily lose control of given limbs. When such functional loss of muscular control dominates the clinical picture the patient is classified as belonging to the *paralytic* type of hysteria.

There are all sorts of motor disability to be found among hysterics. One patient may be unable to walk, another to raise his left eyelid, a third to bend his knee, a fourth to get his vocal cords to vibrate, and a fifth might complain of some other disability. Various technical terms have been introduced to designate these different disabilities. For example, paralysis of a single limb is called *monoplegia,* that of both arms is known as *diplegia,* and if an entire side of the body is disabled one speaks of it as an instance of *hemiplegia.* Similarly, the term *ophthalmoplegia* designates paralysis of the muscles attached to the eyeball. Paralyses of this kind may also be due to structural or organic causes. To differentiate the hysterical kind from their possible organic counterparts one labels them as *hysterical* by speaking of " hysterical hemiplegia," " hysterical diplegia," etc.

c. *The Hyperkinetic Type.* Instead of a functional absence of movement as in paralyses some hysterics suffer from a functional excess of movement or *hyperkinesis.* Consequently, the hyperkinetic type of hysteria is to be thought of as characterized by an *excess* of muscular tension or of movement occurring independently of the patient's voluntary control. In this sense one may observe spasms, tremors, stuttering or even convulsions as manifestations of conversion hysteria. Another common symptom of this type of hysteria is the spasmodic jerking of a circumscribed group of muscles so that at more or less periodic intervals the corner of the mouth may twitch or the nose wrinkle or one shoulder jerk upward. Twitching or jerking of this kind exemplifies what is meant by a *tic.* However, one should not be hasty and regard all tics as indications of hysteria. Neither should all of the other hyperkinetic phenomena be so regarded. Many of them are consequences of neural pathology or of other non-hysterical causes. Without knowledge of such pathology and such causes the amateur diagnostician is apt to be wide of the mark in attributing every tremor, spasm, and tic to some underlying hysterical conflict.

d. *The Paresthetic Type.* Just as *anesthesia* means loss of skin sensations and *hyperesthesia* a heightening of such sensitivity, so the term *paresthesia* means a perversion of cutaneous sensations. When the latter symptom is present the patient complains of tingling in his fingers or that it feels as if insects were crawling over his chest or as if someone were drawing a rake over his shins. Sometimes the complaint may be described as a " burning sensation " in a given skin region. By this time it should be almost superfluous to have to add that in the case of an hysterical paresthesia no organic or objective cause for these tinglings, burnings, and other morbid sensations can be discovered.

e. *The Autonomic Type.* Some hysterical patients reveal a disturbance of digestion or of heart action or of breathing or of elimination as their chief symptom. They are classified as belonging to the *autonomic* type because control of such bodily functions is regulated by the *autonomic* nervous system. All of the glands and smooth muscles associated with digestion, circulation, respiration, etc., are subject to such autonomic control. Disturbance of this control may be due to either structural or functional causes. Even the joint action of both kinds of causes may serve to complicate the clinical picture in a particular patient.

As in the foregoing types there may be a wide variety of specific symptoms associated with this type of conversion hysteria. Almost any of the autonomic systems may be involved. Thus some cases of palpitation of the heart may be of hysterical origin. In fact almost any symptom of excessive fear or anxiety may be thought of as an autonomic function. *Hyperhidrosis* or excessive sweating is not uncommon among hysterics. Neither is *globus hystericus,* the feeling of a lump in the throat caused by functional spasm of the smooth muscles of the gullet. Occasionally one comes across what is technically described as *hysterical edema or blue edema.* This refers to disturbances of circulation in the limbs of some victims of hysterical paralysis. The affected part becomes puffy and bluish as more and more fluid accumulates; hence the designation of blue edema.

There is no need for all such possible autonomic symptoms to be listed. It will be noted that all of them, as was just mentioned, are also symptoms of emotional stress. There is probably a close kinship between many cases of so-called anxiety hysteria and those of this autonomic type. The selection of a suitable diagnostic label in the individual case will depend on which aspect of the clinical picture obtrudes itself more conspicuously. If the patient's apprehension stands out as the more prominent aspect, then the case might be classified as one of anxiety hysteria. Contrariwise, if the patient seems but mildly fearful and centers his complaint on the autonomic symptoms, then the latter aspect is made the basis for classification. In the last analysis this issue of appropriate classification is not nearly as important as that of getting to understand the clash of motives responsible for the emergence of specific hysterical symptoms.

f. *The Amnesic Type.* Understanding the motivation of the hysteric is an issue which applies to all types of hysteria. However, it is particularly prominent in those cases in which the patient seems motivated to push aside or to forget certain ideas or experiences. The symptoms of hysteria in these cases are attributed to the abnormal forgetting or *amnesia* involved in what is taken to be an active, if unconscious, process of thrusting unwelcome ideas away from the center of attention. In the amnesic type of hysteria, in other words, there is a *dissociation* or a splitting-off of one group of ideas from the stream of normal consciousness. The hysterical symptoms are interpreted as a consequence of this cleavage, for the split-off group of ideas is assumed to continue an independent, dynamic existence away from the focus of normal ideational control.

A convenient illustration of this sort of forgetfulness is furnished by what is known as *hysterical somnambulism*. In this kind of sleep-walking the sleeper reacts to his immediate environment. He avoids obstacles in the room as he moves from the bed to the door on his way downstairs to the kitchen. He may help himself to a glass of milk from the bottle in the refrigerator and then walk back to his bed. Upon being awakened he has no recollection of what he did or saw or touched or heard. His *amnesia* for the events of his sleep-walking experiences is seemingly complete. It is as if these events were altogether *dissociated* [3] from those of normal, waking consciousness. In addition to somnambulism there are other trance-like states characteristic of this type of hysteria. The very concept of dissociated personality as exemplified and popularized in Stevenson's *Dr. Jekyll and Mr. Hyde* might thus be included in a catalogue of hysterically motivated amnesic episodes.

An especially dramatic example of this kind of episode is supplied by what is called a *fugue*. This word means *flight* and it is used to designate those cases of hysteria in which the patient flees from his home moorings to a new environment where he takes up a new life and often a new identity. The flight in question should not be confused with that of a fugitive from criminal justice. Unlike the latter, the hysterical patient has no recollection of his former life. His two lives are rather drastically dissociated from one another in his spontaneous memory. This is brought out by noting what happens upon the termination of the fugue. The patient wakes up one morning in a distant city in possession of his

---

[3] The concept of dissociation has been regarded as purely descriptive by some psychologists. Others have invoked it as a genuine explanatory concept. For some contemporary evaluations, see Miller, J. G., *Unconsciousness*, New York, John Wiley & Sons, Inc., 1942, pp. 19, 35, 64–65, 227–230; White, R. W., and Shevach, B. J., " Hypnosis and the Concept of Dissociation," *J. of Abnor. and Soc. Psychol.*, 1942, *37*, pp. 309–328.

original identity and his original memories, but unable to recall or reconstruct the events experienced during the days he was living in this distant city as a victim of a fugue.

It should now be clear why amnesia is singled out as the central factor in this manifestation of conversion hysteria. To understand patients of this type the investigator has to probe into the dynamics of their forgetfulness and ascertain what they had to gain by not remembering what the ordinary man would never forget. According to this approach, the dissociation is motivated and the job of the psychological detective is to track down the guilty motives. Whether he can secure a conviction after tracking them down is another question. What we mean to say by this metaphor is that achieving permanent cures of full-fledged hysteric personalities is a mighty difficult achievement.

PSYCHASTHENIA

The name for the psychoneurosis we have just considered is of ancient origin. Even Greek medicine employed the word *hysteria*. *Psychasthenia,* however, the psychoneurosis we are about to consider, is of much more recent vintage. Pierre Janet, distinguished French contemporary of Sigmund Freud, introduced the term as a means of referring to cases in which persistent and morbid fears, obsessions, doubts, and compulsions stand out as the chief symptoms. Janet regarded such symptoms as the result of the victim's failure to maintain effective bonds between the medley of ideas and impulses every person experiences during the course of daily living. This is another way of saying that some of the ideas and impulses can become detached or *dissociated* from the main stream of control. Under ordinary circumstances, as Janet conceived of it, it requires a certain minimum amount of energy to exert such control. He even ventured to speak of "psychic energy" in describing the process. This is possibly a dubious descriptive phrase, but it must be introduced in order to understand what Janet was driving at in coining a word like *psychasthenia*. Taken literally this term means a lessening or an absence of mental strength or energy.

Many psychologists dislike terminology suggesting that there are two kinds of energy: mental and physical. This dislike is understandable, but we must not permit it to keep us from appreciating the drift of Janet's thinking. After all, even in physics we talk about mechanical energy and thermal energy and electrical energy, meaning merely that there are different ways in which energy can be expended and not that there are qualitatively different kinds of energy. What harm is there in adding to the list a phrase like *psychic* or *mental* energy as a convenient way of indicating that the *product* of energy expenditure was a letter, a poem, a new idea, a decision, a speech, a musical composition or any other achievement commonly classified as a *mental* achievement? This we believe is all that Janet intended by his concept of psychic energy.

Let us digress for a moment to consider a simple parallel to Janet's conceptual scheme. A man going out to mail a letter does not have to carry a burden even if it is a bulky letter. It is easy for him to get to the mail box and complete his errand. The operation calls for no marked concentration, effort, or tension. Contrast this with the picture of the harassed suburbanite rushing to make his train from the city late in December with an armful of Christmas packages and a pocketful of greeting cards to be mailed. Extricating these cards in order to drop them in the box while hanging on to seven or eight parcels is by no means a casual procedure. It requires considerable energy expenditure, adroit balancing, and a fairly complex act of attention. A momentary lapse of vigilance and one or more of the packages is likely to be " dissociated " from the clutches of the frantic shopper. As he bends down to retrieve the fallen parcels, he might strike his elbow against the mail box and drop some of the others. There would then be a " disintegration " of the total pattern of impulses involved in his original intention of mailing the cards, catching his train, and transporting the bundles to his home. Each impulse refers to a separate errand or a separate commission. Organizing his energy in order to execute all these commissions required an " integration " of these impulses, but the lapse of attention or the failure to keep the muscles of the clutching fingers properly tensed resulted in their " disintegration." In Janet's terminology our shopper's loss of control over his packages and their consequent " dissociation " would have been due to this " lowered psychic tension."

As applied to Janet's concept of psychasthenia the foregoing analogy simply means that it requires energy and effort for us to keep our obligations, intentions, desires, and aversions harnessed together in fairly unified or " integrated " fashion. A dangerous lowering of what Janet called the requisite *psychic tension* and some impulse or idea is likely to become dissociated and no longer be amenable to conscious control just as our hypothetical shopper could no longer control the fallen package by flexing the fingers of his empty hand.

Dissociation of the kind met with in cases of psychasthenia gives rise to obsessions and compulsions. Any idea which keeps obtruding itself despite efforts to dislodge it constitutes an *obsession*. In mild form everybody has experienced such obsessive ideas. After a long evening of bridge the tired player finds it impossible to fall asleep because vivid visual imagery of the cards keeps obtruding itself. Some people have great difficulty dislodging distracting tunes that " keep running through their heads." The imagery or the tune seems to have taken possession of the focus of attention and all efforts to shunt out the invader by " thinking of something else " prove futile. When the obsessive idea implies action of some sort, the individual may find himself forced to yield to the summons. It is this motor aspect of obsessions which is stressed by the term *compulsion*. A familiar instance of a " normal " compulsion is the common experience of having to go back to try a locked door to make altogether sure of having locked it. Children often indulge in harmless compulsions on their way home from school by yielding to the impulse to touch every lamp post or to step on every crack in the sidewalk.

The psychasthenic patient's efficiency is seriously curtailed by his obsessive-compulsive trends. He finds them acutely distressing. Often he regards them as signs of impending insanity and this adds to his distress. It should be remembered that we are not referring to the kind of " normal " ones mentioned in the preceding paragraph. The slightly worried student yielding to what he recognizes as a foolish or superstitious impulse to toss a coin in order to learn whether he passed the examination is not a victim of psychasthenia. But his roommate whose morbid fear of germs compels him to wash his hands every time he touches a book, a dollar bill, a door-knob or any other object handled by other people — such a roommate is to be so regarded. Some psychasthenics find it impossible to retire without indulging in a complicated, time-consuming ritual they know to be foolish: the bottles in the medicine cabinet have to be counted three times, the hair has to be brushed a fixed number of times, the discarded garments have to be arranged in a precise order while reciting some prayer ten times, the top button of the pajama coat has to be fastened and unfastened five times before the teeth are brushed, then the last two buttons are fastened — and so to bed.

The vagaries of such obsessive-compulsive troubles are endless in their variety. We once were consulted by a neurologist whose weeping psychasthenic patient complained of the persistent conviction that she might unwittingly have killed somebody. She sometimes drove her car around for many blocks looking for a strange pedestrian she had noticed at some intersection. The search was prompted by the morbid fear that her fender might have struck him as she drove by. Although in one sense she was positive nothing of the sort occurred, nevertheless she was beset by lurking doubts. To achieve inner peace she simply had to hunt for him. If she could not locate him, she would call the police to get a measure of reassurance by being told that no accident had been reported. Or else she would telephone the hospitals to make assurance doubly sure. Her days were filled with such constant preoccupations and morbid uncertainties that she had neither the time nor the energy to devote herself to her domestic duties in efficient manner. Another psychasthenic patient once referred to us was obsessed with the idea of stabbing her husband to whom she was intensely devoted and whom " she couldn't think of hurting."

It is thus possible to catalogue a long list of fears and compulsions of which psychasthenic patients complain. These are often given formidable Greek labels like *trichotillomania* or the morbid impulse to tear out one's own hair, and *mysophobia* or an abnormal dread of being contaminated, and *paralipophobia* or the morbid fear of neglecting something. There is no increase in intellectual grasp of the psychological issues involved by memorizing a long list of Greek compounds. A particular patient may have as one of his psychasthenic symptoms a tendency to be panic-stricken by the possibility of having to manipulate the number *13*. It is easy enough to consult a Greek dictionary and learn that " triskaideka " means *13* in Greek. By adding the suffix *phobia* we get the awe-inspiring word *triskaidekaphobia,* but no more insight into the patient's troubles than we had before our mastery of the new

Greek term. Accordingly, we shall not bother to introduce a list of " manias " and " phobias " symptomatic of psychasthenia. It is more illuminating to find out what lies back of the symptoms than to give them learned labels, and there is always the danger of confusing the learned label with genuine understanding. Moliere's physician, who taught that opium makes people sleep because it contains " a soporific principle," is a classic illustration of such confusion.

Understanding of psychasthenic symptoms is facilitated not only by Janet's concept of " lowered psychic tension," but also by Freud's emphasis on the symptoms as expressions of poorly handled personal conflicts. The individual patient is regarded as having failed to work out an effective way of carrying his mental burdens; hence the dissociation. This is the crux of Janet's contribution.

But why the perseveration and the annoying obtrusion of the morbid doubts, ritualistic compulsions, and distressing obsessions? A follower of Freud might answer, " To protect their victim from some impulse of which he is afraid or to enable him to make peace with a protesting conscience." Thus the morbid fear of dirt and the concomitant impulse to make a ritual of hand-washing may be symbolic of an underlying fear of giving way to some illicit sex impulse. The individual may despise himself for cherishing such an impulse. His extreme precautionary attitude toward contamination might then be interpreted as the result of an impulsive effort to buttress the foundations of his self-respect. In accordance with this view the phobia would serve as a shield to ward off self-accusations and the compulsive washing would be a symbolic expression of the desire to " wash his sins away." The manifest fear of self-contamination could consequently be explained as a reaction to the latent fear of self-condemnation. This type of interpretation will serve as a rough indication of the general drift of Freud's [4] approach to the psychoneuroses.

---

[4] Neither Freud nor his followers adopted Janet's diagnostic nomenclature. For them the group of symptoms which Janet labelled *psychasthenia* were disposed of under a different label. There is no need to discuss the relative merits of the rival opinions in this summary of mental disorders. It suffices to outline the kind of personal difficulty which all agree are representative of *psychoneurotic* disturbances.

NEURASTHENIA

Almost 75 years ago an American physician, George Beard, introduced the term *neurasthenia* as an appropriate designation for what was at one time known as Beard's disease. Its functional nature was not recognized at first. In fact, Beard himself regarded the condition as one of " nervous exhaustion " and this notion is still preserved in the literal meaning of the word *neurasthenia*. However, as employed today, the word no longer carries this literal meaning; for it is now known that the nerves as such are quite undamaged.

The outstanding symptom of neurasthenia is constant fatigue in the absence of any manifest justification for such fatigue. Even after resting, the patient still complains of being tired. In some patients the fatigue disappears by evening only to return the next morning. Along with this chronic fatigue there is the associated symptom of *hypochondria,* or the tendency to be morbidly anxious about one's health. The patient worries about his digestion, his pulse, his diet, his nerves, and every passing ache, pressure, or change in temperature. He may develop the habit of checking on the latter with a clinical thermometer several times each day. He may also develop the habit of going from one clinic to another or from one health resort to another. The glowing claims of patent-medicine vendors arouse his eager interest. He lives in a world of medicine bottles, enema bags, prescriptions, and pills.

Strictly speaking, neurasthenia is not a disease or a clinical entity, but a way of reacting to disease or the threat of disease. In other words, neurasthenic symptoms may accompany or follow any illness or the fear of an illness. A person suffering from a mild heart ailment may become excessively concerned not only about his heart, but about his health in general. A boy may become terrified by what some ignorant friend or some designing quack tells him about the dangers of masturbation. In his terror he begins to look for the expected signs of injury to his health. He begins to wonder whether he is as wideawake and as strong as " normal " boys of his age. This looking and searching lowers his threshold of sensitivity to trivial bodily changes and what the average person would never notice becomes a symptom of disease for him. This sense of concern about the seeming weakness of one's body may easily carry over to other areas and the neurasthenic boy may come to worry about his capacity to do efficient school work or to become popular with the younger set. A general sense of personal *inadequacy* may thus easily develop as the psychological product of hypochrondriacal brooding. What the late Alfred Adler popularized as an " inferiority complex " has obvious roots in neurasthenic attitudes.

THE PSYCHONEUROSES AND THE CONCEPT OF NERVOUSNESS

Before completing this outline of functional disorders it might be advisable to digress a little at this point in order to amplify the meaning of the adjective *neurotic* or *psychoneurotic* as applied to people in such common phrases as " neurotic housewife " or " neurotic personality." It ought to be clear that the neurotic patient is not merely a " nervous " patient. However, as the term has tended to be employed in popular writings, one gains the impression that for many of the writers any manifestation of nervousness is to be equated with a symptom of neuroticism. This is very likely the kind of error which may induce many sensitive readers to classify themselves as neurotics. Because such erroneous self-classification is sometimes a source of personal worry, it might be good mental hygiene to devote a little space to disposing of this common error.

Not all psychoneurotic patients conform to the popular notion of the " nervous type." This is especially true of some hysterics whose very casualness about their functional lameness or anesthesia in itself is a bit abnormal. Of course, many other hysterics as well as most psychasthenics and neurasthenics do strike the observer as " nervous " individuals. Nevertheless, it is probably unwise and inaccurate to base a diagnosis of neuroticism on nothing more than signs of nervousness. The situation provoking the nervous reaction must also be taken into account. In other words, although the discomfort, tenseness, and emotional upset characteristic of nervousness may also be found in cases of neuroticism, there is a difference in the causation of the reaction of nervousness. The normal person is nervous because of a present threat, but the neurotic patient is nervous because of what happened a long time ago and what may have no direct, plausible bearing on the events of his immediate environment. A few simple examples should serve to clarify this distinction.

It is normal to be mildly nervous in a situation of mild stress and extremely nervous in a situation of acute stress. For an inarticulate football hero to show signs of nervousness as he lumbers to his feet to " say a few words " at the victory banquet does not mean that he is a neurotic football player. Nor is the person who finds it impossible to be altogether relaxed and calm while his dentist is drilling away at a molar to be classified as a neurotic, even though careful study should reveal such definite symptoms as heightened blood pressure, palpitation of the heart, sweating palms, constricted throat muscles, and inability to concentrate on the dentist's small talk. Furthermore, people ought not to be classified as neurotic just because they weep at funerals or are nervous and depressed when some member of the family circle is seriously ill. These are all instances of normal, non-neurotic nervous reactions; for the situations provoking them constitute a present threat to the welfare of the victim. With the disappearance of the threat the nervousness will vanish. All of us can understand why circumstances of this kind produce nervous behavior.

In the case of the neurotic patient such spontaneous understanding of his nervousness or fear or anxiety is not to be had. It strikes everybody as queer for the psychasthenic to be so nervous after touching the door knob. His explanation that there might be germs on the knob does not suffice to render his fear understandable. The mere theoretic possibility of contact with germs does not constitute a situation of present stress for the normal individual. Something in the psychasthenic patient's *past* must thus be at the root of his nervousness. He is to be viewed as a neurotic not so much because of his nervousness, but because the nervousness is prompted by dissociated or unconscious experiences in terms of which an intrinsically neutral or harmless situation is reacted to *as if* it were a portent of danger. A neurotic person might thus be nervous about handling unsterilized paper money or reading a story dealing with the theme of divorce or the smell of roasted peanuts. None of these instances would constitute situations of stress for the normal individual. They would not make him nervous as he might be if he received stolen money, became involved in a divorce scandal, or woke up at night smelling smoke. For the neurotic it is his emotionalized past which distorts his present reactions and renders him nervous even when his friends and his own judgment often assure him " there is nothing to be nervous about." Sometimes the neurotic is unable to specify just what makes him so jumpy and apprehensive. He is afraid without knowing what he fears or why he fears. This is very different from the agitation of the convict being strapped in the electric chair or the nervousness of the holdup victim.

Mixed symptoms and miscellaneous groups

The " official classification of mental disorders," upon which the outline being presented here is based, allows for cases whose symptoms fail to conform with any of the syndromes in assured fashion. For example, with reference to hysteria provision is made for a " mixed hysterical psychoneurosis." Similarly, under the heading of " psychasthenia or compulsive states " there is a sub-heading which justifies a diagnosis of " mixed compulsive state." One is even permitted to employ a still broader diagnostic term like " mixed psychoneurosis." All this means that not every case of mental disorder can be pigeonholed with clear-cut definiteness.

Recognition of the existence of mixed symptoms is not enough; for in addition to the need for providing for " mixed " cases circumstances have forced the psychiatrist to introduce a few more diagnostic labels. A somewhat paradoxical one in the " official classification " is termed *without psychosis* and followed by a list of disorders from which the examining psychiatrist is to choose the one most applicable to the given case. What this means is that patients are often sent to a psychopathic hospital for observation or custody even though no psychosis or psychoneurosis is found to be present. Epileptics, alcoholics, and drug addicts need not always be psychotic and may nevertheless require hospitalization. The hospital record will then read: " epilepsy without psychosis " or " alcoholism without psychosis." Similarly, cases of mental deficiency may find their way into a psychopathic hospital and some of these may be complicated by accompanying psychoses, while others may be reported as " mental deficiency without psychosis." Epidemic encephalitis is responsible for another diagnostic complication. This disease leaves some of its victims with psychotic symptoms as we have already explained. However, it may also produce only mild changes so that, while hospitalization may be required, there is no serious disruption of behavior, no alarming loss of emotional control, and no drastic impairment of intellect. In the latter event the hospital entry for this class of patients would read " disorders of personality due to epidemic encephalitis."

Another group of patients whose symptoms cannot be squared with any of the preceding diagnostic concepts is made up of persons possessing extreme difficulties of adjustment to ordinary standards of decent, socially responsible conduct. They are neither psychotic nor neurotic in the sense in which these adjectives are applicable to unambiguous cases of mental disorder. Nevertheless they exhibit a seeming pathological inability to be mindful of routine obligations and sensitive to the rights of others. It is as if they lacked the capacity to appreciate the ethical implications of conduct problems. The word *appreciate* is used advisedly in this context; for with them it is not a question of not *knowing* the " difference between right and wrong," but of not being able to evaluate such a difference emotionally. In a purely cognitive manner they " know " that it is " wrong " to stab a child, to pour acid on a puppy, or to steal money from a blind newspaper vendor. However, they fail to experience the emotional revulsion which crimes of this character arouse in the average man. Such affective responsiveness is probably more necessary in determining ethical choices than abstract knowledge of legal codes. This was rendered quite evident during the prohibition era when vast numbers of " respectable " citizens violated the law because they " didn't *feel* it wrong to take a drink."

The group of patients we have reference to are incapable of *feeling* any act to be wrong. In the older psychiatric literature they are sometimes referred to as victims of " moral insanity " or " moral imbecility." These terms are no longer employed as suitable for diagnostic purposes. Instead the modern psychiatrist calls these patients *psychopathic personalities*.[5] What he means to convey by this designation is that some sort of inherent and presumably in-

---

[5] For a recent discussion of the meaning of *psychopathic personality* in the light of fairly detailed case histories, see Cleckley, H., *The Mask of Sanity*, St. Louis, C. V. Mosby & Co., 1941.

curable character defect dooms the patient to a life of trouble with
organized society. As a consequence the psychopath grows up to
be an *amoral* adult. His misdemeanors and crimes — cheating,
lying, embezzling, debauching, and seducing — bring disgrace
upon his family, but the disgrace has no influence on him. Neither
has imprisonment, punishment, pleading or any other customary
technique of dealing with the black sheep of the human flock. The
psychopath is no more capable of sincere regret or genuine remorse
than he is of experiencing righteous indignation. In despair his
family often sends him to a psychiatric hospital or else he maneuvers himself there in order to dodge a prison sentence. In this way
he and those like him come to be catalogued in official hospital
statistics under the general caption " without psychosis " and the
specific diagnosis of " psychopathic personality."

Another diagnosis appearing under the aforementioned general
caption is that of *primary behavior disorder*. This is further sub-
divided into cases of " simple adult maladjustment " and " primary behavior disorders in children." The former term is applied
to non-psychotic and non-neurotic adults who have trouble in getting on with the family or with their business associates and whose
poor adaptability is not attributable to the possession of a psychopathic personality or as a *secondary* effect of some illness. The behavior disorder is therefore labelled *primary*. Similarly, there are
so-called " problem children " whose troubles are *primary* in this
meaning of the word. Their difficulties of adjustment seem to have
nothing to do with a history of nervous or mental disease, feeblemindedness, malnutrition, etc. Nevertheless, they seem to be unable to learn to rid themselves of socially disturbing habits. They
may indulge in violent temper tantrums, be neighborhood bullies,
too afraid to fight for their legitimate rights, acutely jealous,
chronic liars, sex delinquents, etc. The list of possible complaints
is tediously long. In very extreme cases these " problem children "
along with the " problem adults " may be hospitalized for study
and treatment. Should this happen, they will then be listed in official reports as cases of " primary behavior disorders." They are
not so much medical or psychiatric problems as psychological
ones ; for the underlying difficulties are so frequently matters of
inadequate habit training, unintelligent application of rewards
and punishments, and other features of the psychology of learning.

STATIC *versus* DYNAMIC INTERPRETATIONS

The introduction of such apparently indefinite and vague terms as " mixed compulsive state " and " mixed psychoneurosis " may strike some as a blundering diagnostic procedure. It might seem as if the diagnostician were as mixed up in his thinking as he alleges the patient to be in his symptoms. This apparent lack of diagnostic certainty is by no means eliminated when the psychiatrist seems to make confusion worse confounded by his diagnoses of the cases discussed as illustrations of the " miscellaneous " group. To regard a given patient as a psychiatric case even though he has no psychosis and no psychoneurosis may be going too far in the opinion of those who like problems to be disposed of in neat, clearly organized fashion. For them the introduction of tentative and borderline diagnoses is annoying; indeed, they are apt to view such diagnoses as adverse reflections on the professional competence of the man making them. They are the people who like to argue that a " man is either sane or insane " or a " thing is either black or white." Transitional cases that cannot be tucked away in trim diagnostic pigeonholes are irritating to people of this sort. They are not likely to be favorably impressed by such diagnoses as " psychopathic personality, without psychosis," or " primary behavior disorder."

Actually the use of such diagnostic labels does not necessarily mean that the psychiatrist using them is concealing his ignorance under an impressive bit of unrevealing technical verbiage. On the contrary, it may even be viewed as a tribute to the modern psychiatrist's enriched understanding of the scope and complexity of his task. He has come to learn that people cannot always be classified in rigid categories. He has also learned that it is more important to understand them than it is to classify them. Furthermore, he has come to realize that people — healthy people as well as sick people — are *unique* personalities. Because of this uniqueness they react differently to the stresses and strains incident to making a living, striving for security, and keeping up with the Joneses. The contemporary approach to personality disorders stresses these individual differences in the dynamics of mental life. As a consequence one finds the present generation of psychiatrists and psychologists deeming it more relevant to get at the motives of a disturbed personality than to venture to dispose of the case by finding some suitable diagnostic label.

The older approach to mental disorders was a more static approach. It was more concerned with description and classification than with explanation and understanding. It was following the pattern of older, orthodox medicine in regarding illness as a more or less static entity with fixed characteristics so that one could speak of a " typical pneumonia " or a " typical scarlet fever." The modern medical man now realizes that pneumonia, scarlet fever and other diseases do not always conform to type. He also knows that his job is not to treat a disease, but to treat a sick patient.

In the same way the modern psychiatrist is pursuing a more dynamic approach and regards his job as less that of cataloguing his patients into types and more that of understanding them in their individual uniqueness as creatures of hope and despair, ambition and frustration, petty lusts and noble loves. For him the story of their lives is as important as the condition of their reflexes, the chemistry of their blood, or the status of their endocrine glands.

PART THREE

PREVENTING MENTAL DISEASE

5...
SOME GENERAL
PROBLEMS OF PROPHYLAXIS

O UR HASTY REVIEW OF MENTAL DISEASES IN THE LIGHT OF CON-temporary psychiatric classification should have made it abundantly clear that the mental hygienist concerned with preventing such diseases is tackling a tremendous job. It is not only a difficult job, but an important one in terms of national welfare. Its difficulty is due to the large number of factors entering into the etiology of mental disorders. Furthermore, all of these factors have not yet been worked out and of those which have been isolated not all are clearly understood. Just what this implies will be brought out a little later in this chapter.

For the time being it might be preferable to consider the social urgency of the mental hygienist's task. In what respects does it concern national welfare? To answer this question it is necessary to get some notion of the number of our fellow citizens whose lives are blighted by the handicap of mental disease. One cannot even appreciate the magnitude of the problem by merely reading hospital statistics of such disease. Statistical reports are cold and impersonal. Their adequate appraisal demands imaginative insight so that the naked numerals become clothed with the texture of images symbolizing the distress, the worry, the panic, and the anxiety not only of the individual patients involved, but of their families as well. Often the pain of mental illness is more acute for the family than it is for the patient. Not only does such illness frequently mean months and years of exclusion from the family circle, but also deteriorating changes in mood and impulse. What was once earnest purpose becomes catatonic indifference. The joyous, friendly youngster may become an irascible, troublesome postencephalitic. A young father's devoted interest in his family may change to callous neglect through the years as his alcoholism becomes worse and worse. Children of psychopathic parents worry over the possibility of transmitting mental disease to *their* children. Or else they worry over their own stability and their own chances of escaping mental breakdown. There is no need to become morbid or sentimental about these matters; but there is a need to take cognizance of them if the human implications of prophylactic mental hygiene are not to be altogether lost in the *unimaginative* perusal of the statistical issues to be introduced in the next section.

HOW COMMON ARE MENTAL DISORDERS?

It is hard to furnish a comprehensive and accurate estimate of the total number of people in need of psychiatric aid. Many psychoneurotics never reach the consulting room of a mental specialist so that their cases are never entered on official lists. Those who do find their way to the office of some specialist are also apt to escape the statistician's dragnet, because such private patients are not reported to any central agency. The situation is somewhat different in the case of the psychoses; for these disorders are more likely to call for segregation in state institutions and by examining the records of such state hospitals one can obtain an *estimate* of the prevalence of mental disease as a whole and of the relative frequency of the more common psychoses. The accuracy of the estimate will vary in different parts of the country, since to a certain extent the number of patients hospitalized will depend on the adequacy of the available accommodations and on some other factors as brought out in the following quotation: [1]

Commonly, there are higher hospitalization rates when facilities are available in greater abundance, are easy of access, and when the type of treatment that a hospital provides has the confidence of the community. Even in a State with superior hospitalization facilities there are many persons with mental disorders who prefer to receive treatment from private psychiatrists, visit out-patient clinics, or are able to achieve the minimum degree of adjustment to their everyday environment necessary to obviate psychiatric treatment.

It should thus be clear that mental disorders are more prevalent than is indicated by reference to hospital statistics. Such statistics constitute an underestimate rather than an overestimate. With this understanding the data presented in Table 1 might now be considered.

[1] *Patients In Mental Institutions*, 1938, U. S. Department of Commerce, Bureau of the Census, Washington, 1941, p. 3.

The data in the table of first admissions are taken from page 13 of this same government report.

TABLE 1

ALL PATIENTS ADMITTED FOR THE FIRST TIME DURING THE YEAR 1938
" TO ANY INSTITUTION FOR MENTAL DISEASE, PUBLIC OR PRIVATE,
WHEREVER SITUATED IN OR OUTSIDE OF STATE, EXCEPTING INSTITU-
TIONS FOR TEMPORARY CARE ONLY "

Mental Disorder	Number	Per Cent
Total	110,323	100.0
With psychosis	*93,541*	*84.8*
General paresis	7,827	7.1
With other forms of syphilis of C.N.S.	1,497	1.4
With epidemic encephalitis	332	0.3
With other infectious diseases	456	0.4
Alcoholic	4,940	4.5
Due to drugs and exogenous poisons	634	0.6
Traumatic	624	0.6
With cerebral arteriosclerosis	11,989	10.9
With other disturbances of circulation	720	0.7
With convulsive disorders	1,942	1.8
Senile	8,576	7.8
Involutional psychoses	3,845	3.5
Due to other metabolic, etc., diseases	1,338	1.2
Due to new growth	173	0.2
With organic changes of the nerv. syst.	895	0.8
Psychoneuroses	4,229	3.8
Manic-depressive	12,282	11.1
Schizophrenia (dementia praecox)..........	21,279	19.3
Paranoia and paranoid conditions	1,862	1.7
With psychopathic personality	1,207	1.1
With mental deficiency	3,055	2.8
Other, undiagnosed, and unknown	3,839	3.5
Without psychosis	*16,782*	*15.2*
Epilepsy	641	0.6
Mental deficiency	1,686	1.5
Alcoholism	7,604	6.9
Drug addiction	931	0.8
Personality disorders due to encephalitis	159	0.1
Psychopathic personality	1,095	1.0
Primary behavior disorders	408	0.4
Other, undiagnosed, and unknown	4,258	3.9

This table is particularly illuminating because it gives the relative distribution of cases in terms of the same system of psychiatric classification on which our outline of mental disorders was based. It should also be added that the figures in question were obtained from reports submitted by public and private hospitals. In the original table these are classified separately, but to avoid undue complication these columns have been omitted. It might be of interest though to note that the percentage of frequency of each disorder is not precisely the same for each type of hospital. Alcoholism, for example, is more frequent in the private hospitals while general paresis is more common in the public ones.

Since presentation of this table was anticipated in the two preceding chapters, all of the technical expressions employed have already been explained. It should be observed that about 15% of these " first admissions " are designated as being " without psychosis." As has been previously mentioned, this does not mean the same thing as no mental trouble. The patients of this group do have trouble getting along in the community and their hospitalization follows as a result. One should also realize that the figures in the table refer to " first admissions " only. The " readmissions " and the resident population are not included. When these are added the total population for the year in question is quadrupled; for the " first admissions " amount to 110,323 while the total for all patients equals 444,989. This latter figure constitutes a rate of 342.8 per 100,000 of the general population.

A good way to grasp the import of the figures for the " first admissions " is to realize that they mean an average of more than 300 people being admitted to our mental hospitals every day of the year. Furthermore, Landis and Page estimate that there are practically the same number of mental patients being looked after in private homes, in ordinary hospitals and in other institutions as in the official psychiatric hospitals so that the actual incidence of mental disease is undoubtedly far larger than these figures suggest. In fact, some statisticians working on the problem have ventured to predict " that at least 1 person out of every 20 will become a mental hospital patient at some time during his life." [2] This should not be interpreted to mean that 5% of the total population is

---

[2] Landis, C., and Page, J. D., *Modern Society and Mental Disease,* New York, Farrar & Rinehart, Inc., 1938, p. 24.

doomed to die in a psychopathic hospital; because not all of those hospitalized remain there. Of those listed as " without psychosis," the discharge rate was close to 90 out of 100 admissions during 1938. The corresponding rate for the group listed as " with psychosis " was 50 per 100. Not all of these discharged patients had recovered. Some of them were merely " improved," while others were " unimproved " and still others failed to have a report made on their condition at the time of discharge. The latter are listed as unclassified. These findings [3] are summarized in Table 2.

TABLE 2

PATIENTS DISCHARGED FROM STATE HOSPITALS FOR MENTAL DISEASE DURING 1938 AND RATE * PER 100 ADMISSIONS

Condition on Discharge	Number	Per Cent Distribution	Rate per 100 Admissions
Total	56,756	100.0	56.5
With psychosis	45,841	80.8	51.9
Recovered	15,142	26.7	17.1
Improved	25,514	45.0	28.9
Unimproved	4,734	8.3	5.4
Unclassified	451	0.8	0.5
Without psychosis	10,915	19.2	90.1

* " Rates for patients with psychosis discharged as recovered, improved, and unimproved based on total admissions with psychosis; rates for patients discharged without psychosis based on total admissions without psychosis."

It may be of interest to add that the foregoing figures do not apply uniformly to all of the individual classes of mental disorder; for " the largest proportion of discharges in recovered and improved condition occurred among those psychoses due to " infectious diseases, to syphilis, to the use of alcohol and other drugs and among the patients diagnosed as psychoneurotic, manic-depressive, and as cases of psychopathic personality.

ARE MENTAL DISORDERS ON THE INCREASE?

It would be easy for uncritical alarmists to cite evidence in support of the contention that the entire country " is rapidly going crazy." They could point out that in 1923 the number of hospital-

[3] *Patients In Mental Institutions*, 1938, U. S. Department of Commerce, Bureau of the Census, Washington, 1941, p. 53.

ized mental patients was only in the ratio of 241.7 per 100,000 but that this ratio climbed steadily through the years until it had reached a figure of 351.7 per 100,000 by the year 1939.[4] Statistical evidence of this sort is especially subject to misleading propaganda unless the bare figures are qualified by relevant interpretations. This kind of misleading propaganda is often introduced by advocates of schemes for " improving the human race " by sterilizing the " unfit." They often bracket the mentally diseased with the paupers, the feebleminded, the criminals, the alcoholics, and the epileptics. All these are lumped together into a single group of the biologically unfit which threatens to wipe out the biologically fit by a greater rate of propagation. To ward off this calamity they urge prevention of propagation by means of relatively minor surgical operations[5] on these men and women of " bad stock." By this simple maneuver, so they teach, only men and women of " good stock " will be left to become the parents of the next generation. Eugenical sterilization is thus their proposed means of coping with " the rising tide of insanity." Before examining the soundness of this proposal it would be in order to find out whether their alarm is justified. To do this one must raise this simple question: Does the fact that each year is marked by an increase in the population of our psychopathic hospitals necessarily signify an increase in the prevalence of mental disorder in the country as a whole?

In the opinion of those who have studied this question in critical fashion within the recent past there is no cause for great alarm. The increase does not mean that more people are suffering from mental breakdown, but that more cases of such breakdown are being recognized and committed. It also reflects a greater willingness on the part of the public to permit commitment once antiquated, harsh methods of institutional control are displaced by modern, humane methods. In those states in which new, well-

---

[4] *Op. cit.*, p. 11.

[5] The operations in question should not be confused with those undertaken by the veterinarian when he castrates a male animal and spays a female. Such animal operations involve removal of the sex glands. But this is not involved in the recommendations of the eugenicists. All that they advocate is cutting the vas deferens in the male and either tying off or cutting the fallopian tubes in the female. This procedure renders it impossible for impregnation to occur, but does not result in any secondary changes in physique or personality. The sterilized patient may still marry and still be capable of desiring and enjoying the normal sex act; but parenthood can never follow from such indulgence.

staffed institutions have been erected the relative number of mental patients is significantly larger than in those whose mental hospitals are prison-like structures, inadequately staffed and unattractively equipped. Some of the New England states, for example, have much greater rates of commitment than some of the states in the South. It is significant that the former have much finer hospitals than the latter. It is also significant that these better hospitals are closer to the large centers of population. In general, the more accessible a hospital the greater the readiness of a family to concur in the hospitalization of one of its members. People want to visit their sick relatives and hesitate to send them so far away from home as to preclude frequent visits.

There are still other factors to be taken into account in the effort to interpret the meaning of the statistical data relating to the increase of mental disease. There is little mental disease below the age of 15, practically no paresis before the fourth decade of life and the disorders associated with arteriosclerosis and senility do not set in much before the sixth decade. A large proportion of cases are thus contributed by the aged and the aging. However, as is well known, man's average life span has increased since the turn of the century so that the number of people reaching the age of susceptibility to these disorders has increased from year to year over the period covered by the data. This in itself would serve to explain a good portion of the rise in the curve of incidence of mental disorders without thereby implying any special reason for alarm. If the population as a whole in 1940 contains more old people than the population contained in 1930, then we ought to expect a larger percentage of mental disorders at the end of the decade. But this would not mean that the 1940 stock of old people is biologically less fit than the 1930 stock. On the contrary, since there are relatively more who have " survived," one might be tempted to reverse the argument.

Actually, though, this appeal to biology to account for the statistical increase in number of hospitalized patients is decidedly questionable. Not only can the increase be explained along the lines already suggested, but, as one prominent investigating committee pointed out, " the rate of increase is too rapid to be biologic." [6]

[6] Myerson, A., Ayer, J. B., Putnam, T. J., Keeler, C. E., and Alexander, L., *Eugenical Sterilization*, New York, The Macmillan Co., 1936, p. 27.

This committee was appointed by the *American Neurological Association* in 1934 to study and report on the entire question of the inheritance of mental diseases and associated conditions. Its report was published in 1936 and contains such a wealth of carefully documented material that we shall have occasion to refer to it more than once in the following pages. In the interest of brevity we shall designate it as the A.N.A. report. As may be inferred from the evidence culled from the pages of this report and introduced in this section, this A.N.A. committee does not feel disposed to conclude that there is a genuine increase in the total amount of mental disease. In general, as has already been suggested, the increase shown by annual hospital figures is better explained as due to more cases being reported rather than to a rise in the number of reportable cases.

PROPHYLAXIS BY MEANS OF STERILIZATION

It might be contended that even though no alarming increase in mental disease can be demonstrated, the advocates of eugenical sterilization are nevertheless correct in their basic recommendation: improve the race by sterilizing the unfit. The simplicity and straightforwardness of their argument is superficially compelling in its cogency. It amounts to this: if mental disease, feeblemindedness, epilepsy, crime, and pauperism are fundamentally products of inferior germplasm, then the ideal way of preventing such social pathology is to block off continued transmission of this source of biological contamination. The way to prevent mental disease and associated conditions is to prevent their manufacture by cutting off the supply of biological building material. If the proposal is sound, psychiatrists ought to be able to put themselves out of business within a few generations.

The A.N.A. committee has examined the proposal in detail, studied existing sterilization laws and practices, and evaluated the arguments pro and con. It will not be necessary to introduce all of this detail here. For our purposes it will be enough to point out some of the chief findings of the committee in rather dogmatic fashion. Those interested in considering the evidence upon which the findings are based will have to consult the report itself.

The entire argument of the eugenicists rests on a belief in the heritability of the social pathology they want to breed out of existence. But the committee concluded that the belief in question in turn rests on very shaky foundations. It found relatively little valid scientific data to support such a belief. Furthermore, in its opinion, " neither psychiatry nor human genetics approach at present the status of exact sciences " and " most of the legislation which has been enacted so far is based more upon a desire to elevate the human race than upon proven facts."

These general considerations should not be taken to mean a blanket denial on the part of the committee of significant hereditary factors in the production of some mental and nervous diseases. It recognized, for example, that Huntington's chorea is definitely heritable. As a consequence, it is willing to recommend sterilization for this class of patients " with the consent of the patient or those responsible for him." This reflects the committee's attitude toward all conditions for which either complete or partial hereditary etiology can be demonstrated; namely, that sterilization should not be mandatory but optional with the patient or those acting in his behalf. If sterilization is made compulsory by legislative statute as has been done in many states, the committee suggests that to achieve its ostensible objective the law should not be limited in its enforcement to those who are in the custody of state institutions, but should be extended to apply to patients in private hospitals as well as to those being cared for by private physicians. In the words of the committee: " We see no reason for group or class discrimination."

Of particular interest to the mental hygienist is the committee's attitude toward sterilization of those found guilty of crime and vice. It flatly disapproves of any such action on the ground that too little is known of the part played by heredity in shaping character. In particular it calls attention to the enormous influence exercised by training, education, economic opportunity and other socially determined factors in the development of the ethical aspects of personality make-up. In the eyes of the committee to speak of a " born criminal " would therefore be tantamount to speaking of a myth. Until the time comes when such a myth can be displaced by indisputable proof for the alleged inheritance of a criminal tendency, the committee maintained, it would be " cruel and unusual punishment " to resort to sterilization as a means of preventing crime.

The general drift of the committee's findings is thus all in the direction of skepticism concerning the production of any marked improvement in the race by sterilizing the feebleminded as a class or the majority of the mentally diseased. Even in those cases in which hereditary factors may be regarded as primarily responsible for specific disabilities, the committee maintains that adequate hospitalization in itself serves as a eugenic device; since such institutional segregation prevents propagation. Furthermore, the common notion that the feebleminded as such are "abnormally fertile" is not supported by critical scrutiny of pertinent data. On the contrary, the "normal" population very likely outlives and outbreeds the mentally retarded as is indicated by the following passage: [7]

In spite of all efforts to prolong the life of morons, imbeciles, and idiots, they still fail to survive at the same rate as "normal" persons, especially in the pre-reproductive ages. . . . Nature still selects, even though we are horrified by such examples as the Jukes.

Incidentally, with respect to mental deficiency it must not be overlooked that the spectacular clinical types of feeblemindedness such as cases of Mongolian idiocy, microcephalus, and others for which organic pathology can be demonstrated are not representative of the bulk of the feebleminded population. The most numerous group, as the A.N.A. committee points out, is made up of those [8] "in whose cases no definite pathology has been established and which are only known as they manifest themselves by lower mentality." Mentally retarded children have been known to be born to "normal" or even "bright" parents. In fact, enthusiastic advocates of eugenical sterilization might well ponder over the following sentence taken from a report made by the *British Commission on Sterilization:* [9]

It is impossible in the present state of our knowledge about the causation of mental defect to forecast with certainty whether a child of any given union will exhibit mental abnormalities.

There are a few relatively rare conditions such as amaurotic family idiocy which are definitely known to be of hereditary origin.

[7] Quoted on p. 56 of the A.N.A. report and written by Edgar Sydenstricker.
[8] *Op. cit.,* p. 112.
[9] *Ibid.,* p. 121.

The committee recommends sterilization of adults who are *known* to be " carriers " of such familial diseases. However, it looks with disfavor upon Utopian schemes to rid the world of all of its mentally dull inhabitants; for " in a world which has much low grade work to be done, there is still room for the people of low grade mentality of good character." [10]

Sterilization of the psychotic patient after he is recognized to be a mental patient is not likely to have much influence on the incidence of mental disease in the next generation. Those whose condition is recognized early in life, as in the case of many schizophrenics, are apt to be barred from parenthood by lifelong hospitalization. Parenthetically, this numerous class of patients is below average in marriage rate as well as in the number of children born of such marriages. With respect to those whose mental breakdown occurs late in life it should be obvious that sterilization would be too late to accomplish its purpose; for these patients have already brought their " tainted " children into the world.

To expect a drastic reduction in the total amount of mental disease and mental defect by wholesale sterilization of the victims of such disease and defect is hardly warranted by existing evidence. Of course this sort of attack on the problem has not yet been put to a radical test in this country. It will be interesting to see whether Nazi Germany, which seems to be resorting to this kind of wholesale sterilization, will succeed in eliminating " defective strains " from the *Herrenvolk*. Cynical critics of the " master race " are not very optimistic regarding the outcome, for the presumed psychopaths among the Nazi leaders are not being included among the experimental subjects. Even aside from this oversight there is little chance of pronounced success for the experiment. In its preoccupation with the hereditary factors it is neglecting the equally important *non-hereditary* causes of mental disease. Furthermore, as was just mentioned, the vast numbers of Germans who are themselves " normal," but whose germplasm contains unpredictable determiners of mental disease, will still be free to transmit these determiners to future generations. Nor should one overlook the fact that so very many of the " abnormal " ones are operated upon too late, since they have already become parents by the time their " abnormality " is detected. In brief, wholesale

[10] *Ibid.*, p. 180.

sterilization does not seem to be the answer to the mental hygienist's problem of safeguarding the public from the menace of mental disease.[11]

PUBLIC AND PRIVATE ASPECTS OF PROPHYLAXIS

Rejection of a general program of eugenical sterilization should not be regarded as a denial of heredity as a factor in the production of mental disorder and defect. The average man's concern about marrying into a family with a history of such disorder or defect is not to be dismissed as superstitious fear. He would be wise in consulting a competent psychiatrist to find out whether the particular pathological condition is likely to manifest itself in any children born of the proposed union. Each case merits individual consideration, and the expert in mental disorders is best qualified to evaluate the chances involved.

Some mental defects are due to birth injury and not to heredity. In a case of this sort the psychiatric expert would not hesitate to give the family of the afflicted individual a clean bill of health. Similarly, if the mental deficiency in question should belong to the variety called *Mongolism,* he would not regard this as a eugenic barrier to marriage with some member of the Mongol's family. Just what causes Mongolism is not known, but that it does not " run in families " is known. However, there are types of feeblemindedness of definite hereditary etiology and one of these would, of course, call for a psychiatric warning.

The problem being dealt with here is a little different from that of eugenical sterilization discussed in the previous section. We are now discussing individual rather than public prophylaxis. A few simple examples will clarify this distinction. It is one thing for the mental hygienist to deal with the broad problem of preventing alcoholic psychoses in the entire country and another matter for him to tell a single individual what precautions to take. In the same way his efforts to reduce the incidence of paresis reveal identical public and private aspects. In other words, suitable prophy-

---

[11] This adverse verdict is in accord with the general judgment not only of the A.N.A. committee, but of other students of the problem as well. For example, Landis and Page (*op. cit.,* p. 90), in discussing two of the most common functional mental disorders, write that " extensive sterilization of manic-depressive and dementia praecox patients would have but little effect in reducing the incidence of these two mental disorders."

lactic knowledge is available to prevent either of these psychotic disturbances. Once a person learns to avoid alcohol and syphilitic infection he need never worry about becoming a possible victim of either Korsakoff's psychosis or of paresis. But how to induce the public to exercise the requisite restraint is a problem that has not yet been satisfactorily solved. The general taboo of all traffic in alcohol during the prohibition era failed as a public mental hygiene measure. In the same way merely warning the public of the dangers of venereal infection has not resulted in a unanimous boycott of prostitution by the public. Nor does it seem to help much to have the police " run the prostitutes out of town." Either their customers follow them out of town or else they return and operate clandestinely. What to do about this constitutes a problem of prophylaxis in the realm of public mental hygiene.

Another way to grasp the distinction between the public and private aspects of prophylaxis is to note that mental hygiene has two spheres of application. Any person studying the subject of mental disorders might ask, " What can I do to avoid paresis, or pellagra or schizophrenia or a brain tumor or any one of these disturbances I'm reading about? " This sort of question refers to an application of mental hygiene recommendations to him as a private individual. On the other hand, he might well ask, " What can we as mental hygienists, psychiatrists, educators, public health officials, neurologists and psychologists do to protect our fellow citizens from these disorders? " This latter kind of question would accordingly emphasize the public aspect of the mental hygiene movement.

SHOULD MENTAL DISEASE IN THE FAMILY BE A BAR TO MARRIAGE?

It should now be clear why no inconsistency is involved in the A.N.A. committee's rejection of eugenical sterilization as a general measure and its approval of it in selected individual cases. Both from the viewpoint of public as well as private mental hygiene, questions of sterilization and marriage are not to be disposed of by dogmatic generalizations. There are some general guiding principles to be considered in advising the individual about marrying into a particular family or about the wisdom of having children in the case of marriages already contracted; but, with some exceptions, even these principles are not to be applied too dogmatically. One of these principles, for example, would render it inadvisable for a man whose mother was schizophrenic to marry a woman whose father was schizophrenic, even though both the man and the woman were mentally healthy. There is some evidence suggesting that schizoprenia is not entirely functional, but that it develops in terms of some still not clearly understood inborn predisposition. Because of this possibility, it is altogether likely that the vast majority of psychiatrists would not be very enthusiastic about our hypothetical couple's proposed romance. They would deem it safer for normal children of schizophrenic ancestry to marry into families without a history of what might be a heritable mental disorder. On this basis they would discourage an alliance between families having a history of epilepsy, but not between the normal son of an epileptic man and the normal daughter of some normal family. The general principle is to avoid reenforcement of a possible inborn neuropathic or psychopathic tendency by " inbreeding " of the tendency in question. But, as was just implied, the application of the principle calls for critical evaluation of all the factors governing the individual case. It is necessary to make sure that what was once diagnosed as schizophrenia or epilepsy really conforms to the clinical picture of these disorders, particularly those which may be presumed to rest on heritable factors. Some cases of epilepsy may be more a consequence of severe head injury than of transmissible pregerminal factors. In doubtful cases it is wise to consult a psychiatrist about the risks involved. He is in a better position to evaluate these than any other specialist. The variables to be taken into account are so numerous, and their relative weight so dependent on the case histories of the individuals involved, that it is impossible to dispose of the problem by fixed injunctions like " never marry into the family of a manic-depressive " or " don't fall in love with the grandson of a paretic."

As a matter of fact every family probably has a history of mental or nervous disorder of some kind if the family tree be investigated thoroughly enough. Nobody really knows his family tree completely. To anticipate what will be mentioned again in a later chapter: the ancestors of every person increase in geometric progression. Starting with 2 parents, we have 4 grandparents, then 8 great-grandparents to be followed by twice the previous number of direct ancestors in the straight line of genetic ascent so that the series is 2, 4, 8, 16, 32, 64, 128, 256, etc. This mode of approach neglects collateral relatives entirely. But even so it serves to show the impossibility of securing a complete mental, medical, and social history of *all* one's ancestors for even the last 500 years. Who can be sure that none of his 256 ancestors eight generations ago was either alcoholic or epileptic or mentally retarded or schizophrenic or immoral or criminal? This means that all studies of the family histories both of psychotic and of normal persons are fragmentary and replete with the error of noting the striking cases in the family tradition. The distinguished Mayflower ancestor is remembered by his descendants, but undistinguished ones who have " disgraced the family " have their names conveniently blotted from the family's collective memory. A 1944 hospital social worker tracking down the psychiatric family history of one of her cases is unable to do much more than scratch the surface of this fallible collective memory. Studies of the inheritance of mental disorders [12] are consequently devoid of the certainty and precision with which the laboratory worker can control his genetic studies of plants, fruit flies, or even white rats. Incidentally, the pedigree of a white rat at the Wistar Institute is better known than the pedigree of any human being.

Even with the facts of mental disorder in a given family clearly established, one cannot always be confident that marriage into such a family will result in the kind of children whose lives are a source of regret and disappointment to their parents and a drain on the resources of welfare agencies. As the A.N.A. committee points out,[13] " many valuable members of society, worth more to it than the cost of maintenance of all state institutions put together, would have been lost if sterilization laws had been enacted on a compulsory basis a few centuries ago." The committee supports this opinion by citing an impressive list of " actual men of genius " belonging to psychopathic families. Many of these were

[12] For the nature of such studies as well as difficulties in prosecuting them, see Myerson, A., *The Inheritance of Mental Diseases*, Baltimore, Williams & Wilkins Co., 1925.
With respect to the problem of so-called psychopathic inheritance it is altogether likely that the influence of very remote ancestry is negligible; for, as Myerson points out (p. 130), " it is rare for mental disease to last 4 generations in any one group."
[13] *Op. cit.*, p. 172.

themselves mentally sick. Among them one notes such famous men as the following:

1. Hans Christian Andersen, the distinguished writer of fairy stories, had an alcoholic mother and a psychotic father and grandfather.

2. The composer Beethoven, himself somewhat alcoholic and paranoid in personality make-up, was descended from a drunken father and grandmother.

3. Goethe, Germany's outstanding literary genius, had a sister who was manic-depressive.

4. The famous physicist, Robert Mayer, who first formulated the principle of the conservation of energy, suffered from manic-depressive fluctuations all his life, attempted suicide at one time, and was institutionalized for a whole year.

5. Isaac Newton is listed as a psychotic from his 50th year, the psychosis having been " a late schizophrenia with incoherence, bizarre speech, depressive, persecutory and paranoid ideas."

6. The father of Michelangelo seems to have been a victim of mental disease characterized by delusions of persecution.

7. America's own Edgar Allan Poe failed to measure up to the mental hygienist's ideal of a healthy personality and his family's record would horrify any self-respecting eugenicist. The poet's father is listed as a psychopathic personality and his mother as a " vagrant actress," who died of tuberculosis. Along with a feebleminded sister Poe had one brother who was described as a " half-crazy drunkard." And poor Poe himself was a chronic alcoholic, a victim of delirium tremens, and a drug addict the last 12 years of his life.

There is no need to add more examples. Even these few are enough to show that individuals with a history of unstable or psychopathic ancestry may be taught to view such a history less apprehensively than is the case with people whose understanding of " tainted " family trees is colored by the gloom of Ibsen's *Ghosts*. These examples suffice to show the possibility of eminent accomplishment despite such " tainting." It is sound mental hygiene to stress this. Far too many people are needlessly horrified by the discovery of " insanity in the family " one or two generations back. It is well for them to learn that not all mental disease is heritable; it will also help to buttress their morale by teaching them something about the psychiatric history of the Newtons, the Goethes, and the Poes. Such teaching may serve as an antidote to the bleak prospect of inevitable doom so often accompanying accounts of " tainted " families like the Kallikaks.

6... *PROPHYLACTIC ASPECTS*
OF STRUCTURAL DISORDERS

IT WILL BE RECALLED THAT OUR EARLIER SURVEY OF MENTAL DIS-orders was based on an official classification which presumably stressed the etiology of such disorders. At all events each major caption with the exception of the last was introduced with the same three words: " Psychoses due to . . ." The last of these nine captions, it may be remembered, had to do with " disorders of psychogenic origin." Because of this terminology the first eight were grouped together as having reference to " somatogenic " factors. As we have mentioned before, such a rigid distinction between disorders of mental origin on the one hand and those of bodily origin on the other cannot be preserved in actual practice. In some respects it is a dubious distinction; but it does serve purposes of descriptive convenience and it helps to remind us that the well-being of the human organism depends not only on freedom from infection but on freedom from humiliation, terror, and hopelessness as well.

Since mental hygiene is concerned with *all* mental disorders, there is no justification for neglecting prophylactic aspects of those regarded as somatogenic in favor of those viewed as caused by mental factors. It is true, of course, that the former to a large extent belong to the realm of general medicine, public health, sanitary engineering, and kindred fields. However, no comprehensive program of prophylactic mental hygiene can afford to ignore the problems involved. To the individual or community whose welfare is threatened by mental disease it makes no significant difference whether such disease is theoretically classified as somatogenic or psychogenic. The important job is to ward off the threat. There is thus no reason for the mental hygienist to restrict his job to preventing the functional psychoses and the neuroses and to ignore organically determined mental disorders.

It should be admitted, however, that not all writers in the field of mental hygiene would necessarily agree with this view. Perusal of many of the standard works reveals a conspicuous absence of discussion concerning prevention of organic psychoses. The entire emphasis is on the prevention of behavior disorders, functional disturbances, and kindred topics. Practically nothing is said about warding off Huntington's chorea, Korsakoff's psychosis, epilepsy, paresis, etc. It is almost as if the authors were endorsing a division of labor by which prophylaxis of the latter group of disorders is to be shunted out of the field of mental hygiene and only psychogenic ones reserved for their professional consideration. In fairness to them it must be granted that there is some justification for this view. Adequate grasp of the nature of the organic disturbances calls for a rich background in medicine, neurology, serology, and related fields. Without such a background one is not qualified to handle the problems involved. As a consequence some might argue that the problems involved belong more to the general field of preventive medicine than to the field of mental hygiene.

Although the force of this argument is recognized, we do not believe that the earnest mental hygienist can shirk all responsibility for bearing his share of the load in the onerous task of cutting down the incidence of somatogenic psychoses. This does not mean that he, as a mental hygienist, must ever venture to treat a case of paresis or pellagra. But it does mean that he must know enough about the prevention of such conditions to aid in the general task of educating the public to know what precautions are urged by preventive medicine. He can aid in the dissemination of existing prophylactic knowledge so that those in need of suitable medical guidance will not succumb to the lure of charlatans and the enticements of patent-medicine vendors.

Furthermore, not all of the organic psychoses are to be prevented by exclusive preoccupation with such subjects as serology, toxicology, and biochemistry. To put this more bluntly: paresis can be avoided either by means of chemical prophylaxis or by that kind of intelligent self-control ordinarily called strength of character. Moreover, this sort of self-control is not to be overlooked as a factor in the prevention of drug addiction and acute alcoholic intoxication. How to enable people to gain such control is more of a problem in applied psychology than in preventive medicine. It is a problem for the mental hygienist to solve, and constitutes a significant potential contribution which he can make to those actively engaged in the war on the organic mental disorders. Instead of a division of labor the task calls for team work and mutual aid.

In view of the foregoing considerations the present chapter will be concerned with an inventory of some of the *specific* problems of prophylactic mental hygiene. We shall be concerned with such definite questions as what can be done and what has been done to prevent the mental disorders included in our synoptic view of such disorders. For the reasons just mentioned we shall not limit ourselves to the psychogenic ones. In fact we shall start with the somatogenic ones and try to summarize what is known about their prevention.

PREVENTION OF ENCEPHALITIC AND TRAUMATIC PSYCHOSES

Reference to Table 1 in the previous chapter will show that 0.4% of all first admissions to mental hospitals are victims of encephalitis. This includes both those with and without psychosis. In terms of numbers this represents close to 500 *new* cases per year. What can be done to safeguard ourselves and the public against this disease? Actually there is not much the private individual can do to ward off encephalitis. No sera or antitoxins are available to render him immune.[1] About all that can be urged is avoidance of needless exposure during epidemics; but this is general advice applicable to all infectious diseases.

Prevention of traumatic psychoses is largely a matter of accident prevention. This calls for expert traffic engineering, education of the driving public, elimination of industrial hazards, and the introduction of safety devices wherever possible.

One phase of such prophylactic work is almost entirely medical in nature. We have reference to trauma incident to difficult or prolonged childbirth. To the extent that birth injury may have serious consequences for the child it is obvious that improvement in obstetrical care has mental hygiene implications.

---

[1] Since encephalitis is associated with influenza epidemics, progress made in influenza prophylaxis should have an effect on the incidence of encephalitis. Such progress has been reported recently. Two University of Pennsylvania research men have prepared a vaccine which seems to confer immunity with respect to one particular strain of influenza. Only one boy out of 44 inoculated with the protective vaccine became ill when exposed to the virus of influenza A. In a control experiment of 28 unvaccinated boys, 10 contracted the disease after similar exposure to the influenza A virus. (From a report in *Science*, *90*, 1942, p. 11 of Supplement.)

CAN VASCULAR DISORDERS AND BRAIN TUMORS BE PREVENTED?

Just what to do to prevent " psychoses due to disturbance of circulation " is hard to specify. Cerebral arteriosclerosis and other vascular difficulties are responsible for more than 11% of first admissions. In terms of numbers affected, the problem is thus of great importance. And yet very little positive advice can be given to the person asking, " What must I do to avoid these disorders as I grow older? " Of course one can always temporize by some such stock reply as, " Keep in good physical trim at all times and visit your physician twice yearly for a general check-up." This is probably sound advice, but hardly a direct answer to an entirely legitimate question. How about telling the inquirer to watch his blood pressure, heart action, and kidneys? All these seem to have something to do with the disorders in question; but unless one knows what to watch for this too is not particularly helpful advice. Besides, to make people too conscious of their bodily processes is in itself a violation of an accepted mental hygiene precept.

As a matter of fact the precise etiology of these circulatory disorders is not yet established. Nobody knows just why arteries harden or just why blood pressure shoots up. Under the circumstances preventive medicine has to be content with vague warnings and general admonitions to keep in good health. The neat precision with which it can tackle diphtheria prophylaxis is obviously lacking here.

Some heart specialists believe that mental factors may play an important role in the production of these vascular ills. Many of them regard the kind of high blood pressure known as *essential hypertension* as a direct consequence of poorly managed emotional life. They urge their patients to strive after inner calm and to avoid situations likely to precipitate violent excitement. They evidently regard the maintenance of emotional poise and inner serenity as useful prophylactic measures. Some evidence in support of this belief will be introduced in the final chapter in connection with a discussion of some phases of meliorative mental hygiene. In other words, even if the advice of these heart specialists should eventually prove to be only remotely related to the prevention of these disorders, this need not entail rejection of their advice. Mental hygiene precepts are not to be evaluated solely in terms of prophylaxis. A given precept may have little or nothing to do with the prevention of a mental disorder and still be a valuable contribution to mental hygiene wisdom. But this is a digression and an anticipation of what will be taken up at greater length in the fourth part of this book.

Unlike the vascular disturbances those " due to new growth " do not constitute a large percentage of first admissions. As was shown in Table 1, only 0.2% of first admissions in 1938 or a total of 173 cases belonged in this category. However, it must be realized that the problem of preventing brain tumors is more serious than these figures suggest. Only a small fraction of the cases reach mental hospitals, the majority — even those with severe mental symptoms — being taken care of by neurosurgeons rather than psychiatrists. The actual incidence of brain tumors is not inconsiderable. Rosanoff [2] cites mortality statistics culled from the report of the 1930 Census Bureau showing that almost 10% of all deaths were due to different kinds of tumors: 99.08 per 1,000. Of these .68 per 1,000 were attributable to brain tumor. Although considerable progress has been made in the surgical attack on brain tumors, there is no progress to be reported by those attacking the problem of their etiology. Nobody knows what causes such anarchic proliferation of the tissues of the brain. As a consequence neither brain pathologist nor neuropsychiatrist is as yet in a position to tell the mental hygienist what to tell the public regarding prophylactic measures. There is no known strategy by means of which the rebelliousness of the anarchic cells can be suppressed before it develops. A brave fatalism or a resigned stoicism is all the mental hygienist can urge until future research produces the requisite prophylactic ammunition.

THE PROBLEM OF PARESIS

Once again referring to Table 1, we note that close to 8,000 first admissions in the year 1938 were diagnosed as general paresis. Almost 1,500 additional admissions were attributed to syphilis of the central nervous system. In other words 8.5% of first admissions were a consequence of syphilitic infection. Figures of this sort fail to reveal the actual magnitude of the mental hygiene problems associated with the existence of venereal disease. The

[2] *Op. cit.*, p. 488.

anxiety and distress of the unnumbered thousands who contract these diseases without developing psychotic complications are, of course, not symbolized by these data pertaining to first admissions. Nor do the data in question portray the weeks of tense worry of those who merely fear the possibility of having contracted an infection of this kind. There is thus little danger of exaggerating the importance for mental hygiene of a candid discussion of venereal prophylaxis and its implications. Both from the point of view of individual as well as public mental hygiene such candor has become an imperative need.

On the morning on which this section happens to be written newspapers carrying INS despatches printed the following report under a Washington date line:

U. S. health officials Wednesday blamed legal restrictions and a lack of facilities as being responsible for an " unusual " spread of venereal disease in this war-time national capital.

At a meeting of police and health officers it was disclosed that there are at present an estimated 45,000 cases of syphilis in Washington.

Public Health Commr. Dr. Ruhland declared that of this total, only 6,000 were under regular treatment in venereal clinics, and that possibly 2,500 additional were being treated by private physicians.

No estimate was given for the total of gonorrhea cases, but Ruhland declared that the 2,000 cases being treated in public clinics " obviously are far under the total."

The prevalence of venereal diseases was linked directly to prostitution, and health officers spoke strongly in favor of legislation which would permit isolation of " carriers " until they are cured. They also recommended the establishment of prophylactic stations for persons who have been exposed to the diseases.

The latter course, Ruhland said, would undoubtedly be attacked in some municipal circles as creating an " air " of security " which may actually encourage exposure."

The very fact that the public press prints an item of this sort is both encouraging and discouraging. Not so very many decades ago editors would have blue pencilled this kind of copy as " too daring " or " too shocking " or " offensive to good taste." Its appearance in a contemporary newspaper is thus a sign of progress. The old taboo against open discussion of the problem is either gone or at least on the way out. To fight an evil one must not be too squeamish to face it. However, the content of the item shows the need for more drastic action in the fight. If venereal disease is spreading, then it might mean that the recent anti-syphilis campaign has not been pushed energetically enough. One way to check on this is to ask whether people in need of the requisite information have it at their disposal. According to a recent report,[3] one of our naval medical officers made a direct attack on this question by enlisting the cooperation of *all* of the men on his ship, both officers and ordinary seamen. They were asked to tell what they knew about the nature of venereal diseases, what prophylactic precautions one ought to take, how many lectures they had heard on the subject, to what extent they deemed the lectures helpful, etc.

The results may be summarized very briefly: satisfactory knowledge was demonstrated by only 34% of the men; 66% were either ignorant of the salient facts or had them garbled. These percentages refer to their understanding of syphilis and gonorrhea and the basic differences between these infections. What is of especial interest in the present context is the startling ignorance regarding prophylaxis displayed by almost half of the 200 men examined. In the words of the report, only " 51 percent had a satisfactory working knowledge of prophylactic measures." The men had attended an average of eight lectures on venereal disease. Under the circumstances it seemed to the investigator that lectures were not altogether successful as means for imparting this kind of knowledge. Accordingly, he prepared a printed digest of the essential information and gave a copy to each man on his ship. Not only did it arouse discussion among the men, but it seems to have produced some positive educational results; for in the six-month period following its distribution there was a 50% reduction in the incidence of venereal disease as compared with the preceding six-month period.

Stamping out paresis is thus but part of the larger problem of stamping out venereal disease. As has just been suggested, this

---

[3] The report in question has to do with " venereal disease education in the Navy " and was written by C. K. Youngkin and published in full in U. S. Nav. M. Bull., Washington, *39*, 1941, pp. 535–543. Our knowledge of this report is based on a rather full abstract to be found on pp. 40–41 of the January 1942 issue of *Venereal Disease Information*. This valuable journal is published by the U. S. Public Health Service and should be consulted by all serious students of the problems involved in the campaign to wipe out venereal diseases. By addressing the Superintendent of Documents, Washington, D. C., one can secure the bulletins each month. The subscription price is 50 cents a year.

is not merely a medical problem, but an educational problem as well. The requisite prophylactic knowledge has been available for many years. Of course the ideal prophylactic procedure in terms of individual mental hygiene is to refrain from any kind of pre-marital or extra-marital indulgence. However, in terms of public mental hygiene this might as well be recognized as a counsel of perfection. To safeguard the community those unwilling or unable to exercise the requisite restraint must be held responsible for their indulgence. In fact, there is a twofold responsibility in-volved: (1) a personal moral and social obligation to take pro-phylactic precautions and (2) an equally imperative obligation to report for treatment in the event of infection. Modern public health officials urge legislation by means of which recalcitrant or indifferent syphilitics can be compelled to come for treatment, because without the coercion of police power the public cannot protect itself against the menace of continued spread of venereal disease by those harboring the infectious organisms. Even though complete cures may require very long periods of treatment, the danger of contagion can be eliminated by suitable medication in less than two weeks.

Legislation rendering it possible for public health officials to *compel* infected people — prostitutes [4] and others — to report for treatment is thus a necessary part of the prophylactic campaign. It is also necessary for the legislation to provide legal pressure by means of which infected patients can be induced to reveal the source of the infection. This is not for the purpose of punishing anybody; but merely to enable medical authorities to get at every focus of contagion in the community. The purpose is to eradicate syphilis and not to expose anybody to disgrace or humiliation. This task cannot be accomplished without the joint cooperation of the general public, the medical profession, the police officials, and, most important of all, the patients themselves.

---

[4] Both from the viewpoint of public health as well as in terms of social eth-ics it appears reasonable to argue that, although total abolition of the "ancient evil" should continue to be the final goal, as long as prostitution continues to exist, it is better to have it limited to those free from venereal disease than to have an existing social evil made even more evil by permitting the continued transmission of such disease. For a splendid summary of the chief factors in-volved in this aspect of the problem, see Stokes, J. H., "A Statement on Prosti-tution in Venereal Disease Control," *Venereal Disease Information*, 23, 1942, pp. 195–198.

The success of energetically prosecuted efforts to curb the spread of syphilis has been demonstrated at various times. The knowledge is available but it cannot be put into practice without the kind of cooperation just mentioned. In the army it is somewhat easier to prosecute a successful campaign than it is in civilian life because of the ease with which those who become infected or exposed to infection can be obligated to report for therapeutic or prophylactic treatment. Even in the first World War the success of such prophylactic campaigns was already demonstrated. The late Hans Zinsser, distinguished American bacteriologist, tells of one of these in his delightfully informal volume of personal reminiscences. He recalls that American troops in France were persuaded to report for suitable prophylactic treatment within a few hours after exposure. Careful records were kept to note the success or failure of the treatment. In one series of observations [5] out of a total of 242,000 treatments the number of failures was limited to but 1.3%. In another series in which one group of men was treated and another group remained untreated there was one case of syphilis found to develop for every 37 exposures in the latter group, while in the former the ratio turned out to be only one out of every 247 exposures.[6] Although the prophylactic technique employed was manifestly not 100% perfect, its essential efficacy was thus clearly demonstrated.

Consideration of the actual procedures to be used in preventing venereal infection does not, strictly speaking, come within the province of mental hygiene.[7] It is primarily a medical and public health responsibility. However, the mental hygienist can be of some help in the general task of enlightening the public with respect to the seriousness of the problem and the need for the cooperation of every citizen and every community if the campaign to stamp out venereal disease is to be a success. Far too many indi-

[5] Zinsser, H., *As I Remember Him,* Boston, Little, Brown & Co., 1941, p. 260.
[6] Data of this kind should not be interpreted to mean that *all* men in military and naval service require treatment for this sort of exposure. As a matter of fact, Stokes, in the article referred to in Footnote 4, reports that Colonel Ashburn estimated that almost one-third of the American Expeditionary Force mobilized during the first World War " remained absolutely continent during their service in France."
[7] A discussion of these procedures is to be found in the following report:
Hazen, H. H., Hiscock, I. V., Pelouze, P. S., *et al.,* " The Chemical and Mechanical Prevention of Syphilis and Gonorrhea," *Venereal Disease Information,* 1940, *21,* pp. 311-313.

viduals continue to regard such disease as trivial. Far too many continue to fail to appreciate the vital importance of early and proper treatment of every case of venereal infection. The earlier the treatment the better the prognosis. But this should be competent treatment by trained physicians and not the kind obtained in surreptitious fashion either as a result of a whispered conversation with the clerk behind the drug counter or as a result of succumbing to the advertised guarantees of the charlatans who pay for newspaper space in order to beguile the ignorant, the embarrassed, and the terror-stricken. There has been most encouraging progress in the techniques of diagnosis and therapy of venereal infections in recent decades. For the public to benefit by this progress it is imperative to teach people to shy away from self-medication, reliance on proprietary preparations, and poorly informed or unscrupulous quacks.[8] Instead they should be induced to report any suspicious symptoms to the family physician or the men in charge of hospital clinics. In this way they can be routed to trustworthy, properly trained medical specialists.

This should not be glossed over as " obvious " advice; because, despite publicity given to the current fight against venereal disease, it continues to be a serious problem as shown by recent surveys. To be more specific: in 1939 the rate for *all* venereal disease in the whole Army, according to the Surgeon General, was 29.6 per 1,000. His report for the next year showed an increase to 42.5 per 1,000. (Part of the increase, incidentally, may be attributed to a

---

[8] That this kind of teaching is still very urgent was brought to light in a recent survey by Edwards and Kinsie which resulted in such findings as the following:

" In 35 cities, 62 percent of the 1,151 drugstores visited were willing to diagnose and sell ' remedies ' for syphilis or gonorrhea; 31 percent would not diagnose but did sell remedies, especially if asked for by name; only 7 percent refused to diagnose or sell.. . . .

" There are on the market many different patent ' remedies ' for venereal diseases, apparently sold in large volume.

" There is some indication that the sale of such ' remedies ' is now even larger in volume than 6 to 8 years ago.

" Large numbers of charlatans, herbalists, and other unlicensed practitioners are treating many persons having syphilis and gonorrhea.

" A huge educational task yet remains to be done, judging from a series of replies by men in the street to casual questions concerning proper treatment for syphilis and gonorrhea."

The foregoing quotations are taken from the summary of the results of the field study as reported by the two investigators. See Edwards, M. S., and Kinsie, P. M., "Illegal and Unethical Practices in the Diagnosis and Treatment of Syphilis and Gonorrhea," *Venereal Disease Information, 21,* 1940, pp. 1–10.

change in Army policy: prior to 1940 soldiers who developed a venereal disease were court martialed if they had failed to report for prophylactic injections and discontinuance of this punitive practice is possibly responsible for the increase in question.) Furthermore, it is well to realize that syphilis is still rampant in many parts of the country. A report made in May, 1942, showed the incidence for Louisiana to be 124.2 per 1,000. It was even more severe in Georgia, Florida, South Carolina, and Mississippi. A good portion of this prevalence is due to the high incidence of syphilis among Negro groups. In one sample of the Louisiana population the rate for Negroes was 233.8 per 1,000 and only 30.7 for white men. And in Wisconsin the rate has been found to be as low as 6 per 1,000.

These figures [9] indicate not only what can be done but how much remains to be done. They serve to remind us that the newspaper report of alarming conditions in wartime Washington, as revealed in the quotation at the beginning of this discussion, is not to be dismissed as mere " newspaper talk." And they ought also to remind us that possession of prophylactic knowledge is one thing and its application another. In terms of technical knowledge now available it is as inexcusable for a community to be complacent about the existence of venereal disease in its midst as it would be for it to be undisturbed about a smallpox epidemic. One positive way in which the mental hygienist can help win the war against venereal disease is to shock communities out of their complacency. He can do even more by using his influence to secure the appropriations needed to wage a successful war and he can do still more by aiding in the arduous task of educating [10] the youth

[9] The figures in question were taken from abstracts of articles printed in *Venereal Disease Information, 23*, 1942, pp. 212–213.

[10] Those interested in securing useful bibliographic and factual data pertaining to sex education should consult *High Schools and Sex Education,* Educational Publication No. 7, Washington, U. S. Public Health Service, 1940. By addressing the Superintendent of Documents, Washington, D. C. one can secure copies of this monograph. The price is 20 cents per copy.

For a candid, authoritative, clearly written popular discussion of the medicosocial implications of the venereal disease problem, see Parran, T., and Vonderlehr, R. A., *Plain Words about Venereal Disease,* Reynal & Hitchcock, New York, 1941.

Those in need of orientation with respect to the psycho-physiology of sex, hygienic aspects of marriage, and kindred topics will find the following work useful and informative: Kahn, F., *Our Sex Life,* Alfred A. Knopf, New York, 1939.

For additional bibliographic material pertaining to the mental hygiene of sex of the community to face the imperiousness of sex with attitudes of enlightened insight and courageous self-control. Medical progress has by no means rendered character education obsolete.

CAN ALCOHOLIC DISORDERS BE PREVENTED?

Addiction to alcohol constitutes a serious mental hygiene problem. Once again referring back to Table 1 we note that more than 11 percent of the first admissions are due to alcoholism: 4.5 percent being actual psychoses and 6.9 percent being listed as without psychosis. And once again the larger human implications of these colorless statistical data should be reflected upon. They mean broken homes, neglected families, shattered lives, embittered children, anxious parents, traffic accidents, homicidal attacks, blasted hopes, and wasted opportunity. Nor do they mean these things just for the 12,544 alcoholic patients admitted to mental hospitals for the first time in 1938. For each of these patients and their families prior to 1938 there were years of tense worry, bickering, pleading, quarreling, and the acrimonious abuse associated with chronic alcoholism. It takes years before the family or the community finally has the alcoholic patient institutionalized. As a result the data for *first* admissions in any one year fail to give an adequate picture of the total number of people in the country as a whole whose mental stability and personal happiness is already undermined or in jeopardy. The year 1938 had a crop of more than 12,000 alcoholics disintegrated enough to be institutionalized and presumably equally large crops were being prepared for the psychiatric harvests of 1939, 1940, 1941, and all the years to come. To complete the picture we must also add the thousands who make up the more or less permanent or resident population of the alcoholic groups in our psychopathic institutions. In other words, many of last year's first admissions are always present to welcome this year's crop of psychiatric freshmen. The total cost of such " alcoholic education " in dollars and in human misery is not to be computed by orthodox methods of cost accounting.

In terms of prophylactic mental hygiene there are some inter-

---

adjustment in contemporary society, see also McKinney, F., *Psychology of Personal Adjustment,* John Wiley & Sons, Inc., New York, 1941, pp. 385–386 & 412–413.

esting parallels between psychotic disorders due to alcohol and
those due to syphilis. Both involve pathological changes in the
tissues of the central nervous system. In both the etiological agents
are known. Both have been attacked by efforts to induce the public to steer clear of these known agents. Despite this knowledge
and these efforts, both continue to take their toll year after year.
They both thus serve to remind the mental hygienist of the magnitude of his self-imposed professional tasks and of his lack of
outstanding progress so far. That he cannot do much to help
people ward off mental disorders of *unknown* etiology is readily
understandable and no reflection on his professional competence.
But the case is different with the emotional panic of a delirium
tremens victim or the delusions of grandeur of a paretic. He *knows*
that alcohol causes the first and the pale spirochete the second.
However, mere possession of this knowledge does not seem to be
enough to ensure the success of his prophylactic efforts. Nor does
merely *warning* the public of psychiatric danger appear to be
enough. Syphilis and alcoholism continue to sweep over his carefully erected admonitory barriers. Prophylaxis by admonition
seems to be a failure. The public continues to take chances despite
the warnings in a fashion reminiscent of its reactions to the warnings of traffic safety experts. To refer to those who drink to excess
and who indulge in illicit sex behavior as " speedy " may consequently be more than a convenient figure of speech.

It seems as if what we have referred to as a program of prophylactic mental hygiene is less a record of successful accomplishment than a guide to future effort. Just what direction guidance
is to take if the evils of alcoholism are to be eliminated is not to
be decided in hasty fashion. There are sincere individuals who refuse to regard alcohol as an unmitigated mental hygiene evil. In
their opinion, when used in moderation, alcoholic beverages promote conviviality and gracious sociability, the gaiety of the cocktail hour, and the camaraderie that goes with a whiskey and soda
at the club. They may even remind us that the tired laborer is
entitled to his modest pleasure of a bottle of beer with his supper
after an exhausting day of strenuous work. For them alcohol is a
sovereign means of achieving comfortable relaxation and peace
of mind and freedom from care. All this would make alcohol
desirable from the viewpoint of meliorative mental hygiene; for,

from the latter viewpoint, whatever contributes to the joy of living and to finer individual and group morale merits the support of the mental hygienist. Prophylactic and meliorative mental hygiene are thus apt to clash over the alcohol problem unless these conflicting viewpoints can be reconciled.

In theory the problem appears ultra-simple: to train the public to avoid the evils of excess by seeking the boon of moderation. But just what constitutes an "excess" and what is meant by "moderation"? Does not every chronic drunkard initiate his drinking career by first imbibing small amounts and then increasing his daily dosage by what he deems to be such small amounts that almost before he realizes what has happened, his drinking has become an orgy of uncontrollable excess? Are people of this sort capable of learning to drink in moderation? Can the problem of alcoholism be reduced to graphic form in the shape of a normal curve with the total abstainers at one extreme, the pathological drinkers at the other and those of varying degrees of moderation in between? This should be possible if the basic difference between normal and abnormal drinking is merely a quantitative difference. However, what was said in the first chapter regarding this conventional approach to mental disorders in general applies to alcoholism in particular.

The difference between the "normal" drinker and the psychopathic drinker is a difference in kind. All students of the problem are agreed that the solution does not consist in training the alcoholic to become more moderate in his drinking habits. The "normal" drinker can exercise control over his drinking. Under given circumstances he can take one or two drinks more than is his wont and then turn a deaf ear to pleas to "have just one more." Under other conditions he can do without any alcohol for long periods and not suffer because of the deprivation. But such control is not at the disposal of the abnormal drinker. His choice lies between total and permanent abstinence or a continuation of his overindulgence. He can never train himself or be trained by others to take his place in the middle of the hypothetical distribution curve along with those described as "moderate," or "controlled," or "average" drinkers. As will be shown presently, even his motivation with respect to drinking is different from "normal" drinkers. For all these reasons it is more in accord with fact to conceive of the problem of alcoholism in terms of a bimodal curve: the normal drinkers clustering around one mode and the abnormal ones around the other. For the latter group prohibition of some sort — preferably self-initiated and personally enforced — seems to be the only known prophylactic safeguard.

As the mental hygienist views the problem, the prophylactic goal for potential pathological drinkers will thus have to be rigidly undeviating loyalty to the taboo against alcohol in any form. Rosanoff has expressed this in emphatic language: [11]

From a mental-hygiene standpoint it can be said unequivocally that *the use of alcohol as a beverage in any form should be abolished.* There are some limited uses of alcohol as a therapeutic agent; but, aside from that, the advice of a physician, to an individual patient seeking it, in the light of our present-day knowledge, can be only *total abstinence without compromise.* Nearly 3/4 of a century ago Charles Darwin made this statement: " Through the long experience of my father and my grandfather, extending over a period of more than 100 years, I have reached the conviction that no other cause has brought about so much suffering, so much disease and misery, as the use of intoxicating beverages." — Our experience since Darwin's time has borne out but too well the correctness of his emphatic statement.

Apparently Rosanoff would have advocated a self-denying ordinance on the part of " normal " drinkers in the interests of the public good, for he urged almost unqualified abolition of indulgence in alcoholic beverages. It is also clear from the context that he regarded nationwide prohibition by means of legislative enactment as the wrong way to bring about such abolition. In fact, he reminded us that the incidence of alcoholic psychoses increased so rapidly in the years following the adoption of the Eighteenth Amendment [12] to the Constitution " that many of the most ardent

[11] Rosanoff, A. J., *Manual of Psychiatry and Mental Hygiene,* New York, John Wiley & Sons, Inc., 1938, pp. 776–777.

[12] For a curve showing this increase see Landis, C., and Page, J. D., *Modern Society and Mental Disease,* New York, Farrar & Rinehart, Inc., p. 140. In this connection it might not be amiss to introduce the interpretation Landis and Page give to this increase:

" The effect of ' legal ' prohibition on the incidence of alcoholic psychoses should be an object lesson to the advocates of enforced ' health ' measures. The educational program for temperance was relatively effective from the standpoint of health, it had social approval, and it could be ' enforced.' The Prohibition Amendment, with its resultant social disorganization, undid the educational work of fifty years " (p. 150).

advocates of national prohibition became its bitterest opponents." Furthermore, because repeal of this Amendment has not resulted in a reduction of alcoholic disorders, Rosanoff was unwilling to repudiate *all* governmental regulation of the traffic in alcohol. As specific measures he believed in a return to the local option principle, to a resumption of the earlier educational efforts intended to win voluntary converts to the cause of abstemiousness, and in the investigation of possible hereditary and socio-economic causes of alcoholic excess. At all events it should be clear that prophylactic mental hygiene is not yet in a position to point to any impressive record of accomplishment on the alcoholic sector of its battle against man's mental ills.

This does not mean that the outlook for the future is hopeless. Recent years have brought better understanding of the psychology of the alcoholic. Even the discovery of a relationship between chronic alcoholism and a specific vitamin deficiency can be credited to the asset side of the ledger. Those who have had much experience with alcoholics are coming to believe that the problem has been oversimplified and somewhat distorted in the past. They view the alcoholic not so much as a person with a character defect to be railed against, prayed over, and preached at, but as a mentally sick person who turns to alcohol as a means of getting relief from the agony of persistent feelings of inferiority, inadequacy, guilt, or failure, as the case may be. Genetically considered, feelings of this kind are conceived of as having preceded the first drinking bout in the alcoholic's personal history. In this sense they *caused* the drinking. Of course the deleterious consequences of alcoholic excess then produce more distress — after the initial feeling of exhilaration — and the upshot is the familiar vicious cycle of the " blues " motivating one to get drunk, the latter producing the hangover with its characteristic " jitters," and a " pick-me-up " being necessary to get rid of the " jitters." By this time neither the patient nor his friends are able to separate cause from effect. Alcohol stands out as the prime evil and all efforts are concentrated on getting him to learn either " to leave the stuff alone " or to " drink like a gentleman." These efforts are usually altogether futile.

According to the view being developed here, they are futile because the attack is on the effect or symptom rather than the cause.

The rash is not the cause of measles even though it stands out in such conspicuous fashion. To concentrate on keeping the skin free from blemishes will not ward off measles, chicken pox, scarlet fever, and other exanthematous diseases. Similarly, to concentrate on the alcoholic's appetite for whiskey will not ward off his next attack. We must get back of the appetite, so to speak, and ask why this irresistible craving? What prompted the patient to drink in the first place? Only by getting at the motivating factors can one proceed to help the patient help himself. Usually he is unaware of the precise nature of these underlying psychological factors. He fails to realize that for him alcoholism is a means of running away from himself or of escaping from duties, responsibilities, and obligations. He fails to realize that basically he lacks confidence in himself and that his drinking is a blundering effort to attain self-assurance. He fails to realize that his drinking is symptomatic of the emotional immaturity of the spoiled child or of the timid soul too scared of failure to try to be a success or of the conscience-stricken victim too overwhelmed by feelings of remorse and guilt to believe that self-respect can ever be achieved or restored.

Modern techniques of therapy [13] stress the importance of getting at these psychological factors and doing something about them if the drift toward a psychotic breakdown is to be arrested. Special diets and medical measures are not overlooked, but they are regarded as subordinate to the main job of enabling the patient to build up new attitudes toward himself, his future, and the place of alcohol in his scheme of things. The central task is thus one of re-education. The patient has to learn that his alcoholism is an unintelligent and unsuccessful means of coping with his difficulties. He must come to envisage it in a framework of psychological perspectives and recognize it as an instrument of escape and retreat from the reality of inner distress and outer duress. In terms of this framework he is brought to a recognition of the self-deceptions and rationalizations by means of which he has deluded himself into a

[13] For an interesting popular account of these techniques, see Strecker, E. A., and Chambers, F. T., *Alcohol, One Man's Meat* —, New York, The Macmillan Company, 1938. References to the technical literature are scattered through this volume. There is no need to repeat them here. However, some readers may be interested in one recent development not listed by Strecker and Chambers. This is a movement developed by recovered alcoholics to facilitate the recovery of others. An engrossing report is to be found in Parkhurst, G., "Laymen and Alcoholics," *Harper's Magazine, 183,* 1941, pp. 422–429.

specious, self-justifying approval of his alcoholic addiction in the past. He is also taught to view his inability to " drink like a gentleman " not as a sign of weakness or of " lack of will-power," but more as an indication of an impersonal constitutional quirk akin to the inability of some allergic patients to " eat strawberries like a gentleman." To think of himself as allergic to alcohol just as others are allergic to strawberries serves to bolster up his self-respect by shifting the emphasis from self-condemnatory moral judgments to ethically neutral constitutional factors. This reduces the chances of succumbing to the temptation to convince himself and others of his " masculine " prowess in alcoholic competition. Inability to " carry his liquor " is no longer viewed as a sign of weakness or effeminacy. Consequently it is somewhat easier to turn down invitations to drink since the act itself has been converted from a challenge to his self-respect to a mere threat to the chemistry of his body. He comes to think of himself as having a low tolerance for alcohol just as others have a low tolerance for sugar or the dust of goose feathers or the pollen of ragweed.

The re-education of the alcoholic is a complex and difficult psychological task both for the patient and his mentor. Incidentally, among those who have been particularly successful in this type of psychotherapy are ex-drunkards. They possess a degree of insight and firsthand understanding of the difficulties to be overcome not easily achieved by merely reading about alcoholic psychoses. The very fact that they have been " through the mill " establishes a unique kind of rapport between patient and therapist. Their anticipation of the precise nature of the patient's fears and doubts and tensions makes for intelligent planning of daily schedules and adroit ways of dealing with critical periods. All of this makes for growing confidence in the therapist and in oneself. But the basic change, as has already been indicated, has to do with the substitution of an emotionally mature attitude for the erstwhile childish one: to teach the patient that personal problems are not soluble in alcohol, that they are to be faced in realistic fashion and thought through rather than drowned out.

We have been discussing therapy and not prophylaxis. However, if these therapeutic efforts are based on a sound theory, then a promising prophylactic program may be placed at the mental hygienist's disposal. According to the theory, alcoholism is a consequence of inefficient ways of meeting difficulties: running away from them instead of facing them. Less figuratively, alcohol, now known to be a narcotic rather than a stimulant, first acts on the tissues of the brain cortex and disrupts their efficiency. The result is a blurring of judgment, a blunting of self-criticism, and a boosting of impulsiveness. It is this last result which has given alcohol its spurious reputation as a stimulant, for it makes the drinker feel capable of doing big things in a big way. In reality, however, it is a consequence of the narcotizing action of alcohol. To understand this one must recall that the cortex acts like a brake on the functions of the lower brain centers involved in emotionalized impulsiveness. The cortex thus tends to inhibit their full responsiveness by keeping them under restraint or holding them in check. Alcohol weakens or deadens this holding action. In technical language, it inhibits the inhibition. In mild cases this action may be compared to releasing the brakes of an automobile; but in extreme cases it is more akin to removing or destroying the brakes. And a car without brakes is both a dangerous and an inefficient instrument. Similarly, a person devoid of inhibitions is bound to run amok and be a menace to himself and others. The alcoholic's escape from his difficulties is like a car with poor brakes careening downhill.

In the light of these considerations many students of the problem believe that alcoholic psychoses are to be prevented by training children to face their difficulties in manful fashion. Just what such training implies will be taken up in considerable detail in Part IV. For the present we must rest content with the general statement that it calls for a judicious balance between foresight and impulsiveness, building up attitudes of honest self-appraisal in an inner setting of emotional security, and emancipating the child from tendencies to meet his disappointments by whining, running to others for reassurance, and other childish modes of reaction. This kind of child training is justifiable in terms of meliorative mental hygiene. In theory it ought also to have prophylactic effects by reducing the chances of a child with such training later turning to alcohol as a means of escape from the conflicts and troubles of his adult years. But this had better be regarded as a promising working hypothesis rather than as verified fact.

For ideal verification the scientifically minded mental hygienist would like to see a group of say 1,000 children divided into two groups of 500 each, the two groups being approximately equal in talent, socio-economic background, constitutional make-up, opportunities for schooling and play, and other relevant factors. By stressing this kind of training for the one group and permitting traditional laissez-faire training for the other the stage would be set for experimental verification. If the hypothesis is sound, statistically reliable differences in the number of alcoholics in the two groups should show up some 40 or 50 years later.

It is obviously easier to project such experiments on paper than to carry them out. Unfortunately, the entire field of prophylactic mental hygiene is consequently littered with more or less promising hypotheses, many of them attractive and plausible, but very few, if any, have been subjected to the verification of rigorously controlled check one associates with sound scientific work. A plausible working hypothesis is one thing, but its verification is another. It is easier for the bacteriologist to prove that he can ward off an epidemic of typhoid in a community than it is for the mental hygienist to *prove* that he knows how to safeguard all the babies born into the world today from the menace of alcoholism and its associated evils.

PREVENTION OF CONVULSIVE DISORDERS

Epilepsy, it will be recalled, may require institutional commitment either because of its psychotic complications or because the attacks render it unwise to leave the patient without official supervision. In Table 1 these are listed as " with psychosis " and " without psychosis," respectively. For the year 1938 the number of first admissions in the former category amounted to 1.8% or 1,942 of the total and 641 or 0.6% in the latter category. This means that almost 2,600 or almost 2.5% of those entering a mental hospital for the first time were victims of a convulsive disorder. Since these figures refer to an *annual* admission rate, it can readily be realized how the total number of individuals and families affected is actually much larger for the country as a whole. In fact, Lennox,[14] whose study of epilepsy was mentioned in Chapter 3, estimates the incidence of the disease in the general population to be 0.5%.

[14] Lennox, W. G., *Science and Seizures*, New York, Harper & Brothers, 1941, p. 96.

Stated differently, this would represent 500 cases of epilepsy in every city with a population of 100,000. Applying this ratio to the 132,000,000 people in the country is enough to suggest the magnitude of the problem of epilepsy. To render this more than a vague suggestion it might be added that Lennox [15] believes that possibly 10,000,000 people in the United States are either " subject to or predisposed to epilepsy." Warding off such convulsive disorders is thus a prophylactic task of extreme importance. In discussing its nature we shall avail ourselves of the idea furnished by Lennox.

As was mentioned on an earlier page, epilepsy is associated with disturbed electrical rhythms of the cortex. This so-called cerebral dysrhythmia can be demonstrated by means of an electro-encephalogram (the E.E.G.). Not everyone with an abnormal E.E.G. has seizures, but everyone with genuine epileptic seizures has abnormal brain waves. The electrical disturbance in question is a necessary but not a sufficient condition for the production of epileptic attacks. This is but another instance of a familiar causal relationship: A causes B provided A is accompanied by X or X' or X''. In this formula A stands for the necessary cause and the X's symbolize the associated or contributing causes. In the interests of clarity this formula can be illustrated in terms of a few stock examples. Gasoline (A) is necessary to activate an automobile engine, but this will occur only if the ignition switch is on (X), the battery is up to a minimal voltage (X'), the spark plugs are in order (X''), etc. In analogous fashion one can demonstrate that the mere presence of the cholera organism is not sufficient to start a plague, that mere possession of a gun does not signify murder, that ownership of a ball and bat will not guarantee home runs, and that nearness of a suitable body of water is a necessary but not a sufficient condition for fishing.

In his discussion of the prevention of epilepsy Lennox first considers the possibility of eliminating the fundamental cause, the cerebral dysrhythmia. Inasmuch as this rests on a genetic basis its total elimination could be accomplished only by means of a drastic eugenics campaign. Such a campaign would require an E.E.G. record for every person in the world and all with dysrhythmic records would have to be induced to abstain from parenthood.

[15] *Ibid.*, p. 189.

In theory this sort of attack on the problem ought to make epilepsy a rare or nonexistent clinical condition within a few generations. However, this prediction will probably never be more than a hypothetical goal buried in a textbook like this, for the conditions of its fulfillment are neither practicable nor even entirely desirable. About a tenth of the world's population would have to be sterilized or persuaded to refrain from having children. To select this vulnerable tenth, as was just stated, every person in the world would have to be tested. This in itself would constitute an almost forbidding task. But even if it were executed, the most ardent advocate of racial betterment might hesitate to apply the taboo against parenthood indiscriminately to all of the millions with abnormal E.E.G.'s. Many of these would be possessors of exceptional talents and abilities. Many others would be the potential forebears of Swinburnes and Pascals and Handels and other distinguished epileptics. This is not to imply that great poetry, brilliant mathematics, and inspiring music are caused by epilepsy, but merely to point out that the " welfare of the race " involves much more than freedom from convulsive seizures.

As might be anticipated, Lennox is not enthusiastic about prophylaxis by means of wholesale eugenic control. In particular he deplores what he characterizes as " the blank ignorance of some legislators " and " the stupidity and cruelty " of the law they enacted in Connecticut to prevent epileptics from having children. According to this bit of applied legislative eugenics, no epileptic may marry unless his bride is at least 45 years of age. If he does, he can be punished by imprisonment up to 3 years. Outsiders who assist in the promotion of such a marriage are to be dealt with even more severely: a fine up to $1,000 or a maximum of 5 years in prison, or both. The fact that legislation of this sort takes place is our chief reason for devoting this much space to the eugenic aspect of the problem. Far too many individuals regard " eugenics " as the answer to all questions of prophylaxis in which hereditary factors are operative. With reference to epilepsy, as Lennox views the issue, the question of children is *altogether an individual affair*. Even if all epileptics could be restrained by some such statute as the one just described, the remaining millions with undiscovered abnormal E.E.G.'s would still be free to transmit their latent heritage of convulsive seizures.

There are some specific suggestions offered by Lennox to the victim of epilepsy troubled by the question of advisability of marriage for an epileptic. In the first place the need for honesty regarding the existence of the seizures is to be stressed. To withhold this information from the prospective marriage partner is indefensible deception. In the second place the following facts might aid the individuals concerned in thinking through the problem of the wisdom of such a marriage. A study of the near relatives of 2,000 epileptic patients has shown the incidence of seizures among them to be five and a half times greater than in the general population. Stated differently: seizures are found in one out of every 36 near relatives on the average. To evaluate the risk of having children one may use these data as a basis for prediction. As Lennox implies, the pessimistic patient will conclude that they mean he will be the parent of five and a half times as many epileptic children as a normal parent would be. On the other hand the optimistic patient, with equally impeccable statistical logic, may conclude that if he and his future wife should have a family of 36 children, only one will be subject to seizures. Under the circumstances both patients might welcome additional hints. They ought to know, for example, that the chances of having normal children are greater if one of the parents has a normal E.E.G. They ought also to know that the history of their own attacks has a bearing on the predictions being made. The chances of having epileptic children are greater if the epileptic parent had seizures all his life than if he was free from seizures during his childhood and only developed them subsequent to a head injury or following a serious illness. In the light of the evidence marshaled by Lennox families any of whose members are victims of migraine headaches and some kinds of psychotic disorder are also more likely to harbor abnormal E.E.G.'s. Marriage by a member of such a family or into such a family is thus calculated to heighten the chances of bringing epileptic children into the world. Finally, if the individual patient feels the risks are too great for him, or that there are not enough positive assets in the way of valuable *heritable* traits (to the extent that one can know about such matters) in his family tree to compensate for the risks, he might still consider marriage provided he and his wife are reconciled to making it a childless marriage. This is almost all that can be said at present regarding the public and private phases of the eugenic approach to prophylactic mental hygiene as applied to convulsive disorders. In other words, the prospects for control by eliminating cerebral dysrhythmia, the fundamental cause, are not very bright.

Even though one is born with an abnormal E.E.G., it is possible in many instances to ward off the emergence of actual seizures by control of the secondary or accessory causes. Among the latter Lennox lists all traumatic and infectious disturbance of cortical tissue, or more specifically: birth injuries, fractured skulls, meningitis, middle ear infections, encephalitis, St. Vitus dance, and syphilis of the central nervous system. These constitute some of the X's in our preceding formula. Many individuals are born with cause A, the abnormal E.E.G., but will never exhibit a convulsive seizure provided they succeed in dodging the hazards of these X's. Translated into suggestions for positive action this means that the incidence of epileptic seizures can be reduced by providing the public with better obstetrical care so as to render birth injury less frequent, by educational and mechanical contributions to accident prevention campaigns, and by taking advantage of existing knowledge pertaining to the prevention of those infections likely to act as contributing causes. And for the victim himself, for whom these prophylactic suggestions come too late, there may be comfort in the reflection that modern medicine has made progress in the direction of more adequate understanding and control of his trouble. The new drug, dilantin, as mentioned earlier, shows promise of being a better anti-convulsant than any of its predecessors. But this phase of the subject is purely medical and beyond the province of the mental hygienist.[16]

---

[16] Treatment of epilepsy is, of course, a medical problem; but the mental hygienist can be of some service in using his influence to enlighten the public regarding the dangers of purchasing " cures " by mail or of succumbing to the blandishments of quacks who guarantee spectacular results by " new, secret remedies." Any person needing guidance with reference to problems of epilepsy or associated conditions might communicate with *The Laymen's League against Epilepsy,* 25 Shattuck Street, Boston, Massachusetts. The office of the *League* can furnish the name and address of some reputable medical consultant located near the home of the inquirer.

Another way in which the mental hygienist can be of assistance is to help change the attitude of those members of the public who still think of the epileptic as " queer " or " dangerous." This is a survival of the superstitious doctrine of demonic or spirit possession. Dissipation of the last remnants of this doctrine will make the lot of the epileptic easier to bear. This in itself will constitute mental hygiene progress.

Concluding comments

The general drift of the prophylactic aspects of the more common structural disorders has now been outlined. In retrospect it must be obvious that more progress has been made in formulating the problems than in solving them. There was more cause to view with alarm than to point with pride. Even in connection with mental disorders of known etiology — paresis and the alcoholic psychoses — there was no record of solid prophylactic achievement to report. Prevention of the structural psychoses is still largely a task for future realization. Whether the mental hygienist can submit a more encouraging report on prophylactic aspects of the functional disorders is a question consideration of which had better be reserved for discussion in the next chapter.

7 ... *PROPHYLACTIC ASPECTS*
OF FUNCTIONAL PSYCHOSES: I

BEFORE UNDERTAKING A SURVEY OF EXISTING KNOWLEDGE CON-
cerning prevention of the functional disorders it might be
desirable to review a little of what was said on previous pages regarding the meaning of the term *functional* in contradistinction to
organic or structural psychoses. It will be recalled that one psychiatrist suggested the phrase " mind twist " disorder as a symbol
for the former category and " brain spot " disorder for the latter.
It will also be recalled that functional disorders were divided into
two groups: the functional psychoses on the one hand and the
psychoneuroses on the other. This gave us a tripartite classification comprising the organic psychoses, the functional psychoses,
and the psychoneuroses.

By way of once again showing the justification for such a threefold division, a simple illustration might be considered at this
point. In a baseball game a player may be prevented from taking
his turn at bat because his thumb was broken by a foul tip the
previous inning. This would constitute a structural disorder. Another player might not be able to take his turn because of sudden,
devastating news. A telegram announcing the death of his wife
and child in an automobile accident might leave him so shocked
and bewildered that he has neither the strength nor the interest
to go on with the game. He might even fail to hear his name as the
batting order for this particular inning is announced over the
public address system. Those close to him might report that he
seemed " to be in a trance or a kind of stupor." His personal
tragedy would thus render it impossible for him " to adjust to
the reality " of his professional duties as a batter. In view of this
loss of contact with " reality " his trouble might be used as a convenient symbol for the functional disturbance of the psychotic
type. To symbolize the psychoneurotic type a third hypothetical
situation will have to be introduced. In this situation just as the
batter is about to step to the plate the manager of the opposing

team changes pitchers. The new pitcher may have a curious wind-up: one that reminds the batter of a pitcher he played against in the minors ten years before. This minor league pitcher, he hastily recalls, was finally dismissed from organized baseball because of his violent temper and the frequency with which he threw what batters call a " bean ball," a swift throw aimed directly at the head of the batter. One of his " bean balls " actually killed a player. In vague form these reminiscences are dimly revived at the threshold of our player's consciousness as he watches the new relief pitcher's curious wind-up. He is more vividly and acutely aware of a sudden and to him inexplicable inner panic. He is troubled by a mild nausea and a pounding heart. He wonders if standing out in the sun could have made him sick. He also wonders whether to tell the manager about his symptoms so that another batter can be substituted for him. He is altogether in contact with the " reality " of the baseball environment and his responsibility to it; but somehow he does not feel equal to " adjusting " to it. For the time being his " batting functions " are disordered. Something out of his past is interfering with present adjustment and enabling him to exemplify the concept of a psychoneurotic action for us. We thus have the broken thumb standing for the structural disorder, the tragic telegram representing the functional psychosis, and the curious wind-up symbolizing the neurotic disturbance.

THE MAGNITUDE OF THE PROBLEM

These functional disorders bulk large in the statistics of mental diseases. By turning back to Table 1 and segregating the functional from the structural cases into a separate table, one can secure a serviceable notion of the proportion of first admissions officially classified as primarily functional. Table 3 on page 138 reveals the result of such segregation.

It is thus obvious that almost 40% of the first admissions belong in the category of functional disorders, and that, furthermore, schizophrenia alone accounts for nearly half of them. In addition, the vast majority of neurotic patients are never hospitalized because of their disorder and consequently fail to be included in statistical surveys of this kind. All in all there is little danger of overestimating the importance and scope of these functional troubles. If the mental hygienist could work out some way of warding them off, he would be making a contribution of incalculable value to human welfare.

TABLE 3

FIRST ADMISSIONS FOR THE YEAR 1938 " TO ANY INSTITUTION FOR
MENTAL DISEASES, . . . EXCEPTING INSTITUTIONS FOR TEMPORARY
CARE ONLY " IN WHICH THE NEW PATIENTS WERE FOUND TO BE
VICTIMS OF A FUNCTIONAL DISORDER

Classification	Number	Per Cent of All Cases: Organic Plus the Functional
Psychoneuroses	4,229	3.8
Manic-depressive	12,282	11.1
Schizophrenia	21,279	19.3
Paranoia and paranoid conditions ..	1,862	1.7
Psychopathic personality	2,302	2.1
Primary behavior disorders	408	0.4
Totals	42,362	38.4

FUNCTIONAL DISORDERS: A MENTAL HYGIENE CHALLENGE

Far more than is the case with the structural disorders, these functional ones constitute a direct challenge to the ability, knowledge, and professional status of the mental hygienist. The structural disorders, as we have seen, are basically problems for workers in such fields as general medicine, neurology, serology, sanitary engineering, public health, and whatever else is ordinarily included in the concept of preventive medicine. But the very concept of *psychogenic* disorder modifies the whole picture. It implies the existence of a whole class of disturbances whose primary etiology is mental. One can no longer pass the buck to preventive medicine. The job has to be tackled by those who pride themselves on being specialists in the study of this phase of etiology; namely, psychological factors as causes of disease. Prevention of functional disorders is thus a responsibility to be assumed by the mental hygienist. In many respects the extent of his success in reducing the incidence of these disorders may be regarded as an index of his professional progress.

The soundness of a program of prophylactic mental hygiene can thus be put to a pragmatic test: are there significantly fewer cases of functional disorders in communities served by mental hygiene clinics than in comparable communities devoid of such clinical guidance? This general question ought to be broken up into a series of more specific questions as each of the disorders is taken up separately. Accordingly, the earnest mental hygienist ought to ask himself, " What evidence can I mobilize to demonstrate to this community that I know how to safeguard it from schizophrenia? Have I really got such evidence? Do I know what to tell people about warding off the hebephrenic type of schizophrenia as opposed to the catatonic type? Can I be as specific as this or is my understanding of this psychosis still too vague to justify such specificity? And what shall I tell them about the prevention of manic-depressive disorders? If badgered by some hostile skeptic, could I dispose of his skepticism by pointing to some spectacular instance of a successful prophylactic campaign directed against manic-depressive psychosis? How can I prove to such a skeptic that I really know how to prevent paranoia and hysteria or any other functional disturbance? "

These are challenging questions. They may be irritating, but they have to be faced. No mental hygienist, mindful of his own injunction to face reality bravely and without evasiveness, would be justified in dodging them. They call for a critical sifting of evidence rather than dogmatic enthusiasm. They demand blunt honesty and a readiness to recognize the difference between hope and accomplishment. To handle them adequately one must be familiar with such common sources of error as confusing a plausible working theory with demonstrated fact, substituting symptoms for causes, assuming that knowledge of causes automatically supplies prophylactic control, and that citation of expert *opinion* is preferable to a direct evaluation of the facts upon which such opinion is based. Even though it involves a slight digression, it might pay us to examine some of these sources of error a little more closely.

SOME LOGICAL PITFALLS

In getting at the cause of a disease — particularly a functional mental disease — the unwary investigator is sometimes likely to regard what he takes to be his successful treatment of a patient as proof of the theory underlying his treatment. To illustrate this in terms of a common ailment like tonsillitis: some investigator may assume that because the throat is stiff the basic cause is a lack of lubricating fluid in the body. Accordingly, he prescribes olive oil taken internally and applied externally to the neck muscles as suitable therapy. After several days of such treatment the inflammation subsides and the stiffness disappears. Does this suffice to prove the correctness of the theory? Does seeming therapeutic success constitute scientific proof? Unless careful control experiments are introduced, such proof is worthless. People recover from tonsillitis in the absence of any specialized therapy. *Speed* of recovery might consequently be taken as one criterion of success. If the olive oil therapy administered to 1,000 patients results in recovery in significantly less time than for 1,000 untreated patients, then therapeutic efficacy could be attributed to the oil provided all other conceivably relevant factors such as nursing care, diet, age of the patients, etc., had been kept reasonably equated for the two groups.

But to return to our crucial question: would such therapeutic success also mean that the theory concerning the need for lubrication has been confirmed? By no means. The oil may have been successful because of a possible nutritional effect or because of some hitherto undiscovered vitamin or because of some mechanical effect of the massage on the muscles or blood vessels of the throat. To check on these possibilities additional experiments would have to be planned.

An erroneous theory *may* result in gratifying therapy. To argue from therapeutic success to confirmation of theory is thus apt to be treacherous. Nor can such treacherous logic be circumvented by testimonials from enthusiastic and grateful patients. There are thousands of such patients sincerely convinced that they owe their recoveries either to chiropractic, or to some physician's green pills, or to Christian Science, to osteopathy, to deep breathing, to massage, to mineral water, to removal of tonsils, to a visit to a holy shrine, or to nudism. Similarly, there are thousands who attribute the excellence of their teeth to the very careful daily use of a toothbrush. Just why some equally conscientious devotees of the toothbrushing ritual suffer from dental decay and why some who never brush their teeth escape such decay are questions they blithely ignore, even though the scientifically minded dentist is acutely aware of the relevance of such questions. And as the daily newspapers remind us from time to time there are nonagenarians who attribute their longevity to the moderate daily use of tobacco and whiskey just as there are nonagenarians whose testimony " proves " that total abstention from smoking and alcoholic drinks makes for a long life.

Questions of cause and effect in the realm of health and disease for the most part are too complex to be settled by casual observation, by majority vote, or by general impression. Even " clinical experience " may have to be checked by control experiments and the experience of other clinicians. Nor can the mere citation of expert opinion be taken as an invariably dependable way of disposing of such questions. The history of medicine is replete with instances of experts who backed what we now know to have been the wrong opinion. In the seventeenth century there were experts who opposed what Harvey had to teach regarding the circulation of the blood. And Pasteur's troubles with the medical experts of his day are common knowledge. That Charcot, France's leading authority on diseases of the nervous system in the late nineteenth century, refused to endorse the then novel teaching of syphilis as the cause of paresis, is also common knowledge among those familiar with the history of paresis.

These considerations should not be taken to mean that experts are not to be trusted or that ordinary opinion is as valid as expert opinion. The fact that members of the United States Supreme Court differ from one another on some specific questions of constitutional law does not signify the Court's ignorance of constitutional law. Nor does it justify a contemptuous attitude toward the field of constitutional law. Even those who espouse a minority opinion are more learned in the field than those not professionally trained in this branch of the law. In other words, we are not saying that experts should be ignored but that their opinion on *controversial* issues should not be confused with tested knowledge. What they have to say should be taken as presumptive evidence rather than as coercive proof. As applied to our immediate concern — unsettled questions in the field of mental hygiene — this means that such questions cannot be disposed of by appeals to what " Freud taught " or " Adler advocated " or " McDougall maintained." Appeal to authority is different from a direct and critical scrutiny of the available evidence. What a " doctor " says is probably more often right than what the " layman " says; but when another " doctor " contradicts the first one, then the poor " layman " may begin to appreciate the difference between fact and opinion, between data and their interpretation, or between symptomatology and diagnosis.

THE PROBLEM OF SCHIZOPHRENIA

Some of the difficulties and pitfalls just mentioned can be exemplified by considering the prophylactic issues involved in the subject of schizophrenia. Development of a technique for preventing this disorder would constitute a tremendous mental hygiene contribution. It will be recalled that almost one-half of the institutionalized patients suffering from functional disorders are schizophrenics. What can be done to protect the children born this year and those to be born in the ensuing years from becoming victims of this disease? What shall we tell their parents about building up immunity against schizophrenia comparable to what they can be told about immunizing their children against smallpox and diphtheria? And maybe we ought to enlist the aid of the schools and get the teachers to cooperate in some vast anti-schizophrenia campaign. If so, we ought to be able to plan such a campaign as definitely and as concretely as Dr. Parran and his co-workers planned their anti-syphilis campaign.

Unfortunately, we are unable to be as certain, as definite, and as concrete in our recommendations as those who have undertaken to ward off diphtheria, syphilis, typhoid and similar infections. The essential etiology of the latter diseases is much better understood than the etiology of schizophrenia. There is even some debate as to whether it should continue to be classified as a functional disease. Without going into all of the details of this debate it might not be amiss to introduce a bare suggestion of some of the points raised by the participants, so that the mental hygienist will not be judged too harshly for his failure to stamp out schizophrenia.

There are some who believe schizophrenia may be due to disturbed body chemistry. They point to the fact that so frequently the schizophrenic patients have low blood pressure, slow pulse, and reduced oxygen consumption. Others regard the disease as com-

plicated by brain disturbances as revealed by atypical electroencephalograms. Still others call attention to the seeming beneficial
effects of shock therapy. This mode of treatment was introduced
in the late 1920's by Dr. Manfred Sakel and was tried out in various clinics in different parts of the world in subsequent years. It
consists in producing a rather devastating shock by means of a
preparation like insulin or drugs like camphor or metrazol. The
resulting convulsions, especially from metrazol, may be so violent
that on rare occasions a patient's jaw may be dislocated or some
bone broken under the sudden strain of powerful muscular spasms.
In fact, many psychiatrists are reluctant to employ this mode of
therapy not only because of the injuries it may induce, but also
because of the fear which it arouses in the patients. On the other
hand, its advocates believe the improved mental condition of the
patients following a series of such shocks justifies both the risks
and terror involved. Recently some investigators have reported
success in reducing the violence of the muscular contractions
by using another drug before injecting the metrazol. This other
drug, known as *curare,* when introduced into the bloodstream directly, will paralyze all muscles by blocking the passage of neural
impulses from motor nerves to muscles. Indians in South America
used to apply curare to the tips of their arrows. After being struck
by such an arrow the victim would be left helpless, since he was
powerless to move his muscles. When taken by mouth curare is not
nearly so toxic or dangerous, but will nevertheless continue to
exert some inhibitory influence on the patient's musculature. By
taking advantage of this well-known fact Dr. A. E. Bennett of
Nebraska reports marked reduction in the hazards of metrazol
therapy if curare is administered shortly before injecting the
shock-producing drug.

Just why the schizophrenic patient should be aided by this kind
of drastic treatment is not known.[1] Is the therapy really due to
altered body chemistry induced by the drugs used or is the improvement a consequence of the " mechanics " of the shock or is it
to be attributed to the " mental " results of the patient's *fear* of

[1] Toward the close of his monograph (p. 109) dealing with the shock treatment, as he developed it, Sakel says, " I do not know how the method of treatment I have here described actually works. . . ." For a clearer understanding of
what this treatment entails, see Sakel, M., *The Pharmacological Shock Treatment
of Schizophrenia,* New York, Nervous and Mental Disease Publishing Co., 1938.

the shock? Nobody knows. Some might be inclined to rule out any specific chemical action on the ground that different chemical substances — insulin, camphor, metrazol — can be used for the same purpose of inducing shock. To buttress this argument they might call attention to very recent work in which shock was produced without using any chemicals at all. This is the electroshock treatment developed in the late 1930's in one of the Italian clinics. The technique calls for the adjustment to each temple of the patient of small cushions of rubber. The surface of these rubber pads is covered with some interlacing copper strips which serve as electrodes. To produce the shock a current of less than 100 volts of electricity is shot through the head of the patient for less than a second. This suffices to render him both unconscious and convulsive. As soon as the seizure subsides, the patient relaxes and regains consciousness a few minutes later. Some of the sponsors of this treatment regard it as preferable to chemical means of inducing shock because, according to them, the patient's dread of repeated treatments is less acute than when metrazol is used.

Some success has also been reported for still other forms of nonpsychological treatment of schizophrenics. One of these calls for brain surgery and involves what is technically described as *prefrontal leucotomy*. This is medical Latin for " cutting through the white fibers connecting the thalamus with the cells of the front region of the brain." Nothing is cut out: the connecting fibers are merely severed. Just why this surgical maneuver should bring about improvement or " cure " of the schizophrenic patient is not much easier to explain than " cures " associated with metrazol or electricity. To complicate the whole picture, two Boston investigators have recently reported moderate success in treating schizophrenics by freezing them. Normal body temperature, it will be recalled, is 98.6° F. When this refrigeration therapy is employed the temperature is brought down to 80 or 90°. To accomplish this the patient is wrapped in a special kind of rubberized cloth through which the " freezing fluid " is made to circulate. The duration of each treatment varies from one to three days.

Is schizophrenia really a functional disease?

The relative success of these different methods is still a subject of controversy. An additional subject of controversy is the question of what these reported successes mean in terms of the systematic classification of schizophrenia. Do they mean, as some have taken them to mean, that schizophrenia is really not a *functional* disease after all? Before the mental hygienist can proceed to tell people how to ward off schizophrenia, ought he not come to some verdict on this question?

For the sake of discussion the reality of the reported improvements and " cures " [2] by these various methods may well be granted. In other words, suppose it to be true that schizophrenia can be cured by insulin shock or by camphor shock or by metrazol shock or by electric shock or by refrigeration or by frontal lobe surgery, what then? Does such a finding render a pyschogenic interpretation of schizophrenia either superfluous or untenable? There are some specialists who would be inclined to answer the latter question in the affirmative. They would regard success achieved by chemical, electrical, thermal, or surgical procedures as more in line with a somatogenic interpretation. In many respects such a view seems more plausible and it can be defended by rather obvious arguments. It may therefore be more profitable to consider the less obvious arguments which might be introduced by proponents of the opposing view.

The very fact that the new therapeutic attacks are so *diverse* in nature reminds one of the way in which some admittedly functional symptoms clear up either by massage, by hypnosis, by Christian Science treatments, by some deep-breathing ritual, by harmless placebos, or occasionally following a surgical operation. An unambiguously organic disturbance like a broken arm or carbon monoxide poisoning does not respond to such logically unrelated therapeutic endeavors. What the attending physician does has some understandable bearing on the fractured bone or the

[2] Just how much credence to lend to reports of 100% cures in cases of schizophrenia is subject to debate. Some spontaneous recoveries have been reported right along, even before shock therapy was introduced. Often, though, these recovered cases would suffer a relapse later. Probably the following opinion by one of the best informed workers in the field constitutes a good cross-section of representative expert opinion:

" Dementia precox has been and still is in the minds of many a hopeless condition by and large, but the fact remains that remissions and even what might be considered recovery occur in certain types. The term ' complete recovery ' should be used with caution as there are probably few cases of a well-defined severe type that recover without some ' scarring ' or permanent mental loss." (From Lewis, N. D. C., *Research in Dementia Precox*, New York, National Committee for Mental Hygiene, 1936, p. 280.)

toxic bloodstream. But this is not as convincing an argument as one could desire. It is too much like a weak argument by analogy. A somewhat stronger consideration is furnished by the contention that there is no necessary relationship between the kind of cure employed and the " mental " or " physical " status of the factors involved. Stated differently, a psychogenic symptom may respond to physical measures, as can be demonstrated by means of a simple illustration: a father faints upon receiving a telegram announcing the death of his son in action. The loss of consciousness, a physical symptom, is caused by the sad tidings, a mental event. The symptom could thus be classified as psychogenic. Consciousness can be restored by a *physical* maneuver such as bending the father's head downward or by a *chemical* maneuver such as using spirits of ammonia. However, the success of either one or both of such non-psychological procedures would not justify changing the classification of the cause of the fainting. We would still be justified in attributing the loss of consciousness to the shock induced by the telegram. The father's love for his son would still constitute a causative factor. Analogously, a schizophrenic may be restored to the reality of his surrounding world by chemical or physical procedures without having such restoration mean that mental factors were not responsible for his original loss of contact with reality.

By means of some additional speculation the foregoing admittedly speculative conclusion can be given still more plausibility. All one can do, incidentally, with respect to this phase of the problem of schizophrenia, is speculate; for even the sponsors of the new modes of therapy prefer to stress results achieved and to gloss over the reasons for the results. They are candid enough to admit not knowing precisely why their varied techniques seem to produce cures or improvements.[3] However, the thoughtful outsider must be impressed by one factor all of these treatments have in common: they are all very *drastic* in nature. They all contain features calculated to arouse attitudes of dread in the patients. The shocks are genuine shocks and even the " indifferent " schizophrenic is apt to manifest emotional concern about having to

---

[3] A typical instance of such candor is seen in this statement: " The physiological action of metrazol on the central nervous system is unknown in so far as the amelioration of the mental symptoms in functional psychoses is concerned." (Read, C. F., Steinberg, D. L., Liebert, E., and Finkelman, I., " Use of Metrazol in the Functional Psychoses," *Amer. J. of Psychiatry,* 1939, *95,* p. 783.)

undergo them on repeated occasions. Of course this factor of repetition is absent from the prefrontal leucotomy, even though its drastic nature be admitted; but this particular technique has not been as successful with schizophrenics as with some other types of functional cases. Some form of the shock treatment seems to be productive of better results with the schizophrenics than the surgical treatment. But this constitutes a slight digression. What is of more immediate concern is the possibility that the shock treatment itself may be viewed as a mode of heroic psychotherapy or re-education in line with the use of severe disciplinary measures used in the traditional treatment of incorrigible prisoners or the flogging to which the insane were subjected in the pre-modern era.

What we are suggesting is that punishment may under given circumstances be classified as a form of therapy.[4] To appreciate what this might mean as applied to the schizophrenic patient it is necessary to recall that, according to one view, such a patient has taken refuge in the congenial atmosphere of an inner world of phantasy — that he has withdrawn from the outer world of duty and responsibility and is no longer responsive to the events of the life going on around him. The stuporous catatonic fails to respond to calls, requests, pleadings, or even mild pinches. He acts as if he were completely absorbed in some private world of his own or lost in a daydream just as a normal person can lose himself in the exciting events of a football game he is watching or the fictitious events with which he identifies himself as he reads a fascinating novel or follows some dramatic movie episode. For the time being such a normal person is also put out of touch with reality. In fact he himself might classify such recreational pursuits as " escapes " from the reality of the humdrum events of his everyday world. To arouse the attention of such a preoccupied, normal " escapist " may require a more vigorous push or a louder call than is ordinarily required when he is not withdrawn from the affairs of his

---

[4] That this suggestion is not altogether remote from direct clinical impression can be inferred from the following testimony of a psychiatrist whose article reached us shortly after this chapter was completed:

" Shock treatment, particularly convulsive shock treatment with metrazol or sinusoidal current, *may be interpreted as punishment by the patient,* and may be the reason for the high rate of improvement obtained with patients showing a depressive trend." (Lipschutz, L. S., " Some Administrative Aspects of Suicide in the Mental Hospital," *Amer. J. of Psychiatry,* 1942, *99,* p. 186. Italics not in the original.)

routine environment. The schizophrenic's detachment from his environment is, of course, far more extreme. His absorption in his inner world is far more intense and complete. May it not be, therefore, that more extreme and more intense attention-arousing methods have to be introduced in order to break through the barrier of his indifference to the outside world?[5]

Another way of clarifying this speculative suggestion is to view the shock experiences in terms of what they might do to the inner orientation of a catatonic patient. The latter, it will be recalled, seems to act as if he had adopted a resolute "leave me alone and don't bother me" attitude. If current hypotheses are correct, he wants to be permitted to live out his daydream in undisturbed fashion or to wrestle with his inner affairs in his own way without the intrusion of distracting outside factors. For him this is seemingly the more congenial mode of dealing with the basic problem of adjusting to the problem of living. Under the circumstances he remains secure within his protective shell of unresponsiveness to ordinary means of getting a person's attention. However, the shock treatment is too devastating to be ignored. It renders it impossible for him to continue to live his congenial inner life; for the shocks break through the shell and disrupt the congeniality of life in his mental shelter. If he ventures to resume catatonic housekeeping when consciousness returns, there will be another devastating shock coming his way at the next treatment. This sort of therapeutic bombardment is kept up until the patient capitulates by coming out of his schizophrenic retreat into what we call the "normal" world.

If this interpretation has any merit, then any form of sufficiently drastic treatment might work as well as those that have been used. Severe floggings might work, but psychiatrists would be reluctant to try it. All of the newer methods come within the scope of rec-

[5] Recoveries from schizophrenia have been attributed to such intense experiences as being knocked out by a blow, being the victim of an attack by a snake, or otherwise shocked. In this connection it is pertinent to consider the following quotation:

"A certain number of patients, some of whom have been well advanced in their disorder, have been known to recover after a severe infectious disease or shock, for example, that initiated by being knocked unconscious or bitten by a snake, and undoubtedly many drugs and other procedures which seem to produce remissions in individual cases are of 'shock' import." (Lewis, N. D. C., *Research in Dementia Precox*, New York, National Committee for Mental Hygiene, 1936, pp. 282–283.)

ognized " therapeutic " procedures: prefrontal leucotomy is respectable surgery; insulin or metrazol injections are matters of orthodox pharmacological treatment; and the use of refrigerants or electric currents would be classified as acceptable techniques of physiotherapy. But flogging would be taboo. It would be too reminiscent of the early days of barbarous treatment of the insane. It would suggest punishment rather than therapy. Nor are we urging that this taboo be violated. We are merely suggesting that by violating it an investigator might be able to check on the *modus operandi* of the shock treatment and that if a series of " therapeutic floggings " should produce as many cures and improvements as are now attributed to the new methods, then schizophrenia might continue to be classified as a functional disorder. As matters stand there is no reason to regard the success of the new methods as necessarily requiring complete abandonment of a functional or psychogenic interpretation of schizophrenia.[6]

IS SCHIZOPHRENIA A " CONSTITUTIONAL " DISORDER?

As was just pointed out, the success of shock therapy has cast doubt on the basic functional status of schizophrenia. Closely related to this view is the opinion of those who have long been skeptical of a purely psychological explanation of the etiology of the disorder. In their opinion the schizophrenic's troubles are a consequence of some inherent " constitutional " anomaly: some obscure inborn factor that renders him vulnerable to the ordinary stresses of life. If this opinion is sound, it may supply the mental hygienist with a valuable lead; for by learning to recognize the symptoms of such constitutional predisposition to schizophrenic breakdown, one might be able to shield the victims from stresses beyond their capacity for endurance.

This approach to the problem of schizophrenia assumes the operation of two sets of factors: hereditary factors and factors of environmental stress. It is believed, furthermore, that the former are not always sufficient to produce a breakdown; but that the

---

[6] The neurologist, Foster Kennedy, would probably not agree with this conclusion; for, in the *Preface* to Sakel's monograph, he writes: " The scholasticism of our time is being blown away and whatever may be the verdict of the next decade in reference to Manfred Sakel's contribution to ' schizophrenia ' we shall not again be content to minister to a mind diseased merely by philosophy and words." (From Sakel, M., *The Pharmacological Shock Treatment of Schizophrenia*, New York, Nervous and Mental Disease Publishing Co., 1938, p. xv.)

conjoint operation of both sets of factors must be invoked to account for many of the cases. Furthermore, sponsors of this view are also willing to grant that schizophrenia may occur in the absence of hereditary or constitutional factors. In fact, the A.N.A. committee, mentioned in Chapter 5, endorses this general view of the etiology of schizophrenia. Its findings are embodied in four propositions which may be paraphrased as follows: [7]

1. Hereditary factors seem to play an important part in the etiology of schizophrenic disorders.

2. These hereditary factors are often not sufficient to produce a psychosis.

3. The hereditary factors are not to be regarded as " highly specific " in the causation of schizophrenia. If they were, then whenever one member of a pair of identical or monozygotic twins suffers from schizophrenia, one would expect the other twin to be a victim of the same disease. Studies of mental disorder among twins fail to confirm this expectation. There is a higher rate of incidence among identical than among fraternal twins, but the degree of correspondence in the former group is far from perfect. For example, in one study of 19 pairs of identical male twins 10 pairs were schizophrenic as compared with 11 pairs of dizygotic brothers in which only 3 pairs were diagnosed as schizophrenic. This study revealed 9 pairs of monozygotic twins in which schizophrenia developed in only one of the brothers. However, some of the " non-schizophrenic " twins developed other mental disorders such as epilepsy or alcoholic disturbance. What is of particular importance is the fact that cases have been reported in which the " non-schizophrenic " twin is altogether " free from any neuropsychiatric condition." This suggests — one might almost say proves — that the hereditary factors taken by themselves are not sufficient to render a schizophrenic breakdown inevitable. Incidentally, this is part of the evidence upon which the preceding proposition (2) was based.

4. There are cases of schizophrenia in which no hereditary factor can be demonstrated to play a part; hence it is concluded that such factors are " not essential in the etiology of so-called schizophrenic psychoses."

These four propositions serve to emphasize the blurred nature of our understanding of the etiology of schizophrenia. It is not yet possible to bring the details into sharp focus. Nor is it possible to

---

[7] Myerson, A., Ayer, J. B., Putnam, T. J., Keeler, C. E., and Alexander, L., *Eugenical Sterilization,* New York, The Macmillan Co., 1936, p. 162.

be confident of the precise meaning of the factors involved. This is especially true of the reference to hereditary factors; for, as the third proposition indicates, these are not to be thought of as " highly specific." Under the circumstances one would not be justified in saying that some people inherit schizophrenia. All that the proposition justifies is the statement that some people seem to inherit something — exactly what is unknown — which renders them more likely to become schizophrenic than people who are born without this unknown something. However, the second and fourth propositions indicate that this unknown something is neither necessary nor sufficient to produce schizophrenia: the psychosis may fail to develop despite its presence or schizophrenia may develop despite its absence. One begins to appreciate the difficulties of some bewildered schizophrenic trying to understand the nature of his own illness! And it is not strange that a few years ago a leading psychiatrist [8] was moved to complain " that our research on mental disorders is in a state of chaos. . . ."

Be this as it may, it is particularly relevant to point out that many veteran psychiatrists have tended to regard schizophrenia as in some way more of a " constitutional " [9] disorder than many of the other functional disturbances. Even Southard,[10] the man responsible for the picturesque " mind-twist " *versus* " brain spot " metaphor, seems to have had his doubts regarding the functional status of schizophrenia; for he once referred to it as " the obscure

---

[8] Lewis, N. D. C., *op. cit.*, p. 1.

[9] The term *constitutional disorder* is often employed in psychiatric and medical literature to suggest a condition the writer thinks of as inborn in some way, but which he is reluctant to call hereditary. There are some, of course, who equate the term with genetically determined disorders. Others go beyond this and include rather vague factors. For example, in a recent volume by Bauer one learns that " constitution is not a physical entity but is a panel and plan of the total set-up of the individual personality " and that it " comprises physical and mental traits, visible and invisible characteristics " many of which " may not be detectible " by the investigator. (Bauer, J., *Constitution and Disease,* Grune & Stratton, New York, 1942, p. 9.) With respect to the phrase *mental constitution* similar ambiguity prevails as the following sentence shows:
" There are . . . theoretically two senses in which the word ' constitution ' may be applied to mental constitution: the congenital, probably inherited constitution and the acquired — the latter being the result of persistent maladaptive reactions to experiences so early encountered that the individual's mental development is ever afterward biased by them, and is never known to have been different." (From Gillespie, R. D., *Psychological Effects of War on Citizen and Soldier,* W. W. Norton & Co., Inc., New York, 1942, p. 43.)

[10] Southard, E. E., " On the Application of Grammatical Categories to the Analysis of Delusions," *Philos. Rev.,* 1916, *25*, pp. 196–227.

quasi-functional but probably in some sense ' organic ' disease."
The same lurking doubt is reflected in the following quotation
from the report of the A.N.A. committee:[11]

The psychiatrist, as he deals with these conditions in his practice,
feels that dementia praecox is, so to speak, deeply embedded in the
nature of the individual, that there is a sort of fatalistic destiny
operating.

If this " feeling " should be found to rest on a firm factual foundation, then the outlook for a successful prophylactic campaign
against this disease would not be very bright. To prevent a " fatalistic destiny " from coming to pass calls for extraordinary courage
and more tactical wisdom than the average mental hygienist may
be presumed to possess.

Efforts have been made to justify such a " feeling " by a direct
search for evidence of constitutional differences between schizophrenic patients and others. Kretschmer,[12] for example, in a well-
known study reported that schizophrenics tend to be rather tall,
somewhat undernourished, lean-looking individuals while manic-
depressives, on the other hand, tend to be rather short, plump,
deep-chested individuals. He designated the latter as possessing a
pyknic physique, from a Greek root, *puknos,* meaning thick or
thickset. The schizophrenic body-build was called *leptosomatic,*
which is Greek for thin body. To the extent that one's physique
is partly determined by hereditary factors Kretschmer's observation suggests that both schizophrenia and manic-depressive psychosis are rooted in constitutional factors. Although Kretschmer
mobilized an impressive array of evidence in support of his thesis,
other workers have pointed out some serious shortcomings of the
evidence in question. Some have stressed Kretschmer's failure to
control the age factor: the fact that schizophrenia is more common
in younger age groups and manic-depressive psychosis in older age
groups. Since there is a tendency for people to get more portly as
they grow older, what Kretschmer regarded as a basic constitutional relationship is, according to these critics, more a normal
consequence of aging than of anything else. Other critics have
attacked Kretschmer's endeavor to account for exceptions to his

[11] A. N. A. Committee, *op. cit.,* p. 169.
[12] Kretschmer, E., *Physique and Character,* New York, Harcourt, Brace &
Co., 1925.

generalizations. Their objections are clearly formulated by Klineberg who states: [13]

In the various studies which Kretschmer reports, from one-quarter to one-third of the patients failed to fit into his scheme. Kretschmer explains this discrepancy in terms of mixed heredity, the constitution being inherited from one parent and the disease from the other. This explanation appears to be in flat contradiction to the rest of the theory. If there is a causal relation between physique and psychosis, it is difficult to understand how a case of schizophrenia could ever appear with a pyknic constitution.

Kretschmer's endeavor to demonstrate the existence of a significant constitutional factor in schizophrenia by an appeal to anthropometric data thus turns out to be far from successful. However, the existence of such a factor may possibly be demonstrated by another line of evidence introduced by Landis and Page. These psychologists applied a statistical probe to the general problem. To understand their approach it is necessary to remember that those who regard schizophrenia as a non-constitutional disorder prefer to think of it as a consequence of inefficient habits of dealing with personal difficulties — running away from them into a land of wishful daydreaming. If this is true, then one might expect more cases of schizophrenia following a period of sharp increase in the magnitude of personal troubles to which a large population may be exposed. The World War and the economic depression in the early 1930's constituted two such periods. Accordingly, Landis and Page [14] proceeded to examine the statistics pertaining to first admissions both before and after these two critical periods and their findings with respect to schizophrenia showed no significant changes in the rate of hospitalization. More specifically: in the State of New York the average annual rate per 100,000 of the general population during the two years of America's participation in the war was 25.4 as compared with 24.4 for the two preceding and the two following years. During the three years of the depression, 1929–32, the rate of incidence for schizophrenia was 26.2 as com-

[13] Klineberg, O., *Social Psychology*, New York, Henry Holt and Co., 1940, p. 415. This volume contains references to the original studies undertaken in recent years to check on the validity of Kretschmer's theory and should be consulted by those interested in such bibliographic material.

[14] Landis, C., and Page, J. D., *Modern Society and Mental Disease*, New York, Farrar & Rinehart, Inc., 1938, pp. 145–148.

pared with an average of 26.7 for the periods from 1927 to 1929 and from 1932 to 1934.

What do data of this sort mean? Landis and Page interpret them to mean that schizophrenics are " constitutionally predisposed " to mental breakdown; for they state that " practically every psychopathologist " would agree with the following opinion of Dr. J. V. May concerning the " common belief of the general public " that overwork or " some great emotional stress " is " the immediate cause of insanity ": [15]

> The immediate cause, so called, is usually a mere incident and often not without significance, but bearing little, if any, definite relation to the *fundamental, underlying condition* responsible for the mental breakdown. . . . In the *constitutionally predisposed*, the love affair, the loss of position, the upsetting factor, whatever it may be, is merely the straw that breaks the camel's back and is nothing more than an accident of fate, a pure coincidence.

It should be obvious that this kind of interpretation constitutes a serious issue for those who hope to be able to prevent schizophrenia and other functional disorders by getting at the psychogenic factors. If these latter are " mere incidents," just " accidents of fate," and if the real trouble is some ineradicable constitutional defect, what can the mental hygienist hope to do? What basis in fact is there for such confidence as that expressed by Pressey [16] in writing that dementia praecox " appears to be practically incurable, but it is preventable "? Pressey even urges teachers to be on the alert for early signs of schizophrenia in children so that future breakdown can be prevented. But here we find evidence suggesting that irrespective of what measures teachers take or what precautions parents introduce or even what mental hygienists may preach, the mental hospitals of the State of New York and of other states will continue to receive their annual 25% quota of new cases of schizophrenia year after year with relentless consistency. Neither the turmoil of war nor the panic of economic collapse will influence the steadiness of this schizophrenic stream. And by implication neither would the introduction into the life of the community of a long period of peace and security and free-

[15] *Op. cit.*, p. 145. (Italics not in the original.)
[16] Pressey, S. L., *Psychology and the New Education*, New York, Harper & Brothers, 1933, p. 160.

dom from want, disappointment, and distress. As Landis and Page interpret their evidence, such amelioration of social ills would make people happier, but the psychiatric gods would nevertheless continue to exact their yearly tribute of schizophrenic victims. In fact, as Landis and Page have worded it: [17]

It is clear, then, that war, economic depression, unemployment, and general unrest have not led to an increase in hospitalized insanity. This does not mean that there was no mental stress and unhappiness, but that these psychological stresses and tensions do not lead to an increased rate of hospitalized mental disease.

It will be noted that the authors do not restrict their comments to schizophrenic psychoses. In their opinion *all* of the functional disorders are expressions of underlying constitutional deficiencies. If there are any exceptions, they fail to mention them. Their language is direct and unequivocal as the following passage shows: [18]

Our data favor the argument that the basic etiological factors of "mental" disease are physiological and constitutional rather than psychological. If the basic factors were psychological, then we should find the highest rates of incidence either in those times of greatest social stress, such as war, disaster, or great social insecurity, or particularly at those age periods in the life of the individual when the stress of personal adjustment is the greatest. . . . In actuality not one of these expectations is realized. Adolescence and adulthood are generally the periods of greatest stress and conflict, while later maturity is usually a period of relative social and emotional complacency, yet the highest incidence rates of mental disease are found not among men of 25 to 50 but among those of 70 and over.

Landis and Page are obviously questioning the entire concept of mental factors as causes of disease. They interpret the results of their statistical survey to mean that conflict, worry, anxiety, disappointment, guilt, and humiliation have little if any demonstrable influence in producing mental breakdown. For them not only schizophrenia but all functional disturbances are basically constitutionally determined. They do not venture to guess at the precise nature of the constitutional defects; since their method of attack was not directed at this aspect of the problem. Neither do

[17] *Op. cit.*, p. 148.
[18] *Ibid.*, pp. 151–152.

they venture to explain why some schizophrenics are catatonic and others hebephrenic. Their probing had to do with whole groups of patients and not with any isolated individuals: it was directed at the flock and not at the individual sheep. In fact this is true of all the lines of evidence introduced in this section. They all refer to schizophrenics as a class and pay little if any attention to the individual histories of individual patients. What this might mean will be discussed in the next section. For the time being, though, it is important to note that these varied lines of evidence — groups of schizophrenic twins, the general clinical impression of psychiatrists, Kretschmer's anthropometric data, and the Landis-Page statistics — all point in the same direction; namely, the basic " constitutional " nature of schizophrenia. As has already been suggested, some of these lines of evidence are rather weak and no single line need be regarded as altogether decisive, but can their cumulative effect be ignored?

Group data *versus* individual cases

In terms of the evidence just presented it must be evident that many specialists in the field of schizophrenia would be rather skeptical of any mental hygienist who would venture to boast that he knew how to prevent schizophrenia. As a matter of fact in the present state of our imperfect understanding of this disease it would be very difficult for any such mental hygienist to cite coercive evidence in support of his contention. And yet, as was hinted at on a preceding page, there are many writers, educators, psychiatrists, and child guidance experts who seem persuaded that parents and teachers can be trained to recognize early symptoms of schizophrenia in children in time to ferret out and remove the conditions responsible for these symptoms. Quite manifestly experts of this kind do not regard schizophrenia as " basically constitutional " or the product of a " fatalistic destiny." They seem more inclined to view it as the consequence of poor habits of adjustment to personal troubles. By substituting efficient habits for the poor ones the teacher or parent is supposed to be able to throttle the schizophrenic threat at its inception. Prevention of a breakdown thus becomes a matter of educational control: responsibility for suitable prophylactic measures is shifted from the psychiatric clinic to parent, teacher, and playground supervisor.

How can this approach to the problem be squared with the cumulative evidence summarized in the previous section? If schizophrenia is ultimately an inherent, constitutionally determined tendency to breakdown, how can mere habit-training arrest the imperiousness of such a tendency? Furthermore, how can the emphasis on poor techniques of dealing with personal conflicts as the chief etiological factor be reconciled with the failure of major catastrophes like war and economic depression to increase the number of schizophrenics?

To facilitate discussion of these questions it will be helpful to have definite labels for these two approaches. Accordingly, we shall call one the *constitutional* and the other the *conflict* theory of schizophrenia. The evidence for the former view has already been introduced. How can the advocates of the conflict theory dispose of this evidence and what can they say in support of their own teachings?

Part of what they might say has already been anticipated. They would call attention to the fact that the constitutional theory is based on group data rather than on detailed study of individual cases. It is notorious, so they might argue, that what is true of an entire group need not hold for any individual in the group. To cite some conventional instances of this, we might start with the well-known example of the average number of children in the families of the graduates of a given Harvard class. The class as a whole might have an *average* of 2.2 children and yet no single family would conform to this average. No Harvard father would be able to confirm the statistician's report by holding up two-tenths of a child. And then there is the example of the tourist who returns from his first trip to Chinatown with the verdict that " all Chinamen look alike, you can't tell 'em apart." This sort of generalization will arouse the indignant protest of a person who really knows the Chinese people. To him they are all different and as unique in appearance, personal habits, interests, mannerisms, and personality make-up as any random collection of white people. Snap judgments of a whole group of people may result in a distorted and misleading picture of the individuals comprising the group. Nor is this limited to people. A fruit vendor may arrange his stock of oranges in the form of a pyramid so that a picture of the entire group of oranges will reveal pyramidal contours and yet no single orange will have the shape of a pyramid. What is true of the group need not apply to any individual in the group. In other words, the proponents of the conflict theory might urge that their careful studies of the individual lives of individual schizophrenics have brought facts to light which have escaped the scrutiny of the advocates of the constitutional theory.

But how can the conflict theory still be defended in the light of the Landis-Page results? After all, in view of the distress and misery associated with war and depression one might be justified in regarding these results as bearing directly on the conflict theory itself. And the results were negative. Despite the increase in conflict there was no increase in schizophrenic breakdown. Even though group data were involved, the evidence seems so definite and decisive and so intimately related to personal conflicts that mere reiteration of the weaknesses of group data seems rather futile under the circumstances. Nevertheless a stout defender of the conflict theory might not consider the matter as at all futile. He might proceed to argue that on theoretic grounds he would have expected the very results Landis and Page have reported. To justify this he would explain that by conflict calculated to result in schizophrenia he does not mean just any kind of hardship or adjustment problem. Only those which are symbolic of damaged self-esteem or which signify possible disgrace, humiliation, and shameful failure are the ones to regard as mental hygiene hazards of an acute sort. For a parent to lose a child constitutes a grievous emotional shock; but it is much easier to adjust to such a shock if the son met his death as a hero in aerial combat than if he was executed as a criminal. The troubles of people cannot be evaluated by lumping them together under broad captions such as " death in the family," " country at war," or " economic depression." A mental hygienist made this very clear to us in a friendly discussion regarding the significance of the Landis-Page statistical analysis. In fact, his exposition was so vigorous that despite its somewhat loosely worded, excitedly colloquial nature we shall venture to state it here just as he phrased it for us:

I wouldn't expect the depression to cause more schizophrenia because in a depression everybody gets hit, the rich and poor alike. If you lose your job or go bankrupt nobody accuses you of being shiftless or a loafer or a poor businessman. There are too many good workers

and smart businessmen affected. A depression causes a lot of trouble
for people, but there is no *disgrace* in being in this kind of trouble.
As I see it, only troubles that cause a fellow to think of himself as
disgraced or humiliated are the ones that might make for mental
breakdown. Other kinds of trouble we can take with our chins up.
Fellows can be shipwrecked, have legs amputated, lose the sight of
an eye and suffer hunger and privation without snapping mentally.
Sometimes having something to suffer for — being given a cause to
fight for — is what they need to make real men out of them. So not
any old conflict will cause schizophrenia. Only the ones that make
people say they're no good and will never amount to anything so that
they despise themselves and believe that other people despise them —
these are the ones to look out for. But I wouldn't expect more of these
just because war is declared or because there is a major depression. In
fact it might be that such catastrophes might really prevent some cases
of schizophrenia from developing by giving people a chance to enlist,
to work for the Red Cross, to get on W.P.A. projects, enroll in a
C.C.C. camp. This gives 'em things to do they regard as important.
It takes them away from brooding daydreams and brings 'em back to
the real world. When your country is threatened or your family is
about to go hungry you've got to *act:* you can't just sit around and
dream and wish and feel sorry for yourself. As a matter of fact you
can't tell how war and depression are going to affect people in general.
You've got to study each individual's reaction separately. Some people
are thrilled by the prospect of adventure and excitement of war. And
some people might really have been cheered up by the depression. I
mean if you've been sort of thinking of yourself as pretty much of
a failure because you could never afford a car for your family or a fur
coat for your wife and then you find that nobody can afford these
things, well it makes life a good deal easier. You no longer have to
think of yourself as a failure because you're not running up a big bank
balance. Even the big shots are failures now. We're all in the same
boat. And these wholesale troubles may not be all bad from the mental
hygiene viewpoint. They bring people together and make them more
considerate and helpful and neighborly. The movies — pictures like
" Grapes of Wrath," and " Mrs. Miniver " — show how depression and
war can bring families and communities around to a better spirit of cooperation. Mrs. Joad and Mrs. Miniver had plenty of trouble, but
through it all they never had to blame themselves for causing it or for
handling it selfishly or being cowardly about it. Their families came to
mean more to them than ever before. They had a big job to do and
they rose to the occasion. Even the loss of household goods didn't
seem so serious as long as the family could be kept intact. And all the

time they knew how much they were needed, how much they meant
to others — to their children, to neighbors, and to the neighbor's children. Their morale was good — maybe even better than before trouble descended upon them. As a mental hygienist I always ask about
a person's morale. And I can't find the answer by examining statistical
reports dealing with the incidence of mental disease per 100,000 of the
general population. To get the answer I've got to check up on individual people like Mrs. Joad and Mrs. Miniver and not a statistical
abstraction. Now you ought to understand why I'm not willing to
concede that Landis and Page have disposed of what you call the
conflict theory of schizophrenia. It's still a tenable theory as far as
I'm concerned.

Finally, there is an additional shortcoming of the group data
pertaining to schizophrenia. These data are accumulated by throwing all diagnoses of schizophrenia into a single category. Individual
differences among schizophrenics are overlooked in a procedure of
this kind. These differences, it has already been explained, are so
drastic that some psychiatrists prefer to refer to " the schizophrenias " rather than to a single disease entity to be called " schizophrenia." Others endeavor to do justice to the differences by recognizing clinical types of the disease such as the hebephrenic,
catatonic, simple, mixed, etc. In the group studies purporting to
demonstrate the constitutional basis for the disease these types are
not kept separate and distinct. They are all lumped together and
treated as a statistical unit in the form of an average or a percentage or a correlation coefficient. These units are then interpreted to mean that schizophrenia is fundamentally a constitutional disease. Still, even if this interpretation be accepted, how
can the differences among schizophrenics be accounted for? Are
there as many different kinds of constitutional factors as there are
clinical varieties? Or is there but one type of schizophrenic constitution plastic enough to be molded into varying clinical shapes
by differing social or environmental forces? Questions of this sort
have to be answered if the mystery of schizophrenia is to be
cleared up satisfactorily. An indiscriminate round-up of all " constitutional " suspects is not calculated to supply the evidence upon
which to base an answer. Both the work of Kretschmer and that
of Landis and Page constitute the equivalent of such a round-up;
for they made no effort to segregate their cases into schizophrenic

types, being content to lock them all up in the same statistical hopper. Pooling data in this way is like taking a composite photograph: the uniqueness of the individual is lost in the anonymity of the group.

BOISEN'S STUDIES OF SCHIZOPHRENIA

Since the conflict theory developed out of studies of individual life histories of schizophrenic patients, it ought to be in a better position to shed light on the mystery of clinical types which, as was just indicated, is left unsolved when the etiology of the disorder is attributed to some constitutional quirk. A stimulating interpretation of this mystery has been furnished by Anton T. Boisen, a student of the problem over a long period of years. In fact, Boisen's appreciation of schizophrenia as a mental disorder is more direct, intimate, and profound than that of the ordinary, average writer on the subject. In a very real sense he has made the psychology of this disorder his specialty even though he was handicapped at the outset by not being either a professional psychologist or psychiatrist, his training having been in very different fields. It may not constitute too much of a digression to consider a few biographic details before describing Boisen's specific contributions toward the solution of our immediate problem of accounting for the development of schizophrenic types.

From 1899 to 1903 Boisen taught in the department of Romance Languages at Indiana University. He then obtained a degree in forestry at Yale and from 1905 to 1908 served as an official of the U. S. Forest Service. However, his interest in religion became so strong that he gave up this work, entered the Union Theological Seminary, and received his divinity degree in 1911. For the next period of his life he devoted himself to various phases of church work and during the first World War he was active overseas as a Y.M.C.A. secretary. However, in 1920, while conducting a survey for the Interchurch World Movement, he suffered a mental breakdown of such severity as to necessitate hospitalization. The diagnosis was " catatonic dementia praecox " and his people were given the bleak information that recovery was not to be expected. Evidently Boisen was not informed of this bleak prognosis; for he proceeded to recover. However, at first he had trouble convincing his family that the unexpected had taken place so that he was obliged to remain at the hospital longer than would otherwise have been the case. It was during this period that his interest in his own breakdown and in the troubles of his fellow-patients was born. His efforts to learn something about his own case by talking with the physicians at the hospital proved futile: the doctors, according to Boisen, being advocates of the constitutional theory, deemed it unwise to discuss symptoms with the patients.

Being rebuffed in this endeavor, he proceeded to do his own thinking and observing. He began to study the other patients and undertook to do things for them and with them. He was also struck by the fact that the visiting ministers from the neighboring community who came to conduct religious services had no understanding of the inner life, the special needs, and recurrent worries of the patients. The services at the institution were more or less stereotyped copies of ordinary services. There was also a conspicuous lack of pastoral visiting in behalf of those patients who seemed anxious about their lack of religious guidance. As a result of these observations Boisen determined to prepare himself to be better equipped to supply this lack. As he envisaged the lack, it was not a mere absence of familiar liturgy or pleasing ritual to be introduced in order to make institutional life more bearable for the patients: it was a situation directly related to the problem of mental illness. In a letter written at this time Boisen said,[19] " I feel that many forms of insanity are religious rather than medical problems, and that they cannot be successfully treated until they are so recognized."

Upon his discharge from the hospital Boisen proceeded to secure the additional training he thought a chaplain in a psychiatric hospital ought to have. He did special work not only in the field of religion, but also in the fields of abnormal psychology, psychiatric social work, and psychopathology. Some of this work was done under eminent Harvard professors. But despite the excellence of his work and the breadth of his preparation, he found it impossible to locate a position. The specialty he had carved out for him-

---

[19] Boisen has written rather extensively. The sentence quoted is taken from p. 9 of a book which supplies the most comprehensive discussion of his views. The interested reader may also desire to consult a recent article in which Boisen presents some of his current interpretations of schizophrenia. Boisen, A. T., *The Exploration of the Inner World,* Chicago, Willett, Clark & Company, 1936; " The Form and Content of Schizophrenic Thinking," *Psychiatry,* 1942, *5,* pp. 23–33.

self had never been heard of by hospital superintendents and they failed to register enthusiasm when Boisen outlined its nature for them. So far as they are concerned there was no justification for changing established hospital routine by adding a psychiatrically oriented chaplain to the official staff. It was not until Boisen had put in three years of special study in the fields just enumerated that he at last found a sympathetic superintendent in the person of Dr. W. A. Bryan of the Worcester State Hospital and obtained the newly created post of full-time chaplain at the institution. Later in his career Boisen secured a similar post at an Illinois hospital where he was also enabled to work as " research associate in the psychology of religion." In addition, he served as lecturer at the Chicago Theological seminary and was thus able to give candidates for the ministry the type of training he deemed necessary for the efficient execution of a hospital chaplain's duties. Incidentally, in a very direct way this project of Boisen's serves to illustrate a point mentioned in the first chapter regarding the large number of separate fields of study which may converge in the work of the mental hygienist. Here we find the possibility of a mutually helpful alliance between religion and psychiatry in the interests of the large numbers of patients whose personal difficulties may involve religious conflicts.

It should now be clear that Boisen's contributions to the problem of schizophrenia are apt to be refreshingly different. In some respects his understanding of the disease, as has already been intimated, is more direct and personal than that of the average psychiatrist or clinical psychologist. Having himself passed through an intense schizophrenic episode he obtained an insider's view of the disease. The average student has to content himself with an outsider's view: he can learn about the disease; but intimate familiarity with the mental changes as they are experienced by the patient can never be his. This is somewhat analogous to the effort of a congenitally blind person striving to learn what the spectrum looks like to the rest of us. The blind man can learn a great deal *about* colors, but he can never appreciate them in their sensory immediacy. He has to content himself with building up a conceptual framework in terms of which he can guess at the meanings of words like " blue " and " green " and " red." This is the old psychological distinction between knowledge-about and knowledge of acquaintance. As a result of his own breakdown plus his subsequent years of study Boisen has both kinds of knowledge at his disposal when he writes about the problem of schizophrenia. In this respect he is better equipped than most students of the subject, so that what he has to say about the inner dynamics of the schizophrenic's mental life merits serious consideration.

BOISEN'S EXPLANATION OF SCHIZOPHRENIC TYPES

The central conflict of the schizophrenic, as Boisen sees it, is focused around " an intolerable loss of self-respect." In his attitude toward himself the patient tends to feel isolated from others because he thinks of himself as a social failure: he deems himself unworthy in the eyes of his fellow men. In this connection Boisen points out that the criminal and delinquent also experience this sense of social condemnation, this notion of group disapproval, or lack of complete social acceptability. But there is an important difference in the way in which criminals, as opposed to psychotics, react to the conviction of such social rejection. Criminals may actually be social failures in the eyes of so-called organized society, but they may refuse to accept society's judgment. They form their own groups or gangs in which they can find support for and approval of their antagonism to the conventional standards of official society. By such a transfer of group allegiance the criminal avoids the despair associated with loss of self-respect. His ego may actually be enhanced as he finds newspapers referring to him as a " notorious desperado," " a ruthless killer," or a " dangerous confidence man."

The psychotic, on the other hand, reacts differently to his real or imagined sense of social failure. For him his inferiority is all too true and the consequent inner acceptance of the adverse judgment of society may precipitate the agony of acute self-deprecation that comes with inability to have respect for oneself. Psychotic behavior in general and schizophrenic behavior in particular is an outgrowth of the individual's efforts to cope with his catastrophic loss of self-respect. Boisen distinguishes the following three ways in which patients may deal with such a loss:

1. **Drifting.** Instead of putting up some sort of resistance to his loss the *drifter* surrenders himself to the impulse of the moment, to idle pleasure-seeking, or to congenial daydreaming. There

is no effort to master the situation responsible for the damaged self-esteem — no resolve to make good by some sort of positive achievement. It is as if the patient had adopted an attitude of final surrender and had decided that his cause was hopeless. As a consequence the drifter becomes the ambitionless loafer. No longer does he experience a desire to make a name for himself or to win social approval: what people say about him leaves him *indifferent*. This apathy is, of course, one of the symptoms of schizophrenia. So is the daydreaming. For this type of patient the schizophrenic reaction has become a " way of life." By the latter phrase Boisen means to point out that the drifter is seemingly content to go on drifting all the rest of his life. In our earlier discussion of the *simple* type of schizophrenia it was stated that " many chronic drifters, ne'er-do-wells, prostitutes, hermits, and hoboes " are victims of a functional psychosis. Such characterization, it can now be seen, was an anticipation of Boisen's account of the dynamics of the simple type of schizophrenia.

2. **Concealment by Delusional Misinterpretation.** By thinking of the paranoid type of schizophrenia one can secure an understanding of the second kind of reaction pattern which jeopardized self-respect is apt to provoke. The paranoid patients, it will be remembered, have delusions of persecution or of grandeur or both. It will also be remembered that many of them seem to be troubled by difficulties of sex adjustment. This sort of trouble is particularly apt to be associated with feelings of inferiority, attitudes of self-reproach, and kindred accompaniments of lowered self-esteem. The paranoid patient, unlike the simple type, is not content to surrender and just drift along. He meets the threat to his self-respect by fighting back. And he fights back by blaming others for his troubles. According to his way of looking at the problem, " enemies " are out to get him or " hostile forces " are working against him. He hears " voices " accusing him of sex misconduct and calling him vile names. By thus *projecting* his own erstwhile private condemnation of himself and attributing the voice of his own conscience to the vocal cords of his enemies the patient is making an effort to keep his respect for himself intact. This so-called " externalization of conscience " is a device for bolstering up an ego about to be smashed by the blows of a protesting conscience. It is a way of concealing one's guilt from oneself by build-

ing up a delusional world in which outsiders can be blamed for one's shortcomings and failures.

The paranoid reaction is also a " way of life " — a way of meeting difficulties developed by personalities unable either to acknowledge defeat or to admit error. Instead we have a reaction of self-protective deception by recourse to a misinterpretation of the factors involved in the personal conflict. The resulting delusion may, as just indicated, take the form of blaming imaginary enemies for one's troubles; hence the bitter hatred and suspiciousness of the victim of persecutory delusions. However, it may take a different form. The patient may strive to conceal the latent feelings of guilt or humiliation from himself by a delusion of grandeur — convincing himself of his own importance by taking refuge in the fantasied role of being a president or a pope or a king. The very belief that " the king can do no wrong " may help the patient dispose of his basic difficulty. No longer is there any need to accuse himself of sin or failure. Since the king is privileged to make the laws and can do as he pleases, what applies to the common herd does not apply to him. This disposes of the self-condemnation brought on by loss of self-respect. Furthermore, since people in general look up to and respect and admire distinguished personalities possessing power and prestige, there is no longer any need to worry about the condemnation of outsiders. In this way the delusion of grandeur serves the paranoid type of schizophrenic as a defence mechanism by means of which he saves his self-respect, but at the cost of dangerously twisted interpretations of his own motives and those of others. As such delusional misinterpretations become more and more entrenched, he becomes less and less able to adjust to the reality of his basic difficulties.

3. **Panic.** For most individuals, as Boisen sees it, the reaction patterns adopted by the simple and paranoid types are likely to be shocking in their implications. What he means is that as the troubled individual striving to restore his self-esteem finds himself entertaining ideas of pursuing the " way of life " of either of the foregoing types, there is spontaneous recognition of the dangerous nature of these ideas. To venture to solve his problem in such fashion would mean the loss of much which the average individual deems precious: becoming a bum or a tramp — a drifter — would mean the loss of family contacts, of good reputation, and of eco-

nomic security, while the rush of delusional ideas signifies loss of mental control. In either event the prospect would fill the threatened individual with alarm. He becomes panic-stricken. His inner world seems about to crumble and at first he seems powerless to do anything about it. He may react to this with the emotional excitement of a person trapped in a burning building or with the hopeless despair of a condemned criminal whose last appeal has been denied. By referring back to our earlier account of catatonic schizophrenia one can understand the relationship between these two examples of reaction to panic and what was designated as catatonic excitement and catatonic stupor.

In discussing catatonia Boisen is on home ground; for, as has already been mentioned, he himself experienced this type of breakdown. In the light of this personal experience, as well as in the light of his later studies of other patients, he came to see this panic reaction not so much as a " way of life," but more as " a desperate attempt at reorganization." The panic comes as the result of an awareness of personal danger, and the catatonic reaction constitutes the patient's impulsive effort to deal with the threat — trying to find out what to do and how to do it. In fact, Boisen draws a parallel between the catatonic type of schizophrenia and the emotional turmoil associated with the experience leading up to and accompanying religious conversion. Here too there is panic as the ideas of conviction of sin and the imminence of divine punishment grip the penitent. Here too there may be either profound agitation or the acute apathy of altogether hopeless despair. Out of this agitation or apathy there may come a new way of looking at the world and one's obligation to it as a new perspective is introduced and a new pattern of life is worked out. The penitent describes this as " being born again." By this he means being able to start life afresh with new zest and better attitudes.

But to return to Boisen's interpretation of catatonia. The panic reaction is manifest in the behavior of the excited or agitated catatonic. But what about the stuporous patient? We have already indicated that this may be likened to the postural attitudes of a person in acute despair. It may, however, signify more than the emotional blunting following a devastating shock. It may constitute a resolute effort to think through a vitally significant personal problem. The fixed bodily attitude may — like Rodin's statue of

The Thinker — represent an appropriate muscular adjustment under the circumstances. Such an adjustment facilitates concentration by shunting out extraneous disturbances. It is reminiscent of the attitudes taken by students who are trying to study in noisy dormitories or while riding on noisy subways. Even the mutism and negativism become understandable symptoms in terms of this hypothesis. A person engaged in serious thought about a serious problem is disinclined to chat and averse to being distracted by having to do other things. Of course all of these catatonic symptoms are also compatible with the hypothesis that the patient is lost in a world of fantasy. What Boisen is proposing is that the fantasy need not be restricted to self-gratifying, vainglorious, wishful daydreams — an ideational retreat from the grim realities of the patient's personal difficulties; that it may be concerned instead with an earnest effort to cope with these difficulties by reorganizing his attitudes toward them as he probes into the meaning of issues which are of fundamental importance to him.

These issues may be philosophical or metaphysical or theological in nature and of a kind that nobody can dispose of in certain fashion — issues such as the purpose of life, the nature of God, immortality, the reality of sin, predestination, the existence of hell, etc. To a person who craves inner assurance about such issues in order to plan his life, or in order to achieve a measure of inner peace, a period of long, persistent brooding may be an imperative need. This is especially apt to be the case if his central conflict has to do with what he, as a child, has been taught to regard as the kind of " sin " for which " God exacts punishment." His sense of humiliation or his loss of self-respect may consequently be interpreted as having been " rejected by God " or having failed to " obey God's commandments." The victim of such " conviction of sin " or equivalent feelings of abject, personal guilt is not likely to react to such feelings by an immediate flight into comforting daydreams. He is more likely to indulge in painful analyses of his " sinful " past and laborious searchings for some ritual by which his " sins can be washed away " so that he can start life over " cleansed and forgiven." This is what the theologian means by the search for salvation. And it constitutes the religious aspect of what Boisen calls a " desperate attempt at reorganization." Under the circumstances Boisen cannot regard religion as an " escape from reality." For him [20] " it represents an attempt to deal with those loyalties and values which are regarded as ultimate."

Although we have described Boisen's interpretation of the panic reaction in terms of religious symbolism, this should not be construed to imply religious preoccupation on the part of every catatonic. Boisen recognizes this and it would be a misrepresentation of his views not to call attention to it. However, even a condensation of the entire range of these views would entail too much of a digression. As a consequence, the description of inner reorganization in terms of religious adjustment will have to suffice as a means of explaining the general character of Boisen's handling of the problem.

Some support for this view of the nature of catatonia is to be found in the general opinion of psychiatrists to the effect that the outlook for improvement or " recovery " is better for the catatonic than the other types of schizophrenia. This is based on common clinical experience. Boisen's views furnish an intelligible hypothesis to explain the finding : the catatonic is actually trying to come to grips with his conflict — trying to work out a solution for his troubles. If he succeeds, he is pronounced " improved " or " cured," and if he fails, he may be said to be " deteriorating " or even come to be classified as a hebephrenic.

4. **Hebephrenia.** It may have been observed that up to this point no mention was made of Boisen's explanation for hebephrenia, the fourth clinical variety of schizophrenia. The fantastic ideas, the silly grimaces, the outlandish clownishness, and the general incoherence and unpredictable impulsiveness of this syndrome have already been described. How can such disintegration be accounted for in terms of the conflict theory ? Boisen regards it as the final outcome of the drifting reaction : the end-stage of a process of progressively increasing indifference to group opinion and to what the ordinary man calls his " better self." The drifter has given up the fight and is content to be the shuttlecock of impulse.

A similar outcome may be the lot of the catatonic who fails to work out a satisfactory reorganization of his life. Not all conflicts can be solved. As Boisen puts it,[21] " the case is hopeless if the unfortunate hasn't it in him to be something of a success econom-

[20] Boisen, *Exploration of the Inner World,* p. 53.
[21] *Op. cit.,* p. 160.

ically or socially or if his instinctual cravings are such that he can neither own them nor control them." Such a person becomes overwhelmed by his troubles. Panic may seize him and his initial reaction to the panic may take the outward form of catatonia and the inward form of frantic efforts to save himself from impending disaster. This explains why Boisen regards the catatonic reaction as one [22] " which tends either to make or break." When the patient's efforts to save himself fail, he " breaks " and demoralization sets in. No longer does he struggle against his " instinctual cravings " and no longer does he seek some way of self-mastery. Instead he yields to the forces of disintegration and like the chronic drifter he too becomes more and more hebephrenic. To put this metaphorically: hebephrenia signifies failure to quell a panic by effective mobilization of inner resources. Such failure may be likened to an army whose officers and men, forgetful of discipline, are scattering before the enemy in disorderly retreat. And just as the resulting disorganization of the military pattern constitutes disintegration of the army, so the scrambled impulsiveness of the hebephrenic constitutes the distintegration of a personality. What all this implies for a program of prophylactic mental hygiene will engage our attention in the next chapter.

[22] *Op. cit.*, p. 315.

8 ∘∘∘ PROPHYLACTIC ASPECTS OF FUNCTIONAL PSYCHOSES: II

THE STATISTICAL DATA INTRODUCED IN THE PRECEDING CHAPTER showed no significant reduction in the amount of schizophrenic illness from year to year. The rate of incidence was in fact seen to be relatively constant even during and following such stormy periods as those of the first World War and the depression. It was pointed out in this connection that such constancy in the rate of incidence has been interpreted by some specialists to mean an hereditary or constitutional basis for the disease. For them schizophrenia would hardly lend itself to easy prophylactic treatment; for, as they view the situation, some " fatalistic destiny " is operating here. On the other hand, it was also pointed out that the data in question could be reconciled with the conflict theory. Unless the latter theory or some equivalent psychogenic theory can be salvaged, the prospects for preventing schizophrenia will be anything but bright.

CAN SCHIZOPHRENIA BE PREVENTED?

One positive fact stands out in this welter of uncertainty: mental hygienists have yet to demonstrate that they can prevent schizophrenia. Even if the conflict theory is sound, its advocates have no record of prophylactic accomplishment by means of which to confirm its soundness. The regularity and relative consistency of the annual toll of first admissions is a stubborn statistical fact to which opponents of the theory may continue to call attention with annoying persistence. They might well issue the challenge: " If you know how to ward off schizophrenia, why don't we see a reduction in the number of first admissions as you people establish new clinics, write more books, give more courses, and deliver more lectures? " In and of itself a challenge of this kind is not necessarily a fatal indictment of the conflict theory. As was indicated in our earlier accounts of alcoholic psychoses and paresis, the etiology of a disorder may be known and prophylactic cam-

paigns bog down despite such knowledge. Analogously, the conflict theory may still be sound even though anti-schizophrenia
campaigns based on the theory lack demonstrable success or fail to
give evidence of encouraging progress.

The foregoing analogy is helpful, but not as convincing as a
really good analogy should be. It is defective in implying that the
conflict theory has established the etiology of schizophrenia with
the same degree of coerciveness as characterizes the proof for a
causal relationship between syphilis and paresis or alcohol and
Korsakoff's psychosis. An implication of this kind is unwarranted.
After all, the very fact that animal experimentation has confirmed
the damage wrought by alcohol and by the spirochete renders the
one type of proof more convincing than the other. Schizophrenia
has not yet been produced in animals. As will be brought out in the
next chapter, in the opinion of some investigators *neuroses* have
been experimentally induced in animals by means of simple conflict situations; but no functional psychoses have been so induced.
It should be realized, however, that this is not to be construed as
a serious weakness of the conflict theory. As a matter of fact proponents of the constitutional theory are also unable to appeal to
animal experimentation in support of their views. In terms of
body-types there are doubtless dogs and monkeys whose anatomic
contours correspond to Kretschmer's pyknic and leptosomatic
types, but to the best of our knowledge no distinctive *psychotic*
tendencies have ever been reported as common correlates of such
constitutional differences in animal " physique." [1]

In some respects the failure to find schizophrenia among animals might well be regarded as support for the conflict theory. Our
discussion of clinical types in the light of Boisen's analysis made
an " intolerable loss of self-respect " the crux of the schizophrenic's
adjustment problem. Self-respect, codes of ethics, and religious
perplexities are exclusively human affairs. They are products of
social interaction in terms of the institutionalized standards governing all phases of civilized life: family organization, police systems, commercial practices, church influences, school authority —

---

[1] This should not be construed as a denial of a possible relation between
temperamental characteristics of dogs and their body-types. For a discussion of
" inheritance of form as related to personality among dogs," see Stockard, C. R.,
The Physical Basis of Personality, New York, W. W. Norton & Company, Inc.,
1931, pp. 226–262.

all that comprises the culture of a people. In this sense — assuming the validity of the conflict theory — schizophrenia is a disease of civilization. Under the circumstances it might be as foolish to talk about schizophrenia in animals as it would be to speculate about the religious beliefs of elephants, the self-respect of a turtle, or the humiliation of a rat failing to solve a maze problem. The student of veterinary medicine has to study many subjects, but animal psychiatry is not one of them.

The conflict theory can be made very plausible and more revealing, it seems to us, than the constitutional theory. Its very plausibility may cause some to forget its theoretic status. As a consequence they regard what should in all strictness still be viewed as a stimulating working hypothesis as firmly established fact. It is tempting to respond to such stimulation with the conviction that by teaching people how to meet their personal conflicts we can render them immune to schizophrenic breakdown. Unfortunately, many mental hygienists have succumbed to this temptation. On page 154 we called attention to Pressey's appeal to teachers to be on the alert for early signs of schizophrenia. This kind of appeal has been made by many others. Some of them urge courses in mental hygiene as a prerequisite for all teachers on the ground that teachers with such training will be able to detect the beginnings of schizophrenia and other functional diseases in their charges, and by referring these cases to competent psychiatrists they will help nip in the bud what might have developed into a serious mental illness. Although we are by no means opposed to such courses, we are not yet persuaded that their justification is to be found in their presumed contributions to the cause of prophylactic mental hygiene. As will be brought out in the remaining chapters, the justification can be more readily established in terms of what mental hygiene has to contribute to the fostering of individual and group morale, to the improvement of personal efficiency, and to the other goals mentioned in the introductory chapter as belonging to meliorative, rather than prophylactic, mental hygiene.

Of course there would be more reason to stress the educational value of training in mental hygiene for prospective teachers if *both* the prophylactic and the meliorative objectives could be furthered by such training. However, in the present state of our knowledge it might be claiming too much to emphasize the attainability of the prophylactic objective. That is more in the realm of hope than accomplishment. At all events it would be hard to show that it has been accomplished so far as schizophrenia and the other functional psychoses are concerned. This statement should not be taken to mean that we are endorsing the " fatalistic destiny " opinion mentioned in the previous chapter. On the contrary we believe that such an opinion is also devoid of sufficient evidential support to justify shifting it to the category of established fact. In the present state of our knowledge of the medley of factors which schizophrenia seems to involve dogmatism of any sort is unwarranted. This knowledge is still incomplete and final statements regarding either the inevitability or the preventability of schizophrenia should be held in abeyance.

It would be more in accord with available evidence to say that if the conflict theory is sound, then to the extent that parents and teachers can help children to cope with personal difficulties bravely and realistically they should cause that much of a decrease in the incidence of functional mental disease. This decrease has not yet shown up in hospital statistics. In this sense the conflict theory lacks confirmation. Whether it will show up in the future as more homes and more schools are brought within the mental hygiene orbit still remains to be determined. It may be that the theory is inadequate or that the teaching has been faulty or too limited in scope or that not enough academic generations have been exposed to it. These are all relevant possibilities. But the fact remains that we cannot yet *prove* that schizophrenia can be brought under prophylactic control. To the question, " Can schizophrenia be prevented? " the answer ought not to be an unqualified " No " or a dogmatic " Yes," but a more guarded " Maybe." The whole question of the role of the schools in the prevention of psychotic breakdown should still be regarded as a moot question. The issues are by no means simple and clear-cut. There may even be some mental hygiene hazards involved as will soon be evident.

TEACHERS AND MENTAL HYGIENE ATTITUDES

Although we shall devote a separate chapter to some of the educational implications of the mental hygiene movement, it might be well to incorporate some of this material in the present chapter. This applies particularly to the issue just mentioned; namely, the role of the teacher in preventing mental breakdown.

As we see it, there is a possibility of hurting the cause of mental hygiene by placing too much emphasis on this role. Preoccupation with mental disease just as preoccupation with physical disease is itself unwholesome. What we have called meliorative mental hygiene constitutes better preparation for the teacher than what we are subsuming under the caption of prophylactic mental hygiene. The latter is concerned with the morbid and the negative; the former with the healthy and the positive. The whole subject of hygiene may be viewed in either of two ways: (1) avoiding disease or (2) promoting health. This is what we mean by the negative and positive, approaches. Prophylaxis is primarily concerned with the negative approach. It may be unwise to lend undue weight to this negative aspect in mental hygiene courses intended primarily for teachers unless a specific corrective of the kind we are introducing here is brought to the fore.

What attitudes should the teacher bring into the classroom? Should she view her charges as potential cases of chorea, catatonia, paresis, anxiety neurosis or some other morbid entity, or should she view them as potentially healthy, self-reliant, enthusiastic adults? By adopting the former attitude she would be rendering the cause of a mental hygiene a disservice in more ways than one. Intrinsically innocent outbursts of childish mischievousness might be construed as the beginnings of a manic personality. A devoted friendship between two boys or two girls might suggest an incipient homosexual trend. The quiet, shy youngster would remind her of what she had read concerning schizoid personalities in children. It might even be difficult for her to detect many children who did not manifest some ominous quirk or pathogenic symptom. If this should be the outcome of her training in mental hygiene, it would have been better had she not been given such training.

As opposed to this somewhat extreme picture of what too much concern with prophylactic mental hygiene might do to a teacher there is the prospect of a teacher who has been won over to mental hygiene's meliorative outlook. She will be more interested in promoting classroom morale than in searching for hidden complexes and lurking phobias; more interested in helping the youngsters learn the art of getting along with people than in preaching to them about the horrors of delirium tremens; and more interested in promoting their zest for life in work and play than in guarding them against the menace of mental disease. As a matter of fact the menace is not very great in the lives of children and it might be well to devote some space to this consideration in order to allay the possible apprehension of those whose mental hygiene perspective has been distorted by one-sided presentation of the psychopathic aspects of the subject. Later in this chapter some additional features relating to the attitudes of teachers toward mental hygiene issues will be taken up.

CHILDREN'S FREEDOM FROM PSYCHOTIC DISTURBANCE

There is no large body of dependable knowledge regarding the early signs of later mental disease. This means that it is hard to predict which children in a given school are likely to develop a functional psychosis in future years. As a group, children seem to be relatively free from psychotic disturbance. For example, Kasanin and Kaufman [2] found that out of 6,000 patients admitted to a large mental hospital over a period of three years, there were only 65 under the age of 16. Landis and Page [3] also find mental disease to be rare among children. They state quite explicitly that " before the age of 15, mental disease rarely occurs." According to their figures, out of every 100,000 patients " annually admitted to the mental hospitals in the United States " only 22 are between the ages of 15 to 19. In a still more recent study [4] one reads that " psychoses of any sort are extremely rare in childhood " and that " schizophrenia before the onset of puberty is so unusual that individual cases are still reported as clinical curiosities." [5] Actual mental disease is thus quite evidently a post-adolescent phenomenon. As a consequence teachers need not be unduly concerned about

[2] Kasanin, J., and Kaufman, M. R., " A Study of the Functional Psychoses in Childhood," *Amer. J. of Psychiatry*, 1929, *9*, pp. 307–384.

[3] Landis, C., and Page, J. D., *Modern Society and Mental Disease*, New York, Farrar and Rinehart, Inc., 1938, pp. 28–29.

[4] Bradley, C., *Schizophrenia in Childhood*, New York, The Macmillan Company, 1941, p. 21.

[5] Even Child Guidance Clinics, whose work is especially concerned with maladjusted children, find very few schizophrenics among their cases. In the words of Lewis: " The majority of children seen in the clinic are not immediate precox problems, in fact, only an occasional one justifies the diagnosis of this disorder." (Lewis, N. D. C., *Research in Dementia Precox*, New York, National Committee for Mental Hygiene, 1936, p. 59.)

the possibility of psychotic children disrupting or blocking educational effort.

Why children should be practically immune to psychotic breakdown is an interesting question for speculation. Those who prefer heredoconstitutional interpretations of mental disease can use this fact of children's immunity to support their views. They might even regard it as irreconcilable with the conflict theory. The latter theory, they might say, views functional mental disease as the result of personality-warping brought about by repeated frustrations, and yet childhood is actually replete with frustrating experiences. Taboos and *don'ts* surround the youngster at every turn. His life is enmeshed by a network of commands, rules, prohibitions, and admonitions. It's " go to bed now so that you can be up in time for school in the morning," and this means frustration of the desire to play past his bedtime as well as frustration of the desire to sleep late. Arithmetic lessons have to be finished before he is allowed to yield to the call of the neighborhood gang to " come out and play." And the longing for soda pop has to be suppressed in favor of the inevitable glass of milk. On bright Sunday mornings the lure of the golf links may prove too much for Dad, but it's the same old Sunday School for Junior. Certainly nobody is justified in regarding childhood as a period of uninhibited freedom to do as one pleases. Even in early infancy spontaneous impulse has to be subordinated to the imperiousness of the schedule. All through the developmental years impulsiveness has to be curbed because of what grown-ups call " duty " or " manners " or " decency " or " the right thing to do." If conflict and frustration are such important etiological factors, one might almost expect more mental disturbance during childhood than in subsequent periods of life. And yet, as the evidence shows, despite this elaborate network of frustration surrounding children, they rarely are victims of mental breakdown. In some such fashion as this the advocate of the constitutional theory might venture to nullify the explanatory value of the conflict theory. For him the constitutional theory furnishes a better explanation: the deterioration that characterizes the process of aging is a necessary forerunner of mental breakdown; hence children's immunity to such breakdown. Once they get older and heart and lungs and endocrines and other bodily mechanisms no longer function with youthful vigor, then inherent "psychopathic" trends will crop out.

How can the sponsor of the conflict theory meet such an argument? How can he reconcile his belief in the importance of frustration with the child's resistance to actual mental breakdown? These are challenging questions. To answer them satisfactorily will require not only a closer scrutiny of the concept of frustration, but also the introduction of an additional question. This question pertains to delinquent behavior in children. The delinquent child, as everybody knows, is a potential criminal: his conduct is antisocial. Although psychotic children are "clinical curiosities," delinquent children can be found in any juvenile court. Accordingly, one might well ask whether there is any relationship between their immunity to psychotic breakdown and their vulnerability to delinquency. Both teachers and parents have more reason to be concerned about the possibility of having to deal with a delinquent child than a psychotic child. The prevention of delinquency is consequently a more immediate mental hygiene issue than preventing mental breakdown in children.

DELINQUENT BEHAVIOR *versus* PSYCHOTIC BEHAVIOR

To reconcile the conflict theory with the absence of psychotic breakdown in children despite the presence of almost daily frustration, it is first necessary to recall what was mentioned in the last chapter regarding adjustments to the frustrations produced by wars and economic depressions. It was pointed out that people can tolerate some frustrations heroically, especially those that are bound up with devotion to a cause. No patriot's mental stability is in danger because his government asks him to give up his car, do without meat every Tuesday, or interrupt his career by joining the Army. The frustrations with which the mental hygienist is concerned are of a different sort. They are the ones which signify damaged self-respect and the ones which provoke attitudes of resentment or of humiliation. The conflict theory has to do with frustrations of this kind and not the other sort — with the ones which arouse inner turmoil and distress. It will deepen our understanding of the theory and of the mental hygienist's task to examine these a little more closely here even though we shall have to re-examine them in the fourth part of this book in the light of our program of meliorative mental hygiene.

For the sake of clarity of exposition it might help to introduce a simple example of an easily grasped instance of frustration: a young woman engaged to be married becomes the victim of circumstances which prevent the marriage from ever taking place. Her desire for this particular man is thus balked or frustrated. What this frustration will involve or how it will influence her psychologically will depend in part on the precise nature of the circumstances responsible for it. Her fiancé may have been killed in action. This is one possibility. The resulting frustration would involve no sense of guilt on her part and no feelings of shame or inferiority. There would be grief, of course, but also sympathy and solicitous care from family and friends.

On the other hand, there is a second possibility to be considered: her fiancé may have eloped with a rival. This would in all probability induce a very different kind of reaction to frustration, for it constitutes a threat to her self-esteem. There might well be a medley of embittered and varied feelings: anger, jealousy, disappointment, humiliation, and despair. Resentment and wounded pride would be parts of the psychological picture. She might even find herself toying with the idea of revenge or retaliation or some form of aggressive reaction. In certain cultures the members of her family — her brother or uncle or father — might even feel impelled to take a shot at the perfidious bridegroom. And even in our culture the revenge impulse might assert itself in the guise of a breach of promise suit. Frustration giving rise to anger because of a threat to one's rights or interference with one's plans or ruthless deprivation of one's property is calculated to make for some type of aggressive reaction. It is important to bear this mode of response in mind, for it is back of many of our hatreds and dislikes and belligerent attitudes.

In neither of the two foregoing possibilities did the young woman experience any sense of personal guilt. To complete the usefulness of the illustration it will be necessary to introduce a third possibility by having the woman jilt her fiancé in favor of one who is wealthier and whose family is more prominent socially. By hypothesis the conflict would be the hackneyed theme of the writers of popular romantic fiction: true love *versus* the lure of a life of luxurious ease. Under these circumstances for the woman to make the latter choice would involve frustration of the former

longing. It might also involve feelings of guilt — of having behaved in a despicable fashion, of being unworthy, or of being deserving of contempt. Instead of aggressiveness one would have
self-condemnation as the reaction to frustration under such circumstances. This sort of reaction implies a violation of one's
moral code and the abject loss of self-respect which such violation may entail. It also implies being looked down upon by others
or, in the case of some religiously minded victims, of being rejected
by God. At all events, as will become clearer after reading Chapter
10, this kind of reaction presupposes the activation of conscience.
It assumes moral development in terms of personally accepted
principles of conduct as opposed to more childish notions of right
and wrong in terms of uncomprehended rewards and punishments.

Conscience or what the Freudians call a *super-ego* is not something inborn, but a product of learning. The child *learns* in the
course of its development that society approves of some actions
and disapproves of others. Parental approval or disapproval is
one of the agencies by which the child comes to distinguish good
from bad. At first this is a more or less arbitrary affair for the
child. His wanting " to be good " is altogether a function of wanting mother's approval. Being " bad " means the temporary loss of
mother's affection. Need for such affection or for such emotional
security is an imperious need not only for the child, but for the
adult as well. One psychiatrist [6] has called this need *affect hunger*.
Children who are neglected by their parents or those who are
actually disliked by them or those orphaned youngsters who are
shifted from one foster home to another are all likely to exhibit
symptoms of this kind of emotional starvation. The child who
believes himself to be *rejected* by his parents is particularly likely
to suffer from such affect hunger. Later on, of course, the youngster's craving for the approval or the good will of the teacher, the
hunger for friends, and the desire for prestige of some sort appear
as outgrowths of this primary need.[7] In fact, it is never outgrown

[6] Levy, D. M., " Primary Affect Hunger," *Amer. J. of Psychiatry*, 1937, *94*,
pp. 643–652.
[7] Whether the longing for prestige is, genetically considered, an outgrowth
of affect hunger is open to some question. In the interests of descriptive convenience we are *assuming* this to be a correct genetic picture. However, this assumption should not blind one to the fact that in the developed personality the
longing for prestige or the desire for social status may function independently of
affect hunger. The craving for love is not the same as the craving for admiration.

— all normal people continue to experience the need for fellowship of some kind, to be well thought of by others, and to be genuinely liked by at least some other person. The craving is so strong that dogs or cats or other pets may sometimes be used as substitutes for an object of affection. Even hermits are apt to have a dog with them.

The young child's frustrations incident to its violations of parental precepts are more likely to involve a threat to the gratification of this affect hunger than the abject distress of the conscience-stricken adult who has violated his personal code of honor. The child may experience resentment because of the punishment or be emotionally disturbed because of mother's " being mad " at him, whereas the adult will despise himself. His loss of self-respect may cause him to be sick at heart, to brood, and to wish for some kind of relief from the gnawing feeling of self-condemnation. This kind of catastrophic loss of self-respect can occur only after conscience has developed beyond the childish level of mere expediency as the arbiter of ethical questions. It presupposes a level of moral development beyond that of regarding things as wrong because you get punished for doing them. It requires the acceptance or the personal assimilation by the individual of *principles* of conduct that are *his* principles — no longer just the arbitrarily imposed standards of tyrannical parents or teachers. This level of moral development comes after adolescence. Its full maturity may not be reached until the individual approaches the end of the adolescent period. According to a recent investigation,[8] " maturity in moral judgment " is reached between the ages of 17 and 20 in the case of college students.[9]

Mental breakdown, as has been shown, is also a phenomenon of

One can be a success in business and a failure in marriage. Contrariwise, the socially obscure " forgotten man " may bask in the affectionate devotion of a loyal wife. Some further implications of this issue will be discussed later on in this chapter under the caption, " Security and Mental Hygiene."

[8] Barkley, K. L., " Development of the Moral Judgment of College Students," *Character and Personality*, 1942, *10*, pp. 199–212.

[9] The students in the liberal arts college were found to make higher scores on the moral judgments tests used than those enrolled for the commercial courses. The author attributes this gain to differences in the curricular content and not to differences in intelligence of the groups compared. This should not be interpreted to mean that Barkley regards maturity of moral judgment as independent of level of intelligence. It does mean, though, that ethical sensitivity and insight can be modified by what the schools incorporate in the subject matter to be pursued.

later adolescence so far as its first emergence is concerned. Criminality, on the other hand, seems to be continuous with the delinquency of the pre-adolescent. Alexander and Healy,[10] two students of the problem, report that " in all of the cases " they investigated, " the criminality of the adult was the direct continuation of the delinquency of the child." In terms of Boisen's [11] interpretation of this finding the delinquent child may be regarded as one who has developed attitudes of antagonism toward parental authority. There is refusal to accept guidance and resentment against interference. To the extent that parents symbolize organized society this may be taken to mean resentment against organized society. The rebellious youngster may thus experience feelings of contempt for such traditional virtues as obedience, honesty, sobriety, courtesy, self-control, and whatever else he links up with being a " mamma's boy " or a " little gentleman." Emotionally he identifies himself with other rebels against such teachings and consequently is ready to ally himself with neighborhood toughs or roughneck gangs. His affect hunger is gratified by winning favor with such a gang. Feeling himself alienated from or rejected by his family he welcomes the substitute of a gang of delinquents to which he can cling for emotional support. The gang's standards then become his standards, the gang's ideals his ideals, and the gang's outlook his outlook. For him the gang is the surrogate of organized society and his socialization consists in personal identification with the gang and personal acceptance of its way of life. To put this somewhat paradoxically: he becomes socialized by identifying himself with an anti-social group. This renders him delinquent or criminal in our eyes, but involves no self-disparagement in his. In fact, he may glory in his criminal record: his self-respect and prestige are functions of such a record. And as long as he keeps this self-respect intact, he is in no danger of the kind of inner conflict out of which psychotic disturbance may develop.

As might be anticipated, Boisen regards the psychotic individual as one who has accepted parental guidance. What teachers and parents have stressed as necessary for the good life has become part and parcel of the individual's inner system of values. But it

[10] Alexander, F., and Healy, W., *Roots of Crime*, New York, Alfred A. Knopf, 1935, p. 278.
[11] Boisen, A. T., *The Exploration of the Inner World*, pp. 282–284.

takes time for such a system to develop and to be assimilated by the developing personality. Not until the adolescent period does conscience as a matter of conduct governed by *principle* begin to assert itself. Loyalty to such principle is then no longer merely a matter of loyalty to parents and teachers : it is also a matter of loyalty to oneself. To act contrary to such principle will result in feelings of guilt, in loss of self-esteem, in self-reproach, in self-condemnation, or even self-hatred. The victim feels *as if* he were an outcast. He looks down upon himself because he believes that if his parents and teachers and others in authority knew of his disloyalty, they would look down upon him and no longer be affectionately disposed toward him. Part of his misery is thus bound up with affect hunger. His emotional security is threatened by such catastrophic loss of self-respect. Unlike the criminal, his is a divided self ; hence his mental integrity is in jeopardy.

Psychotic disturbance of the functional variety, according to this view, cannot occur until there is conflict between one's selfish or unsocialized desires and one's code of honor, one's conscience, or one's loyalty to ethical principles. In popular language this can be described as the conflict between our good and evil impulses. For many people the sex impulse is apt to be regarded as synonymous with an evil impulse. The intensification of this impulse with the advent of puberty may consequently mark the beginning of an inner struggle that was relatively non-existent in the previous childhood years. Not only is the sex impulse stronger, but the voice of conscience may also be stronger. The latter voice is no longer a mere echo of the parent's voice, but is now taken to be an expression of one's own " higher " nature. Under the circumstances it is easy to see that the post-adolescent has different conflicts from the pre-adolescent, and why these conflicts may eventuate in mental breakdown in the one age period but not in the other.

Furthermore, one ought to see that the problem is not entirely a consequence of chemical or physiological changes incident to adolescence, but that the ethico-social attitudes in terms of which the adolescent reacts to such changes are very likely of even greater import. Nor should this reference to sex conflict be taken to mean that *all* conflicts leading to psychotic disturbance are rooted in this area of maladjustment ; for the period of puberty is not exclusively a period of activated consciousness of sex. It is also a period of dawning social consciousness — an awareness of what will be expected of the individual as a member of society. The adolescent's problems are by no means restricted to the narrow orbit of sex. He is apt to be worried over his vocational choice, his inability to believe in Biblical miracles, his lack of popularity with the boys at school, or the family's persistence in treating him as a " child." His social attitudes are broadening out in every direction just as his bodily frame is lengthening and broadening. Psychologically he is becoming a more complex creature than he was a few years earlier. It is a process of transforming the simple child into the more complex person of character. And character has to do with one's values, one's aspirations, one's principles. The person of character is not unmindful of what others think of him. His honor is bound up with his reputation. He is proud of what his name stands for in the community. What we have repeatedly referred to as *self-respect* involves all such ramifications of the mature self; hence conflict and frustration have very different implications for the psychologically mature individual than for the psychologically immature. This is the type of difference which the advocate of the conflict theory might well stress in order to account for the pre-adolescent's seeming immunity to psychotic disturbance.

DETECTING THE FUTURE PSYCHOTIC

Many mental hygienists have deplored the ignorance of parents and teachers of basic mental hygiene teachings. In particular, as will be brought out in detail in the next section, they have argued that if the potential schizophrenic were recognized as such by his parent or teacher, preventive or remedial measures could be introduced in time to ward off development of the psychotic trend. Effective training in coping with conflict situations would presumably save such a child from his schizophrenic doom. Although such training is to be regarded as desirable for *all* children, the desirability of any special training for the child possessing what has been called a " schizoid personality " might well be questioned. In general, the latter phrase has been applied to quiet, shy, obedient youngsters. It has been assumed that schizophrenia is an outgrowth of such pre-psychotic personality traits. This rather widely accepted belief ought to be subjected to critical scrutiny. We ought to ask ourselves whether the psychiatrist studying a group of children intensively can select those who will grow up to be psychotic? Can he predict which ones will become hebephrenic and which ones catatonic? Can he point to the future manic-depressives and the cases of potential paranoia? If he can, and if the conflict theory is sound, then it might, of course, be true that specialized educational work with such children might help to steer them away from what, by hypothesis, would otherwise mean a psychotic future for them. This kind of pragmatic test of the accuracy of psychiatric prognoses has never been made. However, there is good reason to assert that most competent psychiatrists would be reluctant to view such a test with professional enthusiasm: too little is known about the factors involved. Detecting the future psychotics in a group of children is by no means as easy as some mental hygienists seem to believe.

The conflict theory as applied to schizophrenia has been defended and elaborated by the psychiatrists connected with the Johns Hopkins University. Kanner, a member of this group, has been especially interested in the adjustment problems of children. As a consequence, it is particularly relevant to note what he has to say concerning the " pre-psychotic personalities " of schizophrenics. Incidentally, it is also relevant to point out that despite his allegiance to the conflict theory, he feels constrained to grant that " heredity plays an important part " [12] in the etiology of schizophrenia. However, he is not disposed to view the situation as hopeless because of this. On the contrary, he urges that those responsible for the training of children make every effort to counteract schizoid tendencies by learning to recognize them and by striving to induce their possessors to avoid wishful, unrealistic evasions of conflict situations. The educational goal to be aimed at is the establishment of effective habits of thinking and acting in all phases of human endeavor — in work, in play, and in social intercourse. The child is to be taught to make friends and to get on with others instead of being permitted to retreat to the solitary refuge of an inner world of asocial, dreamy, ineffectual contemplation. Properly qualified, there is no reason to object to this general educational goal. It is to be viewed as a desirable objective for

[12] Kanner, L., *Child Psychiatry*, Baltimore, Charles C. Thomas, 1935, p. 490.

all children and we have no quarrel with this aspect of Kanner's views. Our skepticism is directed toward his notion that one can learn to recognize symptoms of future schizophrenia in the child. He himself furnishes a list of such symptoms, originally drawn up by Kraeplin, by means of which the characteristics of the " pre-psychotic personality " of the schizophrenic are supposed to be recognizable. Four groups of children are mentioned: [13]

1. Quiet, shy, retiring children, inclined to live solitary lives of their own.

2. Irritable, sensitive, excitable, nervous, stubborn children, especially girls, given to religious preoccupations.

3. Lazy, inactive, unstable, mischievous children, mostly boys, who sometimes become tramps and delinquents.

4. Manageable, good-natured, anxiously overconscientious, industrious model children, mainly boys.

It is interesting to observe the reactions of adults when such a list is read to them without informing them of its psychopathic implications, merely requesting them to decide whether in retrospect they believe one of the four characterizations might have applied to them when they were children. The vast majority are likely to identify themselves with some one of these categories. In one group of about 40 people we found only 2 who failed to make such an identification. As the list stands it is likely to cause needless apprehension in parents and teachers. The latter are apt to decide that almost all of the youngsters in every class are " pre-psychotic " and the former may become alarmed over the morbid condition of sons and daughters they had hitherto regarded as " normal " children. To cause needless apprehension and alarm in and of itself is poor mental hygiene. Under the circumstances one might well question the mental hygiene wisdom of inducing parents and educators to cast a suspicious eye on every child who is quiet and shy or irritable and sensitive or lazy and mischievous or manageable and good-natured. One almost wonders what child can be given a clean bill of mental health in terms of Kraeplin's symptoms of the " pre-psychotic " personality: the so-called schizoid personality.

As a matter of fact there is little if any evidence to support

[13] *Op. cit.*, p. 491.

this Kraeplinian teaching. Nobody has demonstrated that " schiz-oid " children grow up into schizophrenic adults. In the language of the A.N.A. Committee: [14]

> There is no scientific proof to the effect that this personality type necessarily precedes the development of dementia praecox. Moreover those who are so labeled are often the bearers of qualities which make for great personal achievement and for the social welfare.

Whether the child ever exhibits reliable signs of future psy-chotic breakdown is thus an exceedingly dubious issue. Moreover it may be unwise for those in charge of children to be too zealous in the search for such signs. There is always the danger of mis-taking intrinsically harmless bits of behavior for significant evi-dence of underlying abnormal trends. The boastful child does not necessarily foreshadow the development of delusions of grandeur. Nor do temper tantrums in the baby signify maniacal excitement when the baby has grown up to be a man. Prophylactic mental hygiene does not call for the indiscriminate curbing of every mode of childish behavior which bears a resemblance to some symptom of psychotic behavior in the adult. Although this ought to be obvi-ous enough, it is sometimes overlooked by mental hygienists them-selves. The emphasis on " schizoid " personalities in children is a case in point.

Detecting the future psychotic is by no means easy. Overenthu-siastic devotion to the cause of prophylactic mental hygiene may lead the amateur psychiatric detective astray. In the process he may do his cause more harm than good. He may succumb to a logical error to which the enthusiastic and unwary are especially susceptible. This error consists of assuming that disease can be prevented by warding off its symptoms. It would be exemplified by anybody impulsive enough to urge mothers to keep their chil-dren engaged in active muscular exercise during an epidemic of infantile paralysis on the theory that " an active muscle can't be paralyzed." Such a person might also argue that ice packs will pre-vent typhoid fever or that " keeping the baby's skin clean " will prevent chicken pox. In his preoccupation with symptoms or ef-fects he is overlooking etiology or causes. His logic is akin to that of some hypothetical criminologist rash enough to insist that the

[14] Myerson, A., *et al.*, *Eugenical Sterilization*, p. 180.

way to prevent crime is to ward off clues. As applied to mental hygiene such logic would mean that the boisterous, noisy, extroverted child is apt to become a manic adult and the quiet, reserved, introverted child a schizophrenic adult. This is poor logic and poor mental hygiene. It also involves the fallacy discussed in the very first chapter: the belief that the " abnormal " is merely a magnified version of the " normal."

Our chief reason for referring to this problem of detecting the future psychotic is that it has become fashionable in some mental hygiene circles to imply that if parents and teachers could be made to understand the import of alleged pre-psychotic symptoms, the incidence of functional mental disease could be reduced. It has also become commonplace in such circles to indict both parents as a class and teachers as a class for their presumed ignorance of basic mental hygiene principles. The indictment in question is related to the previously mentioned problem of teachers' attitudes toward mental hygiene — particularly its prophylactic aspects. Discussion of its validity will help to bring out some neglected phases of the latter problem.

Mental hygiene's indictment of parents and teachers

The contention of many mental hygienists to the effect that those charged with the responsibility of rearing and educating children are poorly prepared to safeguard the mental health of children is based on the findings of two surveys made some years ago. Publication of the results aroused great interest at the time and the findings were discussed by psychiatrists, clinical psychologists, child guidance experts, mental hygienists, and many educators. Almost every text in mental hygiene has made and still makes some respectful reference to the findings. Professors of education have incorporated the results in their lecture notes so that large numbers of students have been told about the mental hygiene shortcomings of parents and teachers.

The obvious moral to this concerted indictment has been the imperative need for instructing the latter groups in mental hygiene principles if the rising generation was to be saved. There was usually the definite implication that mental hygienists possessed some profound understanding of which teachers and parents were sadly ignorant. More specifically, it has been alleged that investigations of the kind we are about to describe demonstrate how uninformed teachers and parents are regarding symptoms indicative of existing or impending personality distortion. What mental hygienists regard as serious conditions, the other groups either overlook entirely or treat lightly and what the latter view with alarm, the former dismiss as negligible. Stated a little differently, mental hygienists are supposed to be detecting the troubled child while parents and teachers are concerned only with the troublesome child. To appreciate the conventional interpretation of the type of investigation we have in mind the following quotation from a mental hygiene text may be read as a sample representative of many others: [15]

. . . teachers only consider behavior of children a serious problem when it either violates conventional morality or violates school regulations leading to disturbance of classroom routine which makes teaching of the 'child or others difficult. It is important to note that only *aggressive* behavior is regarded by the teacher as serious. Those displaying recessive traits such as shy, " good," sensitive, unsocial, imaginative lying, dreaminess, etc., are rarely reported as problems. Yet from the mental hygiene standpoint, the non-interfering, timid and withdrawing child is perhaps a graver problem than the overtly socially aggressive child. The former type is apt to be left alone, to construct fantastic daydreams which take him away from the business of facing and adjusting to life as it is rather than as he imagines or wishes it to be. Left to himself, such a child often fails to become happily socialized. If the process of abnormal introversion goes unchecked, we see developing the recluse, the queer, the odd, the incongruous, and the pre-schizophrenic and schizophrenic (dementia praecox) types. . . . It is obvious that many teachers fail to recognize serious mental hygiene problems in children and to give them the necessary individual treatment to keep them in good contact with reality and to cause them to be happily socialized.

THE WICKMAN-STOGDILL STUDIES

On what kind of evidence are interpretations of the foregoing sort based? Is there really this sharp difference of opinion regarding " problem " behavior between mental hygienists on the one hand and parent-teacher groups on the other? To answer these questions the original investigations themselves must be examined. We shall restrict our examination to two pioneer studies: one by Wickman [16] and the other by Stogdill.[17] The latter studied parental attitudes and the former investigated those of teachers. In both studies the general method employed, although differing in details, was essentially the same: a rating of problems by a group of mental hygienists and a rating of the same problems by a group of teachers and a group of parents. The problems had to do with such issues as " bullying," " tattling," " nervousness," " obscene talk," " cruelty," " masturbation," " playing with fire," and so on.

Each item was separately considered by the individual judge and its degree of seriousness indicated by means of a graphic rating scale. The latter, it might be explained, consists of a line one end of which is taken to symbolize a minimum of seriousness by giving it the caption " of no consequence," while the other end symbolizes the maximum degree as indicated by a caption like " an extremely grave offense or problem." Intermediate degrees of seriousness were recorded by having the judge check the point on the line which he regarded as marking the appropriate point on the scale between these extremes. To facilitate locating such points, captions like " of only slight consequence " and " makes for considerable difficulty " were interpolated between the ends of the line. A composite rating for each group of judges was obtained by determining the average point on the line for each item as checked by each group.

Incidentally, it might be pertinent to call attention to the fact that Wickman's instructions to his two groups of raters were different. Consider the following excerpts from the instructions to the teachers: [18]

" How serious is it for the individual child who shows this behavior? " In other words, how much does it make him a problem child, disturbing, or a misfit? This amounts to the same thing as asking, " How undesirable is this behavior in the school child? "

Make your ratings as rapidly as possible.

[16] Wickman, E. K., *Children's Behavior and Teachers' Attitudes*, New York, The Commonwealth Fund, Division of Publications, 1928.
[17] Stogdill, R. M., " Parental Attitudes and Mental Hygiene Standards," *Mental Hygiene*, 1931, *15*, pp. 813–827.
[18] Wickman, E. K., *op. cit.*, p. 201. (Italics not in original.)

The foregoing should be contrasted with the following excerpts from the list of instructions given the mental hygienists: [19]

Then rate each of these items according to this criterion: What is your professional opinion of the seriousness or importance of this behavior when occurring in any school child with regard to its future effect in limiting his or her happiness, success, and general welfare after leaving school and on entering adult social and industrial life? In other words, how much will the possession of this behavior trait by a child generally handicap him in his future adjustments as an adult?

Furthermore, Wickman tells us that the mental hygienists were not asked to work rapidly. In his own words: [20]

Instead of securing quick responses, as were required from teachers, the mental hygienists were cautioned to give careful attention to their reports and to weigh their responses from a purely professional and intellectual point of view.

It should be manifest that the task set the teachers and the mental hygienists was not at all identical. In addition, by requesting the teachers to work rapidly and allowing the other group to work at a leisurely pace Wickman set the stage for getting impulsive judgments from the former and more considered ones from the latter. Under the circumstances it is hardly to be wondered at that the two groups differed in their ratings. However, Stogdill corrected this defect in method by having the same wording in his instructions to his two groups of judges. Nevertheless, he too secured marked differences in the judgments of his groups of parents and mental hygiene experts.

GOODWIN WATSON'S CRITIQUE OF THE WICKMAN-STOGDILL STUDIES

Many of those who have accepted Wickman's conclusions have seemingly regarded Stogdill's work as supplying adequate confirmation. And yet, as Goodwin Watson [21] has pointed out, Stogdill's study is by no means free from methodological shortcomings. It will consequently prove a valuable excursion to note some of the points raised by Watson in his critique of studies of this kind.

[19] *Ibid.,* p. 210.
[20] *Ibid.,* p. 209.
[21] Watson, G., " A Critical Note on Two Attitude Studies," *Mental Hygiene,* 1933, *17,* pp. 59–64.

One defect of the method has to do with the failure to delimit the meaning of each item to be ranked by the judges. Stogdill, for example, placed 70 items in front of the judges with instructions to " score each of the following items of child behavior as to seriousness or undesirability. *Work Quickly.*" The items themselves were just bare designations like " stubbornness," " over-activity, restlessness," " depressed," and " excessive modesty." If one dwells on the possible situations likely to provoke attitudes of this kind, various judgments are apt to come to mind. Whether " stubbornness " is to evoke approval or disapproval will vary with the situation. Most people would applaud the stubborn little boy who refuses to tattle on his friend despite the threats of a domineering teacher. On the other hand, they would not applaud the sulky kind of stubborn behavior associated with the negativistic defiance of the spoiled youngster who meets every parental request with a blunt, " I won't and you can't make me." Unless the circumstances are specified in more sharply delimited fashion, one cannot be sure that the judges are endowing each item with the same meaning. The judgments are consequently *ambiguous* judgments.

Furthermore, some of the items have rather technical, specialized meanings for those familiar with symptoms of mental disease. As Watson points out, " depressed " has a different connotation for the psychiatrist than for the ordinary parent or teacher. Stogdill's mental hygienists regarded " depressed " as the most serious item because for them it suggests an alarming symptom. However, to the layman who is thinking of a child's disappointment or sadness when rain interferes with picnic plans, " depressed " is merely regrettable rather than alarming. Telling the judges to " work quickly " is hardly calculated to aid them in reaching a common meaning for the various items. Unless the context is specified, people with different backgrounds are not likely to react in the same way to an isolated word like " daydreaming." Many of the mental hygienists realized this, for, as Watson reminds us, more than half of them " refused to answer."

Wickman employed 30 mental hygiene experts and Stogdill used 50. How well did these two groups of experts agree with one another in their judgments? This was a question Watson proceeded to answer. He found " 39 items clearly common to both studies " and by arranging the respective rankings of these 39 items by the two groups he was able to compute the coefficient of correlation. Such a coefficient furnishes a measure of the reliability or consistency of the expert opinion in a situation of this kind. The coefficient turned out to be only .61. What this implies can be made clear to those unfamiliar with correlation technique by considering Watson's own explanation: [22]

Suppose that instead of bothering the busy psychotherapists, Messrs. Wickman and Stogdill had written each behavior item on a card, placed them all in a box, shuffled well, and drawn them in random order, calling the first drawn the most serious, the second the next most serious, and so on to the most trivial. Then suppose they had put the cards back, reshuffled, and drawn again. The average difference between the ranking of an offense in the first drawing and the ranking on the second drawing would be about 13, on the scale of 39. Actually, the average difference between the rank of one of these offenses by Wickman's set of experts and the rank by Stogdill's was about 8 ranks, a difference less than 40 per cent smaller than the disagreement had one or both been made up by lot drawing.

Some of the items showed very striking differences in the judgments of the two juries of mental hygienists. For instance, Stogdill's experts placed " domineering (self-assertive)" in 34th place, and Wickman's experts ranked this item in 12th place. " Cheating " was listed in 7th place by one group and in 24th place by the other. " Destructiveness " was also characterized by a difference of 17 places in the two rankings. In the case of " sensitiveness " the difference was 21. This lack of agreement among the mental hygienists themselves is possibly even more worthy of emphasis than the discrepancies between the experts on the one hand and the teachers on the other. In fact, on the basis of some statistical analyses of Stogdill's data which we need not introduce here, Watson concludes that these data " may reasonably be interpreted to show that a group of parents agrees with some experts as well as one group of experts agrees with another group of experts."

A more direct exposure of the inadequacy of the Wickman-Stogdill type of finding was furnished by Peck.[23] This psychologist was particularly interested in checking on Wickman's contention

[22] *Op. cit.*, pp. 61–62.
[23] Peck, L., " Teachers' Reports of the Problems of Unadjusted School Children," *J. of Educ. Psychol.*, 1935, *26*, pp. 123–138.

to the effect that teachers are more disturbed by behavior disruptive of classroom morale than by behavior indicative of grave personality disturbance. A significant point made by Peck is Wickman's failure to get at the problem directly by asking the teachers such questions as, " What children under your charge are most poorly adjusted? Why do you consider them poorly adjusted? " Instead, as was suggested earlier, Wickman used an indirect rating technique dealing with the relative seriousness of a long series of behavior items.

The procedure employed by Peck was more straightforward than this. She secured a total of 175 case studies from 175 teachers in response to an optional assignment to describe what they considered the case of some poorly adjusted pupil. The instructions were simple and brief: " Tell why you consider the pupil maladjusted, explain as well as you can the factors tending to cause the maladjustment, and state what you think should be done for the child." Incidentally, these teachers had received no special instruction along mental hygiene lines prior to their completion of the written assignment. To consider the detailed tabulation of Peck's statistical analyses of the case studies is not essential in the present context. For our purposes it will suffice to note the following excerpts from Peck's conclusions:

. . . the teachers concerned in the present study gave overwhelming emphasis to undesirable personality traits, considered the various classes of disciplinary offenses as least serious, and placed a median emphasis upon violations of moral standards and of school work requirements. The opinions of the teachers studied in the present investigation resembled those of Wickman's clinicians rather than those of Wickman's . . . teachers. . . . The teachers studied in the present investigation reported their reactions to the specific problems of actual children. Reports thus obtained probably have greater validity as representing the real attitude of the teachers toward the behavior of their pupils.

Indicting teachers as a class for their seeming ignorance of basic mental hygiene principles is thus hardly warranted. Certainly the Wickman-Stogdill type of study has failed to justify any indictment of this kind. Furthermore, as Watson [24] has pointed out, it may also be in order to question a common belief of the many

[24] *Op. cit.*, pp. 62–63.

authors who have quoted Wickman and Stogdill with uncritical approval. According to this belief, mental hygienists as a class are presumed to have a more correct and more profound understanding of desirable personality traits than is possessed by teachers as a class. In the words of Watson: " The Wickman study is often quoted as if the mental hygienists were right and the teachers naive."

What Watson means by this is that the teachers in rating isolated behavior items like " masturbation " and " truancy " were making their evaluations in terms of a larger perspective than the more restricted professional horizon of the clinicians. The teachers may have been altogether correct in assuming dire consequences for the child and for the school by outraged community opinion if conventional sex taboos were regarded as inconsequential. Similarly, their concern about truancy was also altogether understandable; for how can the goals of education be reached if children refuse to attend classes? Of course, as we have already indicated, many of the discrepancies between the teachers and the experts in Wickman's study are to be attributed to the fact that the two groups were asked to answer *different* questions about the significance of such behavior items and were not given equivalent amounts of time in which to think of their answers. However, this criticism does not apply to Stogdill's work. And yet, as Watson demonstrates, the latter investigator failed to make due allowance for understandable differences in outlook between parents on the one hand and mental experts on the other. By way of proof Watson calls attention to the item " playing with fire." The parents regarded this as relatively serious, inasmuch as they ranked it in 8th place. For the experts this was not nearly so serious, since they ranked it 44th. In Watson's opinion this difference of 36 ranks may merely reflect the difference between the detached calm of a clinician speculating about the theoretic import of a child's desire to play with matches and the poorly controlled excitement of a father whose property might go up in flames.

In defense of shy children

Even though it may call for some repetition of what has already been stated, one additional feature of the Wickman-Stogdill studies ought to be discussed. The experts who participated in these investigations rated symptoms of shyness and introversion as relatively serious. In other words, they were regarding symptoms of this kind as indicators of schizoid trends. The logic back of this view, it will be recalled, takes the form of assuming that because the schizophrenic patient seems to have withdrawn from effective contact with his social environment, therefore shyness in the child, which may also be characterized by a tendency to withdraw from social contact, is to be classified as a psychiatric danger signal. It will also be recalled that convincing evidence for the existence of such a relationship between pre-psychotic personality traits in the child and the psychoses of adults has yet to be produced. Furthermore, in the light of what has already been said about this kind of logic, the Wickman-Stogdill experts should have been equally concerned about items like " destructiveness," " quarrelsomeness," and " over-activity "; for such symptoms might, if the soundness of the logic be granted, presage an eventual outburst of the manic phase of manic-depressive psychosis. Their failure to do this may possibly have been due to the common tendency to think of the latter disease as a disturbance of maturity, while schizophrenia still suggests *dementia praecox,* which has already been explained as the Latin for " adolescent insanity."

Quite manifestly, there is little need to devote too much space to this relatively minor issue. What may be of more immediate importance is to call attention to the fairly widespread agreement among many laymen and some mental experts that shyness and introversion and similar personality characteristics are somehow less desirable than their opposites. The child with push and go is regarded as better adjusted than the more thoughtful, less obviously self-assertive child. In the field of education it is often taken for granted that schools ought to be training " leaders " and " doers " and " future executives " for the world of tomorrow. Whether such an apotheosis of leadership and action is in accord with a sound philosophy of mental hygiene is to be seriously questioned.

If one criterion of a sound mental hygiene philosophy be the happiness of adults living in accord with such a philosophy, we might ask just what personality characteristics does one find in children who grow up into happy adults. Is it true that youthful extroverts have a better chance of developing into joyous adults than youthful introverts? Does the poised, self-assured youngster necessarily have a better chance of becoming a well-adjusted adult than his more timid, less confident brother? It is hard to find much data bearing directly on these questions.

There is one study which Watson mentions in the article to which we have already referred that seems to have some bearing on the issues involved. According to Watson,[25] he and Eleanor Ruth Long selected 36 graduate students from a group of several hundred. These 36 were chosen because they " believed themselves unusually happy " and seemed to be definitely successful in their work as teachers. Success was indicated not only in terms of their steady professional advancement, but also in terms of " better-than-average income." Moreover, these 36 adults, relatively mature, their average age being over thirty, not only rated themselves exceptionally happy, but also felt that they were enjoying the finer rewards of successful living. Upon probing into the youthful backgrounds of these people some thought-provoking findings came to light. Marked emotional sensitivity in childhood was reported by 64 per cent. Two-thirds of the group " felt themselves seriously handicapped by bashfulness in earlier years." There may be some question of the trustworthiness of such recollections. However, in the absence of contradictory data, the study may be taken as supplying presumptive evidence in favor of the view that timidity and bashfulness in children need not necessarily be interpreted as signs of future mental trouble.

The absence of any assured relationship between shyness in the child and schizophrenia in the adult has been demonstrated in another way. This consisted in checking on the childhood personality characteristics of 101 schizophrenic patients admitted to a given State Hospital. To avoid the bias of selection the cases were taken in consecutive order just as they entered the institution. The sociologist making this study [26] was interested in finding out whether the schizophrenic trait of seclusiveness was already manifest in childhood. In 53 of the 101 cases there was not sufficient evidence to reach a decision. Of the other 48 cases, 21 were found to have been seclusive children, while 27 " were definitely reported to have

[25] *Op. cit.*, p. 64.
[26] Faris, R. E. L., and Dunham, H. W., *Mental Disorders in Urban Areas*, Chicago, The University of Chicago Press, 1939, pp. 175–177. (One of the co-authors of this book was the original investigator.)

been normally sociable in their childhood." In other words, both sociable as well as shy children may develop schizophrenia.

Evidently factors other than shyness must be taken into account. Some of these are suggested by analysis of the individual cases for the purpose of detecting the causes of the eventual social isolation of the patients. In 29 instances there was evidence that the patients had been "spoiled children." The spoiled child is apt to antagonize others. They may retaliate by making him the victim of sarcastic comments, practical jokes, or actual persecution. For the victim this may constitute evidence of rejection by the social group: isolation and seclusiveness may then develop. Another factor mentioned as making for the latter kind of development had to do with exceptionally strict religious and moral standards imposed on the children. There were 4 cases of which this seemed to be true. These were not " spoiled," but they had trouble reconciling their beliefs with their impulses as shown by strong feelings of guilt associated with sex episodes. Such a person, as we have already indicated, reacts to himself as if he were an outcast from " respectable society " or what he believes such society to be. There were other patients whose seclusiveness was an outgrowth of deafness: not being able to hear cuts one off from social contact and may even induce delusional beliefs. In addition, there were various other sources of interference with healthy social interaction such as difficulty with English, self-consciousness as a result of disfiguring bodily handicaps, and parental objection to playing with other children. All such factors merit consideration by the mental hygienist engaged in ferreting out the causes of the kind of seclusiveness that makes for schizophrenia; for not all seclusive behavior is to be viewed as a menace to mental health. Only that which is caused by the notion of having been spurned by one's fellows is to be so regarded.

It is important to realize that many shy, quiet, reserved people are well liked by others. Their seclusiveness is in no sense a social handicap. In some instances their very shyness endows them with a unique charm. It would be a grave mistake to interpret the mental hygienist's concern with seclusiveness as a schizophrenic danger signal to mean that all shy children — and adults — are to be urged to make themselves over into the pattern of the self-assertive, go-getting " life of the party." The only sort of shyness which deserves to be classified as a sign of possible future trouble is the kind that signifies acute self-disparagement because the victim regards himself as a social outcast. One individual may be shy and seclusive because, like Greta Garbo, he merely prefers " to be alone." There is no reason to worry about such a person's stability. The one to worry about is the one who remains aloof because of the conviction — real or imaginary — that people do not like him, or would not like him if they discovered the secret sin or weakness responsible for the self-disparagement. And there is also reason to worry about the seclusiveness of the lonely foreigner who can't make friends because of the language handicap. But this is very different from being worried about shyness or seclusiveness in the abstract.

THE PREVENTION OF MANIC-DEPRESSIVE DISORDERS

As was indicated in Table 1, next to schizophrenia the most common form of hospitalized functional disease is the manic-depressive variety. Its prevention is consequently an important mental hygiene problem. Unfortunately, aside from a few general hints, there is little tested prophylactic knowledge available. Taken by and large students of mental disease are less sure of what to do by way of reducing the incidence of this disease than they are in the case of schizophrenia. For one thing the hereditary factor seems to be more definitely established in the former than the latter. For another the psychodynamics of the conflict theory has been worked out more plausibly for schizophrenia than for manic-depressive psychosis.

Even with reference to the hereditary background of the psychosis there has been reluctance to recommend prophylaxis by eugenical sterilization or abstention from marriage into a family with a history of manic-depressive disorder. Luxenburger, a student of this question, is quoted with evident approval by the A.N.A. Committee [27] for urging great caution with respect to this attack on the problem because of " the fact that from marriages of manic-depressive couples children may emerge " who may be the possessors of abilities " of great positive social and eugenic value." Each case is to be evaluated on an individual basis. Furthermore, Luxenburger reports it to be a fact that, regarded as a

[27] Meyerson, A., *et al.*, *Eugenical Sterilization*, p. 110.

whole, manic-depressives " are socially productive and success-ful." In addition, " he demonstrates clearly " that their families belong predominantly to " the higher social strata." Before fol-lowing up this clue, however, it is necessary to hunt for possible contradictory clues.

Such contradictory clues are not hard to find. For example, a recently published volume [28] states that " while schizophrenia is a poor man's disease, *manic-depression strikes rich and poor im-partially*." The authors base this verdict on evidence submitted by Faris and Dunham [29] whose study of mental diseases was just referred to in the previous section. However, examination of the study in question leaves one uncertain about the unqualified validity of the verdict mentioned. The work by Faris and Dunham is important and will engage our attention in somewhat greater detail in Chapter 15. In the present context it will be sufficient to restrict our comments to their views regarding the relationship between manic-depressive psychosis and socio-economic status.

It is true that the general drift of the evidence mobilized by Faris and Dunham seems to justify the impression of the absence of any correlation between the incidence of manic-depressive psy-chosis and measures of social status. In fact, in their final chapter devoted to an interpretation of their findings, the two sociologists state explicitly that " the ecological and statistical evidence does not bring out any relationship between this disorder and the social milieu." [30] Nevertheless in the *Introduction* to the book, written by another sociologist, one finds a " brief summary of the facts discovered by the authors " and learns that they discovered the highest rate of incidence of " manic-depressive psychoses in areas with higher rentals." [31] And in the body of the text the authors themselves write: [32]

While the pattern of manic-depressive rates in any distribution of such cases does appear to be extremely random, the correlation co-efficients with certain selective indices indicate the *tendency of the manic-depressive cases to come from a higher social and economic*

[28] Maslow, A. H., and Mittelmann, B., *Principles of Abnormal Psychology*, p. 200. (Italics not in the original.)
[29] Faris, R. E. L., and Dunham, H. W., *Mental Disorders in Urban Areas*, pp. 63–81.
[30] *Op. cit.*, p. 172.
[31] *Ibid., Introduction*, p. x.
[32] *Ibid.*, p. 79. (Italics not in the original.)

level in contrast to the schizophrenic cases. Some additional evidence on this point . . . is obtained in contrasting the manic-depressive patients with the schizophrenic patients in terms of median rental paid in the subcommunities.

There is thus a discrepancy between the conclusion reached in the final chapter and statements made both in the *Introduction* as well as in the body of the text. This is all the more perplexing since the point made regarding the " higher social and economic level " of the manic-depressive cases is cited as one of the " conclusions " at the end of the chapter devoted to analysis of the data pertaining to these cases. This conclusion is worded as follows: [33]

There is a tendency, although not clearly defined, for the manic-depressive cases to come from a higher cultural and economic level than the schizophrenic cases.

Under the circumstances it is easy to understand how the authors cited at the beginning of this discussion were misled by the statement already quoted from the final chapter of Faris and Dunham's report. This statement does seem to justify a teaching to the effect that " manic-depression strikes rich and poor impartially." Moreover, such a conclusion is at variance with the findings of Luxenburger. However, as was made evident by the other quotations from Faris and Dunham, their own conclusions from their own data can also be cited in support of the Luxenburger finding. The latter finding is also in line with the results of other surveys of this aspect of the problem. Landis and Page,[34] for instance, state that " the social status of manic-depressive patients is above that of all the organic psychoses and of dementia praecox " and that " comparatively few " of them " come from either the low educational or economic levels." Accordingly, we can regard this as a reasonably well-established conclusion and proceed to examine its implications for possible prophylactic suggestions.

It is customary to regard manic-depressive psychosis as a disturbance of emotional life. The prominence of such affective symptoms as overexcitement, prolonged despondency, or extreme agitation renders this understandable. In some respects, however,

[33] *Ibid.*, p. 80.
[34] Landis, C., and Page, J. D., *Modern Society and Mental Disease*, pp. 64–65.

placing primary emphasis on disturbed emotionality may fail to render the manic-depressive's psychology understandable. His chief trouble, as we see it, has to do with what may technically be described as poor management of the conative rather than the affective aspect of mental life. *Conation* has to do with striving, with ambition to reach a goal, with struggle to attain an objective. Of course the intimate relationship between such striving, ambition, and struggle on the one hand and emotional fluctuations on the other is not to be overlooked. But the emotional fluctuations are functions of our conative dispositions. Conation may remain the same while the gamut of affective changes is experienced.

The foregoing abstractions can readily be exemplified by a concrete illustration. In many respects football spectators, provided they are genuinely partisan and provided the game's outcome is in doubt, exhibit behavior not so very different from that of a manic-depressive patient. Manic excitement prevails among the followers of the team scoring the first touchdown while depressive gloom descends upon the supporters of the rival team. All of the partisans have the same conative set: they want *their* team to win. Nevertheless the same " stimulus " — a moving football — affects them differently and produces elation in some and dejection in others. In the presumably neutral referee who is not supposed to be a partisan or to take sides this vision of a football moving over the touchdown marker produces no affective change whatsoever. Joy or sadness, in other words, are dependent on existing conative sets or attitudes — on what we want to happen or, in terms of the players themselves, on what we are striving to make happen.

The goals we set for ourselves have much to do with our emotional status. Even defeat may, under certain circumstances, be accompanied by the joy of victory. When an outclassed team is pitted against an unscored-on team of championship caliber and enters the game not expecting to win, but merely determined to make one touchdown, then, although the final score may be 93 to 7, the losers may feel like winners. They will feel this way because they will have attained the object of their conative set: scoring a single touchdown against opponents of overwhelmingly superior ability. It is also desirable to note that under the given circumstances the winners may feel despondent at the end of the game; because their ambition to finish the season without being scored upon has been frustrated. Joy or satisfaction are thus relative to the ambitions we cherish. Our level of aspiration has much to do with our self-appraisal of personal accomplishment. Whether a man thinks of himself as a success or a failure depends not so much on what he has done with his life as on what he endeavored to do with it. The world's second best violinist may rate himself a failure if his ambition was to be the very best. And yet one who set out " to play the fiddle just for the fun of it " may deem himself a great success merely because he has been invited to play in an amateur symphony orchestra.

In the light of the foregoing considerations manic-depressive behavior can be viewed as a disturbance of conation. It is bound up with such matters as personal ambition, competition, social striving, the longing for prestige, the desire to " keep up with the Joneses," and other manifestations of the craving for ego-enhancement by an elevation of social status. Upper-class families are more likely to set high goals of accomplishment for their members than families at the subsistence level. The maintenance of family respectability calls for conformity to relatively high standards with respect to dress, deportment, education, housing, medical care and recreation. To have to depend on charity would be a blow to family pride to one brought up in this type of social setting. Similarly, in terms of this pride the head of such a family wants his children to live up to the traditional level of the family's socio-economic aspirations. In a competitive culture this means constant striving and constant threat of disappointment. This may possibly explain the association between the incidence of manic-depressive breakdown and the high-rent districts of urban areas.

It may also explain why this type of breakdown appears to occur less frequently in Russia than in our country. Although there is some uncertainty about the precise figures, there is little doubt about the existence of a difference. One American psychiatrist who visited Russia in the early 30's went so far as to say that Moscow professors were having trouble finding cases of manic-depression to demonstrate to their pupils. This is very likely a rhetorical exaggeration. However, estimates published by Landis and Page [35] suggest that the rate of incidence in this country may well be double that of Russia. They refer to a report coming from

[35] *Op. cit.*, p. 115.

Kiev in 1935 from which it appears that "more than 5 per cent" of the "hospitalized insane are manic-depressive cases." The equivalent figure for our hospitals is about 12 per cent. This difference may reflect the beneficent influence of a lessened emphasis on personal financial success as the measure of a man's social worth. This clue to possible prophylactic control of manic-depressive disorders is not devoid of psychiatric endorsement; for, according to Rosanoff,[36] "there is sufficient ground for assuming that if in the United States, or in any other country, the problem of *unemployment* were solved, *economic security* established for the masses, and *insurance against sickness and disability* provided, there would be a great reduction in the incidence of manic-depressive psychoses."

SECURITY AND MENTAL HYGIENE

As was just pointed out, there seems to be a close relationship between jeopardized socio-economic security and manic-depressive disorder. Although the importance of *security* for the promotion of mental health will be elaborated upon in Part IV, it may facilitate understanding of the preceding sections to outline some of the ramifications of the concept as it bears upon the functional psychoses.

From the standpoint of the individual, the maintenance of emotional security is of central importance for his mental health. This kind of inner security involves two related but somewhat differing aspects of personality. They have to do with what might be called *self-respect* as the one aspect and social *status* as the other. These overlap, of course; but analysis reveals them to be not altogether identical. One is an outgrowth of affect hunger and the other is more a function of our longing for prestige. Violation of the one is likely to engender feelings of guilt and violation of the other feelings of inferiority, of humiliation, or of embarrassment. The child craves its mother's affection as well as its mother's admiration. Even as adults most of us want to be both liked and admired by others. In many respects these are independent variables. All of us know people we like but do not admire and others whom we admire but do not like. There are people who respect Hitler for his

---

[36] Rosanoff, A. J., *Manual of Psychiatry and Mental Hygiene,* 7th Edition, New York, John Wiley & Sons, Inc., 1938, p. 609.

diplomatic and political exploits, but who loathe him as a man. And many a parent of a prodigal son continues to love the boy long after the last vestige of potential respect for him has vanished.

Complete emotional security calls for due attention to both these personal needs: the need for love and affection and the need for status of some kind. Our *self-esteem* is a function of the adequacy with which these two needs are being satisfied. (There may be some question about the suitability of the terminology being employed here, but there is little to be gained by attacking it. It is unimportant just what terms are selected, provided the dynamics of the psychological factors being described are understood and appreciated.) In other words, self-esteem involves both self-respect and social status. A student who fails to graduate from the university may suffer a loss of self-esteem. If his failure was due to a violation of the institution's honor system, his suffering will entail guilt feelings and a concomitant loss of self-respect. On the other hand, should his failure be due to inability to pass his courses despite conscientious effort, his suffering will involve more of a feeling of chagrin or humiliation and — in the ideal case — no feelings of guilt. His friends will feel sorry for him and will continue to like him even though, in his opinion, they may regard themselves as superior just because they are the possessors of academic degrees. The difference is the difference between wounded pride and a guilty conscience. For complete emotional health the individual has to be reasonably secure with respect to his ability to maintain the integrity of his self-esteem. This means no serious threat either to his status or to his self-respect. To put this a little differently: freedom from the threat of functional disturbance involves the inner security that prevails when one's sentiment of self-regard — one's self-esteem — is undergirded by confidence in one's moral strength and social standing.[37]

In terms of this analysis it should be clear that the schizophrenic disturbance is more a consequence of damaged self-respect while

---

[37] It may be of interest to point out that this general view in some respects constitutes a fusion of Freudian and Adlerian approaches to the troubled personality. Freud, it will be recalled, tended to search for the root of the trouble in sex maladjustments, guilt feelings, a protesting conscience, or some vagary of what he termed the Œdipus complex. Adler, on the other hand, preferred to probe into matters of balked ambition, real or imagined physical handicaps, humiliating experiences, or some vagary of what he called the *inferiority complex*.

the manic-depressive upheaval is more a consequence of balked prestige. Furthermore, the very fact that so commonly a given personal conflict involves both sets of factors may explain why psychiatrists are often uncertain as to whether a given patient is to be diagnosed as a victim of schizophrenia or a victim of manic-depressive psychosis. It may also serve to explain the reason for the " mixed type " of the latter psychosis mentioned in Chapter 4.

At all events, if this analysis is sound, then it ought to be possible to ward off psychotic breakdown by training people to cope with situations calculated to disturb their emotional security. The hypothetical nature of this statement should not be overlooked. As we have already indicated, the mental hygienist cannot yet prove that he can reduce the incidence of schizophrenia by pointing to an actual record of accomplishment in this respect. The same applies to the prevention of manic-depressive disorders. Prophylactic efforts ought consequently to be viewed more as promising leads than as tested techniques. It would be more accurate to say that we have *hopes* of being able to prevent these disorders. This is different from saying that at last we are *confident* of our ability to teach people how to bring up their children so as to render them immune to functional psychoses.

Since we are not yet able to justify these teachings in terms of their *proven* prophylactic value, it might be better not to claim too much for them. As matters stand these teachings can be justified in terms of common sense contributions to human welfare. Parents can be urged to cater to the child's need for emotional security in order to promote the happiness of the child. Similarly, and for the same reason teachers, coaches, and club leaders engaged in the task of helping children develop skills and attitudes conducive to the re-enforcement of self-respect merit the approval of mental hygiene. Training the youngster to accept defeat without brooding self-recriminations and without recourse to alibis and self-deceiving projections is good mental hygiene training. Training him to be a gracious winner mindful of the courteous respect to be accorded less fortunate competitors is good mental hygiene training. Training him to prefer genuine effort to wishful fantasy is good mental hygiene training. Training him to face his personal problems honestly and intelligently is good mental hygiene training. Training him to be a socially effective and likable citizen is good mental hygiene training. These kinds of training are good not merely because they typify the educational implications of the conflict theory. They are good because, if successful, they will bolster morale and contribute to the joy of living. If, as we hope, they will also prevent functional mental disease, so much the better. But even if the future should demonstrate this to have been a vain hope, still, in terms of meliorative mental hygiene, these kinds of training will nevertheless continue to be good mental hygiene training.

PREVENTING PARANOIA

Consideration of the possibility of preventing paranoia will serve to emphasize and clarify the distinctions just introduced. In some respects the behavior of the paranoid patient reminds one of the behavior of a poor loser in golf or tennis or some other sport. He is convinced that he has not gotten a square deal; the officials are prejudiced against him; in reality he is a better player than the victorious opponent, but " if the umpire is crooked, what can you expect? " Here we can note the acrimonious attitude, the delusion of persecution and the beginnings of a delusion of superiority or grandeur along with a definite tendency to project the blame for failure from the self to outside sources. It seems as if the paranoid patient had failed to learn to be a good sport. He takes defeat or the threat of defeat so seriously that to keep his self-respect intact he has to build up a delusional system. Or, in some cases, it seems as if the chief trouble centers around erotic desires of an illicit nature. To acknowledge these as his desires would damage the paranoid's self-esteem. Accordingly he spurns these as his by attributing such libidinous desires to his " enemies." This is the familiar mechanism of projection. How can such warped thinking be prevented? Is it enough to say, " by training children to think straight and to be honest with themselves "?

Quite obviously, to the extent that one can teach such matters, children ought to be induced to think straight and to foster attitudes of fine sportsmanship. They ought to be given the opportunity to assimilate wholesome, self-ennobling attitudes toward sex so that guilt feelings will have as little to do with the subject of sex as with the subject of money. The control of lust, like the control of greed, is a matter of learning. Whether a child develops into a pervert or a crook depends on the training it receives. In terms of individual and social welfare it is thus important to include straight thinking, good sportsmanship, healthy sex attitudes, the habit of honest self-appraisal and kindred non-paranoid traits among the educator's objectives. Indeed, even if there were no such disorder as paranoia, objectives of this kind would continue to merit endorsement. Stated differently: even if the incidence of paranoia should remain the same despite the earnest pursuit of these objectives, this disappointing result would not divest the objectives of their educational value. Their attainment would continue to promote mental health by lubricating social relationships, facilitating the resolution of personal problems, and inhibiting the common tendency to blame others for our shortcomings. A given practice may fail to ward off disease and still be a hygienic practice, provided it contributes to the joy of living, the enhancement of morale, and the elimination of petty irritations — or major ones. In other words, the educational objectives in question can be justified independently of their value for prophylactic mental hygiene.

TEMPERAMENT AND MENTAL DISEASE

The general nature of the factors to be considered in a prophylactic campaign directed at the functional psychoses has now been outlined. In connection with each psychosis the possibility of the campaign's failure was not overlooked. The main reason for the absence of an attitude of dogmatic assurance of success had to do with our inability to demonstrate a significant reduction in the incidence of these disorders on the basis of American hospital statistics. Only the evidence coming from Russia encouraged belief in the attainability of the campaign's objectives; for manic-depressive disorder seemed to be on the wane in that country. However, in addition to this main reason there was a less obtrusive one reflected in our discussion. This had to do with the recognition of a possible factual basis for the contention of those students of the problem who lay so much stress on a constitutional predisposition to functional disturbance. Even such an ardent advocate of the conflict theory as Kanner, it will be recalled, wrote that " heredity plays an important part " in the etiology of schizophrenia.

Often this appeal to constitutional factors takes the form of asserting that a given disorder is the outcome of some particular temperament. The literature is replete with references to a *cyclo-thymic* temperament as characteristic of manic-depressive patients or a *schizothymic* one as giving rise to schizophrenic trends. Some psychiatrists attribute paranoia to some ineradicable constitutional factor they designate as a *paranoid* temperament. Their " clinical experience " teaches them that the paranoid patient is temperamentally disposed to develop into a humorless, suspicious, grimly earnest type of personality.

If this approach to mental disease in terms of temperamental predisposition is sound, then the mental hygienist has to face it. He must recognize that the import of personal conflicts will vary with the temperamental make-up of the individual. In some instances he may even have to consider the desirability of changing a person's temperament. Whether temperament can be changed in any radical way is a moot question. The whole problem of the nature and modifiability of temperament is still largely unsolved. Whether a person's temperament is altogether a function of hereditary constitution or largely a function of training and experience continues to be a debatable issue. Under the circumstances the mental hygienist ought to guard himself against the temptation to disregard unsettled technical issues consideration of which might be likely to shake his confidence in the complete adequacy of his projected prophylactic campaigns. Neither ought he go to the other extreme and magnify the difficulties to insuperable proportions. In fact, when it comes to these allegedly hereditary or constitutional barriers to mental hygiene efforts it might be wise to follow the advice of the psychiatrist who stated that the following quotation from Buckle's *History of Civilization in England* " ought to be ingraved in every clinic and on every writer's desk " : [38]

We often hear of hereditary talents, hereditary virtues, but whoever will critically examine the evidence will find that we have no proof of their existence. The way in which they are commonly proved is in the highest degree illogical, the usual course being for writers to collect instances of some mental peculiarity found in a parent and in his child, and then to infer that the peculiarity was bequeathed. By this mode of reasoning we might demonstrate any proposition; since in all large fields of inquiry there are a sufficient number of empirical coincidences to make a plausible case in favor of whatever view a man chooses to

[38] Myerson, A., *The Inheritance of Mental Diseases*, Baltimore, Williams & Wilkins Company, 1925, p. 52.

advocate. But this is not the way in which truth is discovered; and we ought to inquire not only how many instances there are of hereditary talents, etc., but how many instances there are of such qualities not being hereditary. Until something of this sort is attempted we can know nothing about the matter inductively; while until physiology and chemistry are much more advanced we can know nothing about it deductively.

These considerations ought to prevent us from receiving statements . . . and many other books which positively affirm the existence of hereditary madness and hereditary suicide; and the same remark applies to hereditary disease.

Concluding Comments

Henry Thomas Buckle died in 1862. His demand for suspension of judgment on technical questions until research gives us the relevant data upon which to base confident action thus goes back many decades. Although considerable research has been undertaken since his day, it is altogether clear that with respect to our knowledge of the basic causes of the functional psychoses we need still more research. We are still fumbling and still groping and still guessing — often in the dogmatic manner of Buckle's contemporaries. But taken by and large, progress has been made. Our insight into the nature of the problems and our appreciation of their complexity is more profound than that of the " alienists " of earlier generations. And considering how little money society has devoted to the requisite research, those responsible for what progress has been made are all the more deserving of our gratitude. Furthermore, it may not be amiss to point out in this connection that there may be more than an accidental relationship between the previously mentioned encouraging reports of reduction of some types of mental disease in Russia and that country's willingness to support scientific research. At all events it may be pertinent to reflect upon the possible significance of what Bernal,[39] a British investigator, has to report on the subject. According to his figures, the " Budget for Science in 1934 " in Russia was 1,000,000,000 rubles or " at least 1 per cent of the national income at the time." This was relatively ten times the amount being expended by Britain for the same purpose and three times as much as our country

[39] Bernal, J. D., *The Social Functions of Science,* The Macmillan Company, New York, 1939, p. 224.

was devoting to the cause of research. Maybe, after we too start laying aside 1 per cent of our national income for the general purpose of encouraging continued and systematic study of our scientific problems, future generations of mental hygienists will be able to substitute the certainty of touch that comes with the accumulation of tested knowledge for the present fumbling, the present groping, and the present guessing.[40] Without a solid foundation of such tested knowledge the prophylactic campaigns of the mental hygienist will continue to be more of a tribute to his earnest hopes than a record of positive accomplishment.

[40] Such fumbling, groping, and guessing along with controversy and differences of opinion among the experts, are consequences of the complexity and difficulty of the scientific quest for understanding of mental disease. In this connection it may be of interest to note that in the *Epilogue* to his scholarly survey of the history of psychiatry, Dr. Gregory Zilboorg declares that " psychiatry still lags behind medicine as to the certainty of its task, the sphere of its activity, and the methods to be pursued." He is also of the opinion that " after more than 2000 years of medical history, neither psychiatry nor the public has yet reached any understanding of what mental illness is " and that " our ignorance still outweighs however much we may appear to know." Furthermore, he reminds us that " there is still confusion as to what a psychological reaction is, and medicine and psychiatry and various schools of psychiatry still do not see eye to eye on this subject." (Zilboorg, G., *A History of Medical Psychology*, W. W. Norton & Co., New York, 1941, pp. 519 and 520.)

9... *PROPHYLACTIC ASPECTS OF NEUROTIC DISORDERS*

IN THE PRECEDING CHAPTERS IT WAS QUITE EVIDENT THAT THE extent to which the conflict theory serves to account for the functional psychoses is still subject to debate. This uncertainty is not nearly so manifest in the case of neurotic disorders. Practically all students of the neuroses are agreed that conflict of some sort accounts for the morbid doubts and compulsions of the psychasthenic, the chronic fatigue of the neurasthenic, and the varied assortment of somatic anomalies of the hysteric. Just how conflict results in such disorders is still a somewhat unsettled issue in the sense that adherents of different schools of psychology are still engaged in controversy regarding the details; but that conflict constitutes the focus of neurotic disability is a point everybody seems willing to concede. Accordingly, the task of the mental hygienist interested in preventing this kind of disability resolves itself into a study of the factors responsible for conflicts and the search for suitable means of coping with them. The task is complex and the search is arduous. In fact the present chapter will be largely concerned with laying the groundwork for the job. All the remaining chapters will have a bearing on the long quest for means of efficient prevention and control.

NEUROSES AND EMOTIONAL DISTORTION

The prevention of neurotic reactions may be viewed as the equivalent of preventing abnormal emotional attitudes. To a large extent the neurotic individual's difficulties center around the general theme of fear. Words like anxiety, apprehension, worry, and uneasiness occur over and over again in discussions of the neuroses. There is also much talk of the bodily signs of fear: nausea, indigestion, lack of appetite, diarrhea, palpitation of the heart, trembling muscles, cold sweat, etc. In addition one is struck by the frequent references to such concomitants of fear as doubt, indecision, feelings of helplessness, of impending doom, of loss of confidence, and even of panic.

Chapter 4 contained a discussion of the distinction between nervousness and neuroticism. It was pointed out that these terms are by no means identical in meaning; since the nervousness or agitation of the convict being strapped into the electric chair, to revert to our earlier example, is very different from the panic of a neurotic when he smells roasted peanuts. The one kind of nervousness strikes one as normal and understandable, while the other seems uncalled for and bizarre. The one is a normal fear reaction and the other is a neurotic fear reaction. In the latter case we are dealing with an obvious distortion of emotional reactivity.

What produces such distortions and how they can be prevented are questions of extreme interest to the mental hygienist; for, as has already been mentioned, neurotic disturbances are far more common than the statistics for first admissions to psychiatric hospitals indicate. The majority of neurotics are never hospitalized and not infrequently, when those who do reach a hospital clinic because of the prominence of the physical signs of their underlying fears, the very prominence of such signs — the indigestion or the cardiac disturbance — may lead the unwary clinician astray. The resulting mistaken diagnosis will conceal the neurotic etiology. Every veteran in the field of psychological medicine knows of such mistakes. He knows of colleagues whose lack of psychological insight caused them to suggest drugs, tonics, and even surgery for what was basically an acute fear reaction. For adequate recognition, treatment, and prevention of neuroses it is necessary to secure the requisite psychological insight. It is necessary to remember that the victim of a neurosis is often not aware of the fact that distorted emotion is responsible for his troubles. He fails to realize that his insomnia, loss of weight, and lack of appetite — the symptoms of which he complains and concerning which he consults a physician — are in any way related to his secret fear of the vitriolic tongue of a nagging wife. And the latter fear may be prompted by a more obscure fear that the nagging wife may eventually discover a basis in fact for her suspicions of infidelity on his part. Such a patient will regale his doctor with minute descriptions of the symptoms of disease, and be altogether silent on the subject of his fears; because he honestly believes they can have no bearing on his symptoms. In this sense the patient himself is sometimes partially responsible for misleading the diagnostician. But this constitutes a digression. For the time being it is more important to realize the general bearing of emotional control on the control of neurotic manifestations.

THE CONCEPT OF REDINTEGRATION

During the First World War there was much discussion of " shell-shocked " soldiers. In these cases there was loss of control of all sorts of bodily functions, not as a result of actual injury by shell fragments but as a result of the panic occasioned by the sight and sound or thought of bursting shells or the general apprehension of impending danger. Fright showed itself in terms of the symptoms already discussed in connection with hysteria : paralysis of muscles, loss of vision, spasms of the digestive tube. In some cases the soldiers would collapse and remain in a stuporous condition for hours. Others would reveal tremors, speech disturbances, and other signs of motor agitation. Obviously disabilities such as these rendered the victims unfit for active military service. They had to be hospitalized both in France and in England. Many of them were sent home to a military hospital in this country. This gave the American psychologist, H. L. Hollingworth, who was an Army officer at the time, an opportunity to study these cases of so-called shell-shock. The results of this study were subsequently embodied in a book [1] which developed a theory of neurotic disorder that will serve as a stimulating point of departure for analysis of the psychological factors involved.

The chief problem for Hollingworth was not the fact of the original breakdown as the soldier was moving up to the front in France. After all, widespread bodily commotion is too commonplace an accompaniment of terror to occasion astonishment. Nor can one regard the reaction of fright to the threat of being blown to bits as an abnormal reaction. But what was astonishing and somewhat abnormal was the behavior of some of these soldiers after they had seemingly recovered from the overt symptoms of the " shock " and were safe in the security of the base hospital far from the scene of battle. This hospital, located at Plattsburg, New York, afforded the patients an ocean of safety from the hazards of combat. Nevertheless, it sometimes happened that an intrinsically

---

[1] Hollingworth, H. L., *The Psychology of Functional Neuroses*, D. Appleton & Company, New York, 1920.

harmless event like the sudden sight of a uniformed officer or the backfiring of a passing motorcycle would precipitate a return of the shock symptoms. The recovered patient would once again be rendered the victim of a mild panic and would suffer a relapse and be unable to talk or would stammer or rush down the company street in a frenzy of excitement. Hollingworth's problem was to explain the nature of such a relapse.

The solution proposed by Hollingworth was based on the concept of _redintegration._ This term had been introduced into psychology about the middle of the last century by Sir William Hamilton. As used originally, the word was intended to designate the familiar memory process by which a small " reminder " of some prior experience serves to recall the totality of that experience. For example, forty years after her wedding a woman rummaging through an old trunk may come across a yellowed announcement of the marriage. This bit of paper may then suffice to bring back a welter of details: the name of the dressmaker who sewed the wedding gown, the argument with her mother about the guest list, the proud look on her father's face as he marched down the aisle, the usher whose collar was too tight, the helpfulness of the minister's wife, and many other items connected with the ceremony. The paper, in other words, reinstated or redintegrated the past. A part or fragment of an original experience was enough to revive the whole of that experience.

Hollingworth modified this original meaning of the word _redintegration_. He used it to refer to the fact that people often _respond_ to a fragment of an original experience as they previously responded to the experience in its entirety. For Hamilton redintegration meant that a part may reinstate the whole, while Hollingworth changed it to mean that a part may induce us to act _as if_ the whole were present. The act may express itself in words, deeds, emotions, or in any two or in all three of these modes of expression. Thus, in terms of the example just introduced, the " reminder " of her wedding may — without recalling the multiplicity of ideas associated with the ceremony — cause the woman to mumble " I do " or to tense her muscles as if she were dodging an avalanche of rice or to experience a quickened sense of excitement. Behavior has its verbal, gestural, and affective aspects as this example illustrates.

It is necessary to realize that what we call " having an experience " involves more than mere observation. It is not solely an affair of seeing and hearing and otherwise noting external events. The way in which we react to such events is just as much part of the experience as the sensory impressions which stand out so vividly as we tell about it later. In technical language, experience is *both* an afferent or sensory as well as an efferent or motor process. This unity of experience is destroyed when we analyze it into parts for purposes of psychological analysis. In analogous fashion the unity of the body is destroyed when the anatomist dissects it. However, analysis and dissection are the means of giving us enriched insight into the subject being studied. We have a better understanding of the subject because of such examination. But unless analysis is followed by synthesis and dissection by conceptual reconstruction, the understanding will be inadequate and warped. The enterprise of scientific examination must start with a relative unity and finish with a relative unity. The goal is not to understand the parts, but to understand the whole as a dynamic unit. This, in brief, is what the advocates of configurational psychology keep reminding us and this is also what Hollingworth's concept of redintegration implies. To this extent his modification of the word's meaning constitutes an advance over Hamilton's original usage. Hamilton was restricting it to refer to the sensory aspect of experience; but Hollingworth applied it to experience as an organized whole involving a dynamic interplay not only of sights, sounds, smells, and pressures but words, actions, and emotions as well. For those who prefer physiological descriptions this can be paraphrased by saying that experience is not limited to the mere having of sensory impressions, but also includes changes in the larynx, the striped musculature, and the visceral mechanisms.

As applied to the case of the neurotic soldier the theory of redintegration includes the totality of impressions and reactions involved in the original shock experience. The apprehensive soldier, becoming more and more tense as his company moves closer to the scene of action, finds himself talking with a corporal, who happens to be leaning on his motorcycle, while the troops are resting in an abandoned French village. Across the road an officer is adjusting his holster. The soldier also chances to note the flight of a wild duck silhouetted against the sky. At that moment the garden wall in back of the soldier collapses with a loud crash. Both he and the corporal are covered with debris. Let us assume that the corporal is merely startled while the soldier is shocked. Under these conditions the experience in question will be very different for the two men. The corporal will scramble to his feet unhurt, while the soldier in his panic will be convinced of the seriousness of his injuries. His pounding heart, trembling muscles, feelings of general weakness, along with his inability to cry out will all be very real to him. His shock experience will thus involve something more than a reaction of disruptive fear to the sound of the crash. The medley of sensory details comprising the setting in which the crash took place will also be embodied in the experience. These details may not be logically related to the shock; but they are nevertheless of *psychological* relevance. On a subsequent occasion — this is the crux of Hollingworth's concept — the sight of a wild duck or the sight of a corporal leaning on his motorcycle or of an officer adjusting his holster may suffice to touch off the symptoms of panic. Stated in more general terms : any detail of an earlier experience *may* suffice to instigate the consequents of that experience. Such a redintegrative pattern does not presuppose any necessary recall of the original experience. The instigating detail is followed by the kind of reaction made to the original experience just as if the latter were being relived in its totality.

This approach to the neurotic reaction can be rendered even more plausible by citing a few familiar illustrations of redintegrative sequences from daily life. A mother may respond to the sight of the lock of hair pasted in the " Baby Book " with tender feelings, cooing words, and an impulse to cuddle a child — and this may happen even though the original possessor of the hair is now a bald major serving at the front. To take another example : even though we are not thinking of visiting the dentist's office, the mere sound of a dental drill or the mere whiff of oil of cloves may suffice to produce an attenuated version of our original response to the pain of having a dentist's instrument touch an exposed nerve. There may be incipient nausea, vocal protest, and an actual shudder both in response to the original pain as well as to the " reminder " of the pain.

Many of our likes and dislikes are thus to be regarded as products of the redintegrative process. It should also be noted that the item or detail touching off the attraction or revulsion need not be recognized as a " reminder " of a given experience in order for the redintegrated reaction to be touched off ; hence the neurotic soldier may honestly be unable to account for his neurotic behavior. He may be unable to isolate the significant factor from the new setting in which it has become embedded. In this sense he reacts to it " unconsciously " or without explicit awareness of its existence. A simple illustration of such " unconscious " or implicit observation is that of the man who confessed disliking a certain Indian rug the first time he saw it. He was unable to account for his dislike and was perplexed by it, because ordinarily he was an admirer of Indian art. Not until a friend called his attention to the fact that part of the rug's pattern resembled a swastika did he, a refugee from Nazi Germany, perceive a relationship between his present esthetic judgment and his old violent antipathy for an oppressive political regime.

Some students of psychology might be inclined to classify these examples of redintegration as conditioned reflexes. There is no serious objection to this classification, provided they permit the phrase *conditioned reflex* to mean no more than a certain technique of changing reactions by means of the laboratory technique developed by Pavlov. Actually, of course, the examples in question are too complex both neurologically and psychologically to be called reflexes. If the term *conditioned response* were substituted, the emphasis on conditioning as a process would be less objectionable. It might also be well to modify the concept of conditioning to be broad enough to include the *totality* of sensory impressions influencing the organism while undergoing training. In addition, the totality of responses to these impressions ought also to be included in the concept. It is precisely because redintegration avoids the atomistic connotations of the phrase *conditioned reflex* that it constitutes a better designation for the processes giving rise to neurotic reactions. In brief, as was just indicated, provided the concept of conditioning is divested of its early suggestion of a mechanical linkage of isolated " reflexes," there will be no great harm done by using it as a convenient synonym for redintegration.[2] In this way those who have become enamored of Pavlov's approach to problems of learning will not have to sacrifice their customary descriptive vocabulary.

CONSTITUTIONAL FACTORS

Although neurotic reactions are acquired or learned in the sense of being products of redintegration or conditioning, both clinical observation as well as animal experimentation indicate differences in the facility with which such learning occurs. In other words, there is evidence to the effect that constitutional factors play a role in the etiology of neurotic behavior. Any discussion of suggestions for preventing neuroses must consequently take such factors into account.

Adherents of very different schools of psychology seem to have been impressed by the existence of a predisposition to neurotic behavior. Alfred Adler [3] conceived of what he variously described as " organ-inferiority " and " constitutional inferiority " as the biological basis for the emergence of neurotic character traits. And Hollingworth concluded that the neurotic " is characterized . . . by a constitutional proneness toward responses "[4] of the redintegrative type. For him " this predisposition toward redintegrative conduct . . . constitutes or characterizes what may conveniently be called the psychoneurotic constitution." Furthermore, Pavlov [5] also reported constitutional differences in his experimental animals in terms of which he endeavored to account for differences among " neurotic " as well as among " normal " dogs. He even posited the existence of different " types of nervous systems " among them and conceived of some of his animals as " specialists " in inhibition and others as " specialists " in excitation and still others as predisposed to exhibit a balance between inhibition and excitation. Nor is this recognition of constitutional fac-

---

[2] It should be clearly understood, however, that Hollingworth does not regard redintegration as a synonym for conditioning. (*Op. cit.,* p. 159.) For him redintegration is both broader than and different from simple conditioning. Cf. Hollingworth, H. L., *Psychology: Its Facts and Principles,* D. Appleton & Co., New York, 1928, pp. 56–63.

[3] Adler, A., *The Neurotic Constitution,* Moffat, Yard & Company, New York, 1916, pp. 1–34.

[4] Hollingworth, H. L., *Psychology of Functional Neuroses,* p. 159.

[5] Pavlov, I. P., *Lectures on Conditioned Reflexes,* Liveright Publishing Corporation, New York, 1928, pp. 370–378.

tors overlooked by contemporary students of the problem; for, in a recently published volume, Karen Horney [6] states that " neurotic trends " are the consequence of " the combined effect of given temperamental and environmental influences " and she actually uses the phrase " constitutional factors " in referring to the former influences. She also grants that less is known about such factors than about the environmental ones. In fact, she fails to elaborate upon them; because, as she puts it, they are not " susceptible of change."

The genesis of neurotic behavior, according to Horney and these other writers, is thus not altogether an exclusive product of learning or unfortunate experience. Neurotic behavior, it is often maintained, can be recognized by signs of emotional agitation. More specifically, such agitation may involve nail-biting, temper tantrums, stuttering or other speech difficulties, and loss of control of bladder functions. The emotionally disturbed child, they also remind us, is likely to be a thumb-sucker. Of course, if the previously mentioned distinction between nervousness and neuroticism is sound, then symptoms of this kind need not be positive evidence of an underlying neurotic conflict. Furthermore, some of these items of behavior may sometimes signify nothing more than inadequate home training. Failure to control bladder functions, or what is technically called *enuresis*, may thus mean neither nervousness nor neuroticism. Nevertheless, there have been investigators who allege that such items of behavior are to be attributed to constitutional factors. For example, some years ago Michaels and Goodman,[7] on the basis of a statistical study of the incidence of temper tantrums, speech impediments, nail-biting, thumb-sucking, and enuresis, concluded there was evidence of an " innate predisposition to this type of symptom-complex." The evidence was by no means decisive and the numerical data lacked

[6] Horney, K., *Self-Analysis,* W. W. Norton & Co., Inc., New York, 1942, p. 43.
[7] Michaels, J. J., and Goodman, S. E., " Incidence and Intercorrelations of Enuresis and other Neuropathic Traits in so-called Normal Children," *Amer. J. of Orthopsychiatry,* 1934, *4,* pp. 79–106.
Incidentally, with respect to the diagnostic significance of thumb-sucking it might be well to read the article by D. M. Levy in the same volume of this journal. He supplies rather persuasive experimental evidence to the effect that this alleged sign of a " neuropathic trait " is entirely a matter of regulating the duration of each nursing period and has nothing to do with " innate predispositions." (Cf. Levy, D. M., " Experiments on the Sucking Reflex and Social Behavior of Dogs," *Amer. J. of Orthopsychiatry,* 1934, *4,* pp. 203–224.)

statistical reliability so that the authors did not claim to have *established* such a conclusion. Instead they contented themselves with saying that their " findings " caused them " to favor " such an interpretation.

At all events it is pertinent to call attention to the existence of this type of approach to problems of the neuroses. It will be remembered that appeal to constitutional factors disturbed our efforts to work out a simple and clear-cut prophylactic program with reference to the psychoses. Now we find similar barriers standing in the way of a facile disposition of what at first inspection seems like a simple question: " How can neuroses be prevented? " In the case of psychotic disturbances it was found impossible to reach a final verdict on the existence and importance of the presumed constitutional factors. The situation is a little different with respect to the neurotic disturbances; for recent experimental work with animals renders the contention of Hollingworth, Adler, Pavlov, and Horney affirming the reality of such constitutional factors in the etiology of neurotic behavior more plausible than might otherwise be the case. For the time being we shall not be so much concerned with the conflict aspect of neurotic behavior as with the emotional aspect. In other words, for our immediate purposes it will suffice to ask whether a tendency to emotional agitation can be inherited and if so, what this implies for mental hygiene in the way of training for emotional control.

EMOTIONALITY IN THE RAT

A stimulating attack on the problem of emotionality is to be found in the work of animal psychologists. Some of their results are of significance for the mental hygienist because of the more rigorous control which can be introduced in working with animals as compared to experimental work with human beings. Of course one must guard against indiscriminate and uncritical application of results from the human realm to the animal and *vice versa*.[8] The uncritical attribution of human traits to animals constitutes the well-known fallacy of *anthropomorphism*. The converse fallacy of an uncritical reading of animal nature into distinctively

[8] On the question of the legitimacy and value of such application, see Katz, D., *Animals and Men*, Longmans, Green & Co., New York, 1937, pp. 230–258; Cook, S. W., " A Survey of Methods Used to Produce ' Experimental Neurosis,' " *Amer. J. of Psychiatry*, 1939, *95*, pp. 1259–1276.

human nature is called *zoomorphism*. However, provided these tendencies to error are avoided, there are valuable hints for the mental hygienist to be gleaned from the field of animal psychology.

In the light of recent studies [9] of emotionality in the white rat the task of the mental hygienist appears to be somewhat more complex than is ordinarily realized. This applies very definitely to the specific task of deciding whether timidity is invariably a handicap to the achievement of mental health. As was seen in our earlier discussion of shy children, most mental hygienists have tended to be somewhat concerned about introvertive, unaggressive, easily scared youngsters. They regarded more extrovertive, mildly aggressive, courageous children as better mental hygiene risks. Some reasons for being skeptical of this customary view have already been introduced.[10] Additional reasons come to the surface when certain theoretic questions are raised: Will the timid person be more upset emotionally in a situation of crisis than the person who ordinarily impresses others as a self-contained, unemotional man of action? Is it possible that people who seem poorly adjusted emotionally to situations of mild stress will be better adjusted than the average " normal " person to situations of extreme stress? Or to put some of these possibilities more concretely: Will the shy, easily intimidated group of young recruits, who tremble when the tough sergeant barks at them, be more likely to go to smash mentally in the excitement of active combat than a group of emotionally poised, seemingly thick-skinned recruits for whom a veteran sergeant's vitriolic vocabulary is more a source of amusement than of terror? Are the Dick Tracys of this world necessarily better adjusted emotionally than the Mr. Milquetoasts of this world? On the basis of experimental data about to be described, we shall venture to contend that when confronted with an acute emergency Milquetoast might be better

---

[9] The studies in question dealing with emotionality in the rat have been conducted by numerous investigators. For an excellent introduction to these studies as well as for adequate bibliographic references to the entire group of studies, see Martin, R. F., and Hall, C. S., " Emotional Behavior in the Rat," *J. of Comparative Psychol.,* 1941, *32,* pp. 191–204.

In referring to specific results reported by these numerous investigators we shall not give the original sources. Those interested in consulting the original articles will find the necessary bibliographic information in the report by Martin and Hall.

[10] See pp. 248–252.

equipped *physiologically* to cope with danger than the more re-sourceful Tracy; for Tracy might be having a convulsion while Milquetoast is still conscious and still running.

By means of selective breeding it has been possible to produce two strains of rats: an emotional strain and a non-emotional strain. The difference between the two strains shows itself in various ways. The emotional rats are more disturbed in a strange situation than the others. This disturbance is manifested by excretory reactions. (That fear influences bowel and bladder action even in human beings is too well known to require more than an incidental reminder.) C. S. Hall has demonstrated that in the rat measurement of such eliminative functions under stress of environmental strangeness constitutes " a reliable and valid test of emotionality." The investigator, M. M. Parker, has shown that when the degree of emotionality of one rat, as measured by amount excreted, is compared with other rats in a variety of situations calculated to arouse fear there is approximately the same degree of disturbance manifested by each of the animals in the different situations. The individual differences, in other words, are relatively constant. Still another investigator, F. Y. Billingslea, has checked on the general behavior of the two strains. His observations show the emotional group to be more timid than the other group. However, these more timid animals, while less aggressive, are nevertheless " more active and probably more persistent than the unemotional rats." [11] In addition to such temperamental differences there are differences in glandular equipment, the work of Yeakel and Rhodes having demonstrated that the non-emotional animals possess *smaller* thyroids, pituitaries, and adrenals than the other strain.[12] This is significant in view of the known relationship between the functioning of such glands and the organism's excitability and energy level.

Under ordinary conditions the timid rats seem to be less efficient than the aggressive group. Their timidity seems to interfere with

[11] Unless otherwise indicated all quotations are taken from the article by Martin and Hall mentioned in footnote 9.

[12] This result should not be interpreted to mean that all temperamental differences in human beings are exclusively due to glandular differences. The investigation of Yeakel and Rhodes was concerned with biologically pure strains. Examination of the endocrines of human beings has failed to reveal consistent differences in terms of emotional and other personality characteristics. Cf. Freeman, W., " Personality and the Endocrines; A Study Based upon 1400 Quantitative Necropsies," *Annals of Internal Medicine,* 1935, *9,* pp. 444–450.

their adjustments to a maze-learning situation. At all events E. E. Anderson has found them inferior to the non-emotional strain in this kind of performance. One would expect them to be more profoundly upset by almost any kind of shock and would anticipate greater disorganization among them the more acute the shock. But this expectation was not realized when the matter was put to experimental test. Martin and Hall found that the timid strain is less disorganized by such acute stimulation than the non-emotional strain. In their experiment they took 50 rats of the latter group and 40 of the emotional group and bombarded them with the current of air coming from the kind of device used to inflate tires. This type of air-blast is known to produce a devastating effect on the behavior of rats. Some investigators have even called the result an " experimental neurosis." Others have used such descriptive phrases as " epileptic attacks," " convulsive seizures," and " running attacks." There can be no doubt about the effectiveness of the air-blast as a means of inducing emotional crises in the rat. Probably the least controversial designation for the reaction is to call it an *audiogenic seizure*.

In noting the kinds of reactions precipitated by the air-blast Martin and Hall divided them into two categories: running attacks and convulsive seizures. As their descriptions show, the convulsive seizure constitutes a far more disruptive panic than the running attack. The latter is characterized by impulsive running of a blind sort. The animal may scurry at random over the floor or dash around in circular fashion, " pivoting within the length of its body." Often the animal indulges in " scrabbling." This term refers to agitation of the feet during which they move rapidly even though the animal's body fails to move rapidly. It is akin to moving forward while " running in place." The running or scrabbling is of short duration. After about 10 seconds the animal comes to a sudden halt and remains immobile and tense. The animal is said to be in a " freeze." For a few minutes after the running attack the animal seems to be in a mild stupor: it may lie on its back in a relaxed, dazed condition. In fact, it may be so relaxed that the experimenter can mold its limbs in a manner reminiscent of the lead-pipe flexibility mentioned in our account of the symptoms of catatonia.

The so-called running attack is thus a manifestly serious upset.

However, the convulsive seizure is still more devastating. In fact it actually follows the running attack. Stated differently, the convulsive seizure is a running attack plus. The plus may take one of three forms. In one type the running becomes poorly coordinated and the animal keels over and remains rigid for about 10 seconds. Then it relaxes into a deep coma. Martin and Hall report that sometimes breathing is almost imperceptible during this phase. The comatose condition may last a few minutes after which the animal may slowly recover. In another type of convulsive reaction the animal fails to become relaxed. The running is followed by clonic convulsions which in turn may be followed by a stupor. The third type of seizure is manifested by less widespread clonic movements. Instead of generalized or diffuse agitation as in the preceding type there is more circumscribed or focalized agitation: the animal may stand on its hind feet while the front legs jerk spasmodically and rapidly and then the rat may topple over backwards. Sometimes these animals show a curious kind of locomotion: they move spasmodically and then stop in a freeze and then hop convulsively. As in the other two types these animals also become stuporous. If the experimenter touches the animal while it is in this stupor, " the rat leaps like some mechanical robot." Incidentally, the convulsive seizures were observed by some psychiatrists and they noted a close resemblance between them and epileptic attacks in human beings.

The results of the experiment showed that the timid rats were less seriously affected by the air-blasts than the aggressive ones. In fact, there were a total of 335 attacks of both kinds produced: 238 running attacks and 97 convulsive seizures. The rats of the emotional group had only 5 of these convulsive seizures, while the other 92 occurred among those of the non-emotional strain. And of the running attacks there were 113 among the timid animals and 125 among the others. Under these conditions of severe stimulation the rats of the emotional strain made a better adjustment than the unemotional ones. Their attacks were both fewer in number and less devastating in nature.

Some interesting possibilities confront the interpreter of findings like these. It is obviously incorrect to regard either of these two groups of animals as better adjusted than the other with respect to all environmental difficulties. The non-emotional strain seems better able to cope with mildly disturbing situations. However, when the disturbance reaches emergency proportions, then the timid group seems better able to adapt to it. This might mean that a low threshold of sensitivity to emotion-arousing stimuli is a handicap or an advantage depending on the intensity of stimulation. The slogan " always keep calm " might require some qualification in order to be an acceptable mental hygiene slogan. The " calm " animals were the ones who were less able to avoid panic than the " excitable " ones when the air-blast stimulus was introduced. Martin and Hall suggest that emotionality might serve as a " safety valve " for the emotional strain. Their channels of discharge for the energy of emotional release are more open and more ready to function than the corresponding mechanisms of the nonemotional strain. Because the latter animals do not possess " effective means of discharging tension " they are more likely to " break down under very strong stimulation when the tension accumulates beyond a certain point." The experimenters point out that such " reversals " of adaptability can also be observed among human beings. In fact, their comments on this point have such obvious mental hygiene implications that the following quotation merits careful study: [13]

There are many illustrations of similar dramatic reversals in emotional stability among human beings under the impact of intense " press." A " neurotic " person may respond with calmness, efficiency and dispatch when a real crisis occurs. The " strong, silent man " surprisingly goes all to pieces when beset by frustration. Many a suicide is unexpected because the person taking his life has given no prior indication of serious emotional instability. The timid soul may muster considerable fearlessness in the face of extreme danger.

To revert to our earlier figure of speech : there may be occasions when Mr. Milquetoast will astonish onlookers by behaving like Dick Tracy and sometimes the Dick Tracys may find themselves playing a Milquetoast role.

AUDIOGENIC SEIZURES AND THE CONCEPT OF NEUROSIS

If our earlier distinction between nervousness and neuroticism be accepted as valid, then it would probably be incorrect to regard

[13] Martin and Hall, *op. cit.*, p. 202.

the rat's panic-stricken behavior in response to the air-blast as neurotic behavior. The audiogenic seizure is neither a consequence of learning nor the product of an inner conflict. Unlike the neurotic soldier, the agitated rat is not torn between the duty of facing danger and the strong desire to scurry to a place of safety. Its agitation is more akin to the distress manifested by human beings when *startled* by explosive sounds like a clap of thunder or by irritating ones like a siren blown directly into one's ear. The rasping screech produced by excessive pressure of chalk while writing on a blackboard is another instance of such an irritating, startle-stimulus. Our distress under these circumstances is not as devastating as the animal's reaction to the air-blast, but it is analogous to the extent that it is an unlearned reaction to an auditory stimulus. Moreover, it might well be that prolonged exposure to a rasping screech of an intense sort might render some people almost as frantic as an animal having a " running attack." [14]

Any excessively intense type of stimulation of an irritating kind when prolonged is calculated to precipitate disorganized, frantic behavior. Police officials, for example, have been known to resort to the maneuver of shining a very bright light into the eyes of a

---

[14] Entirely apart from the problem of neurotic conflicts, the influence of noise on mental health comes within the scope of the mental hygienist's interest. Noise is apt to be more than a nuisance; it may be a menace to bodily well-being, to efficiency and contentment. In a recent summary of the " harmful effects of noise," Best and Taylor cite evidence to show that intense and protracted sounds may injure the internal ear and that explosive ones may damage the ear drum and parts of the middle ear. They also point out that irritability, waste of energy, and " nervous strain " may be the consequences of exposure to noisy environments. Noise militates against the efficiency of workers engaged in tasks requiring some degree of attentive application such as mail sorting and typesetting. In one study it was found that noise produced a loss of from 50 to 60 per cent in the accuracy of workers engaged in a certain factory operation. In another study the efficiency of telephone operators was increased by reducing the amount of noise from 5 to 3.5 bels. The latter reduction in noise resulted in a 42 per cent reduction in wrong numbers. With respect to the physiological effects of noise the authors call attention to the following observations: noise may increase oxygen consumption by about 25 per cent for a person engaged in work like typing; it may increase heart action, speed up respiration, influence muscle tone, and raise the blood pressure. Noise may also influence the general disposition of a person. In one case referred to by Best and Taylor the " good nature " of an elderly clerk " became altered in an unaccountable way " when he was transferred from quiet to noisy surroundings. Once he was transferred back to his old office he became his old, kindly self. There can thus be no question that noise-abatement programs are to be viewed as contributions to the cause of mental hygiene. (Cf. Best, C. H., and Taylor, N. B., *The Physiological Basis of Medical Practice*, The Williams & Wilkins Company, Baltimore, 1940, pp. 1695, 1702–1703.)

balky criminal suspect in order to render him more cooperative. The suspect's resulting tenseness, squirming movements, and general lack of muscular control would be more appropriately classifiable as signs of nervousness rather than neuroticism. This would be true if his distress were exclusively a product of the overintense, retinal stimulation. However, if a portion of his distress were due to a conflict between his determination not " to squeal on his pals " and his desire for relief from torture, then it would be more of a neurotic type of distress.

This analysis assumes that without conflict there can be no neurosis. Whether agitation aroused by *any* conflict situation should be regarded as a neurotic process is still a debatable issue. For instance, it is possible to produce what Pavlov [15] has called " experimental neuroses " in dogs by the conditioned reflex technique. This is done by training the animal to respond to a visual stimulus like a circle as the signal for food and teaching him to differentiate the latter signal from a similar one like an ellipse. In other words, a positive response is evoked by the circle and a negative one by the ellipse. The positive reaction involves activation of the salivary glands while the negative reaction involves inhibition of these glands. To accomplish this result the animal is fed in conjunction with the circle and not fed when the ellipse is visible. After a series of such laboratory experiences the animal responds to the circle as if it signified the expected introduction of food. But its response to the ellipse is different. There is not a mere absence of salivation as is evidenced by the fact that shortly after the ellipse has been shown the circle will fail to elicit the customary salivary reaction. Pavlov has taken this to mean that the inhibitory process aroused by the ellipse does not subside the instant the ellipse is removed. Inhibition and excitation are thus to be conceived of as genuine but differing neural events. They are comparable to the physicist's concept of negative and positive electricity. Just as a negative electric charge is not to be confused with absence of a charge, so an inhibitory neural process is not to be confused with mere absence of a neural process.

Pavlov's approach to mental hygiene problems is largely in terms of this concept of neural excitation and inhibition. What he describes as the " proper balancing " of these two processes con-

[15] Pavlov, I. P., *Lectures on Conditioned Reflexes*, pp. 329–349.

stitutes "the basis of a normal life for both man and animal." [16]
The dog reacting positively to the circle and negatively to the
ellipse shows such " proper balance " and its behavior is " normal."
To throw it off balance or render its behavior abnormal the shape
of the ellipse is changed to approximate the circle. The animal is
confronted with signals that are ambiguous: they might mean
food is coming or they might mean no food is coming. In the
language of neurology, they tend to elicit antagonistic or contradictory neural impulses. This conflict between excitation and inhibition results in agitated behavior on the part of the animal.
Instead of being a quiet, docile experimental animal as before, the
dog now refuses to stand still in his harness; he bites at the apparatus; he fidgets and squeals and shows excitement by violent
barking when being brought to the laboratory room. This kind of
emotionalized reaction, so different from the dog's erstwhile response to the laboratory situation, is what Pavlov regarded as an
experimental neurosis.

The type of experimental neurosis just outlined was first produced in Pavlov's laboratory in 1914. Since then many other workers in other laboratories have duplicated the work.[17] The technique
has been applied to sheep, to rats, to the pig, and to the child.
Maier [18] introduced an interesting change in the technique by com-
bining the air-blast with a discrimination problem. A full description of his various experiments cannot be supplied without too
much of a digression. Instead we shall have to content ourselves
with a general account of the essential nature of his procedure.

In his experiments Maier first trained his rats to learn to jump
from an elevated stand through a window cut out of a screen. By
jumping through this window they landed on a platform raised to
about the same level as the stand. This required a horizontal leap
from stand to platform rather than a vertical dive. Food placed on
the platform was the reward for successful jumping. After this
jumping habit was acquired the animal was confronted with a discrimination problem. As it stood poised on the stand it now faced
two " closed " windows in the screen. This was accomplished by

[16] *Op. cit.,* p. 373.
[17] An excellent survey of this work is to be found in Hilgard, E. R., and
Marquis, D. G., *Conditioning and Learning,* D. Appleton-Century Co., New
York, 1940, pp. 279–308.
[18] Maier, N. R. F., *Studies of Abnormal Behavior in the Rat,* Harper &
Brothers, New York, 1939.

placing a card in front of each opening. The cards differed from one another not only in visual appearance, but also in the way in which they were fastened. One card, used as a positive stimulus, had a black circle on a white background and was held in place very loosely by a light weight so that when the rat jumped against it the card flopped over and the animal reached the food on the platform. The other card, used as a negative stimulus, had an equally large white circle on a black background; but this card was securely fastened by means of a latch so that when the animal jumped against it, there was no yielding. The rat received a bump and dropped into a net below. Reacting to the black circle thus gave the animal a reward of food while the white circle came to mean punishment in the form of a bump and a fall. Sometimes when the animal was slow in reacting to the cards Maier induced speedier action by using the air-blast. By giving the animal 10 trials each day a discrimination between the two circles was established in four or five days. To make sure that the discriminatory reaction was genuinely established the experimenter continued with the training until the rat made 30 correct choices in succession. On the average the rat required about 80 trials (50 plus the latter 30) before he was ready for the actual experiment.

Once the animal had mastered the problem of correct discrimination various conflict-producing changes were introduced. One of these consisted in making the black circle the negative stimulus in one trial and a positive one in another so that the established discrimination no longer sufficed to make a correct solution possible. The animal was balked by an insoluble problem: a given stimulus symbolized either reward or punishment. The impulse to jump was blocked by a counter-impulse not to jump. By means of the air-blast the animal was then forced to act. In other experiments the rat was confronted with only a single card so that differentiating it from the absent card was too difficult a problem. In still other experiments the two cards were made identical or almost identical in appearance. Neurotic behavior was induced by compelling the animals to choose when no basis for choice was available.

The animals used in Maier's experiments were not members of the emotional and non-emotional strains employed by Martin and Hall. Consequently the results of the two series of experiments are not comparable in all respects. This is significant because, with very few exceptions, Maier failed to observe full-fledged seizures when he exposed his animals to the stimulus of the air-blast alone. In general he found behavior suggestive of extreme fear rather than convulsive behavior. He is inclined to believe that the neurotic symptoms exhibited by his animals were thus due, not to the action of the air-blast as a disturbing stimulus, but to the combination of this goad to action in a situation evoking incompatible or deadlocked tendencies to react. Nor will any goad to action result in neurotic behavior; for Maier found that the substitution of a mild electric shock for the air-blast induced the animals to jump, but did not precipitate convulsive behavior. He takes this to mean that the localized electric shock changes the problem for the animal. Its task is to jump away from the painful grill rather than to decide which card to jump at. It solves this problem by escaping from the jumping apparatus.[19] In the case of the air-blast " the animal seems to continue to be oriented to the cards," [20] as if the task were not so much to get away from the blast as to react to the cards. The adequacy of this interpretation may be doubted in view of the fact that audiogenic seizures can be produced without the complication of an insoluble discrimination problem. It might be sufficient to account for the observed differences among Maier's animals by stressing the fact that the diffuseness of the auditory stimulation renders escape from annoyance less feasible than escape from the sharply localized electric shock. It is harder to do something about some disturbing noises than the pain occasioned by stepping on a jagged rock at the beach.

Both the conditioning experiments as well as Maier's work bring out the importance of a conflict situation in the production of what many animal psychologists regard as a neurosis. It is also important to note the existence of individual differences in susceptibility to this kind of breakdown. There were some animals belonging to the same litter who " failed to become neurotic in the same experi-

[19] The difference in the experimental setting between the use of the jumping apparatus and the apparatus used in conditioning experiments may explain why what seems to be the same kind of problem situation results in neurotic symptoms in the latter case, but not in the former. Actually the problem situation is not the same. In conditioning experiments the animal is confined by means of a halter or a harness. It cannot run away from its troubles. The jumping apparatus leaves the animal with greater freedom of movement so that, as in the present instance, it can escape from the electrified grill by leaping from the stand.

[20] *Op. cit.*, p. 68.

mental situation " [21] in Maier's investigations. And in the study of Martin and Hall it was evident that the air-blast did not produce a seizure in every rat. Why some animals are affected more than others and why some are not at all susceptible to audiogenic seizures or neuroses are questions for future research.[22]

FROM NEUROTIC ANIMALS TO NEUROTIC PEOPLE

It has already been intimated that not all students of the neuroses are in agreement regarding the nature and import of the experimentally induced abnormalities reported by the animal psychologist. Some of them are reluctant to classify these derangements of animal behavior as neuroses. As they conceive of a neurotic reaction, it is not to be defined as emotional agitation aroused by *any* conflict situation. For them the conflict situation must transcend the animal level of biological security and reach the more distinctively human level of ethical obligation, social pressure, and personal aspiration as exemplified by such familiar dilemmas as the following:

The conflict between one's desire to have a " good time " and the need to obey the stern behests of " duty " will serve as a generalized example. A clash between father and son over the latter's vocational ambitions might serve as another more specific example. So might the distress of a talented, sensitive Negro musician balked in his efforts to become a symphony conductor because of prejudice. An additional instance is supplied by the woman who, though grievously disappointed in the outcome of her marriage, finds herself trapped by the fact that her church refuses to sanction divorce. There is no need to add more examples at this point. The ones mentioned suffice to show how human conflict situations are enmeshed in the demands of social institutions. Church, army, school, family, law, business and industry and labor unions all have something to say about the what and how of the lone individual's conduct. His freedom of action is curtailed on all sides by the majesty and imperiousness of institutional taboos. Family

[21] *Op. cit.*, p. 48.
[22] Martin and Hall (*op. cit.*, p. 192) attribute the differences in question to the likelihood that " susceptibility to attack " is bound up with " differences in temperament and to the underlying factors upon which temperament is based." And Maier (*op. cit.*, p. 53) grants that " direct stimulation may account for a few " of his cases, but, as he contends, " it in no way accounts for the attacks of the majority of them."

ANIMAL *VERSUS* HUMAN NEUROSES

233

pride and social custom and religious teachings may have a say in
what he shall wear, what he shall eat, how he shall earn his living,
whom he may marry and sometimes even what he may read. It is
as if the Great Society had conspired against him to make him a
socialized robot instead of a free man free to follow the spontaneous dictates of his own impulses.

This, in brief, represents the kind of setting emphasized by
those who are skeptical of the validity of the concept of " neurotic
dogs " or " neurotic rats." They reserve the term *neurosis* for conflicts between the individual and the demands of society. As they
envisage the problem, neurotics have trouble with their *social* adjustments. These involve not only other people but the patient's
own notion of himself as a member of society. That is to say, he
may have trouble reconciling a conflict between what he is today
and what he should like to become in the future. His prestige is
involved. And prestige, personal ambition, " making good " and
similar expressions are all reflections of what people mean by
being a useful member of society.

In a recent volume Gillespie [23] stresses this general viewpoint
by classifying neuroses as " social disorders of individuals." For
him " the essential pathology of psychoneurotic reactions is a social psychopathology." [24] In fact, he believes that as a result of
studying such reactions " psychiatry becomes a social science." In
his formal definition of neurotic reactions he designates them as
" abnormal mental states " resulting from " persistent mental conflict over *personal relationships* . . . in regard to others or to
oneself." He also differentiates them from organically determined
abnormalities in that they " are susceptible of cure by psychological means."

[23] Gillespie, R. D., *Psychological Effects of War on Citizen and Soldier,* W. W.
Norton & Company, New York, 1942, pp. 36–39.
[24] However, despite this emphasis on a " social psychopathology," Gillespie
seems reluctant to rule out constitutional predisposition as a significant etiological
factor. In fact, he devotes the second chapter of his book to a discussion of " constitutional factors in psychoneuroses." Although he appears to regard the bulk of
the evidence in favor of the existence of such factors as suggestive rather than
conclusive, he nevertheless seems persuaded of their probable existence. In general he believes mental instability to be in some way related to those biochemical
factors having to do with the regulation of " mental energy." He refers to " the
pathology of psychopathy as essentially one of the quantity and distribution of
mental energy " (*op. cit.,* p. 61). This is very much like that of Janet's approach
to the psychoneuroses which we discussed in Chapter 4 in the section dealing
with psychasthenia.

It must be granted that if neuroses be regarded as exclusively products of disturbed social relationships, then the abnormalities described by the animal psychologists are not to be classified as neuroses. It must also be granted that examination of neurotic human beings entirely justifies this emphasis on the social factor. However, the absence of the latter factor need not render it impossible to produce a neurotic reaction. This is true provided one regards the crux of the reaction in question to be a compulsion to act in the face of a situation provoking interfering or incompatible reaction tendencies. Such interference or incompatibility makes the situation a conflict situation. The neurotic feels himself *trapped*: he wants both to fight and to run away, to love and to hate, to speak up and to be silent, to take risks and to take no chances, etc. Whatever the dilemma happens to be, it is one of importance for the neurotic; hence he becomes emotionally wrought up over it. The emotional attitudes aroused by the dilemma are antithetic in nature. One thus finds what are technically described as *ambivalent* attitudes as more or less characteristic of the neurotic reaction. A child who both loves and fears his father would be said to cherish ambivalent emotions. So would a wife who loves her husband for his kindness when sober but who loathes him for his brutality when drunk. In terms of these emotional factors one might say that, psychologically speaking, the neurotic is trapped by his ambivalent attitudes.

In order to avoid both anthropomorphic as well as zoomorphic errors it might be well to note in what respects the experimentally induced abnormalities in animals are comparable to the neurotic reactions of people. Such comparison calls for observation of both likenesses and differences.

The abnormalities are alike in being the consequences of the simultaneous arousal of contradictory reaction tendencies. In Pavlov's dogs these took the form of excitation and inhibition. Maier's rats were both attracted and repelled by the same stimulus card. Under the experimental conditions it was impossible for the animals to adjust to the problem by arbitrary suppression of one reaction tendency in favor of the other. Two rival possibilities of adjustment were kept in conflict with one another. In this sense the ambiguous stimulus cards were arousing ambivalent adjustments. Ambivalence is thus a constituent part of the neurotic picture for both the animal subjects and human patients.

One chief difference between the two sets of abnormalities lies not in the fact of ambivalence, but in the nature of the provocative situations. For the animal subjects the latter never go beyond the instinctive level of biological safety. The animal's dilemma has to do with some such relatively simple task as getting food under threat of pain or shock. However, the dilemmas of neurotic patients are ordinarily not so simple. Their troubles are much more complex and involve the impact of social forces — often antithetic or contradictory social forces. Their worries have to do with the maintenance of self-respect and self-esteem. The animal subject is trapped by physical forces, but the neurotic patient is trapped by social forces, by problems of civilized living, and by the demands of his culture. His anxieties have to do with economic security, social prestige, living up to the real or imagined expectations of his family, building up a reputation, being worried about his good name, being able to make good and to do good, winning friends, gaining popularity, learning to know the right people, avoiding disgrace, and adjusting his cravings to the accepted folkways of his people. In this sense his anxieties — his neurotic difficulties — are products of civilization. Neither the rat nor the dog is ever enmeshed by such difficulties.

Under ordinary conditions the animal is not a victim of contradictory teachings; hence its neurotic symptoms are almost altogether the result of artificial laboratory techniques involving the arousal of contradictory impulses. The human being, however, is exposed to contradictory appeals in the course of his everyday living. He has to learn to adjust to the contradictions implicit in the society of which he is a member. Karen Horney [25] has called attention to some of these contradictions. One of them is the contradiction between our actual worship of competitive business success and our presumed worship of the ideal of brotherly love. How can a business rival be outsmarted and driven into bankruptcy and at the same time be treated with affectionately solicitous concern for his welfare? The attitudes involved are antithetic. An-

[25] Horney, K., *The Neurotic Personality of Our Time,* W. W. Norton & Company, New York, 1937, pp. 287–289.

other contradiction pointed out by Horney has to do with the constant arousal of desire for new and different material possessions in the absence of the means for gratifying such desire. We are constantly bombarded by commercial appeals to get new luggage, new cars, new clothing, new furniture, and new gadgets. The fact that most of us cannot afford such constant replacement of our existing equipment by " the latest model " means, if the advertising men are successful in their appeals, a chronic state of dissatisfaction. Needs are aroused in people whose restricted income renders gratification of such needs a matter of perpetual postponement.

Somewhat related to the latter contradiction is another less obvious one mentioned by Horney. Although she does not give it this label, we might call it the *Horatio Alger Success Delusion*. Children are indoctrinated with the notion that life is a game in which every player is *free* to be a winner provided he avails himself of the virtues of effort, efficiency, and dogged determination. Every poor boy possessed of these virtues is presumed to be a potential success in business, in marriage, in sport and in whatever other field of endeavor to which his ambition may be directed. Failure is supposed to be impossible. The path from rags to riches or from obscurity to fame is supposed to be open to any child who chooses to pursue it. Anybody is supposed to be able to get anything he wants provided he tries hard enough to achieve its attainment. This is the great dream of individual success conjured up for the masses of people by many parents, by commencement orators, by inspirational preachers, and by those who write " success stories " for the pulp magazines. Belief in such a dream must give people, as Horney suggests, " a feeling of boundless power " in guiding their own destinies. And yet, as will be brought out in detail in Chapter 15, the dream is an idle dream for the vast majority of people. Ambition and hard work are not sufficient to guarantee success. They are not even sufficient to guarantee economic security. We are not merely thinking of the many posthumously famous writers, artists, composers, and inventors who died in obscurity and poverty. We are thinking of the thousands and sometimes millions who cannot find work because there are not enough jobs to go around. We are thinking of the conscientious, hard-working, able small business men and small manufacturers unable to withstand the economic pressure of chain store competition, of powerful mergers, or of other tremendous corporate rivals. We are thinking of the millions whose dreams of fame and fortune can never be realized because of the handicaps of poverty, of disease, of racial prejudice, of religious discrimination, of ignorance, and of not knowing the " right " people. For such millions the realities of these handicaps must engender, to use Horney's phrase, " a feeling of entire helplessness." As a consequence they become the victims of the ambivalent attitudes of " boundless power " on the one hand and of " entire helplessness " on the other. In commenting on these issues Lynd brings out still more mental hygiene implications as the following quotation reveals : [26]

One can elaborate Dr. Horney's list by the addition of many other contradictions: between saving and spending; between playing safe and " nothing ventured, nothing gained "; between " you've got to look like money in order to make money " and spending your money for the things you really want; between (if you are a woman) having " brains " and having " charm "; between things that are " right in theory " and " wrong in practice "; between change and stability; between being loyal and " looking out for Number One "; between being efficient and being human; between being democratic and " getting to know the right people." Human beings are, as Freud has pointed out, inevitably ambivalent at many points, but a culture which encourages unnecessary ambivalence is recklessly careless of the vital energies of its people.

The ambivalent attitudes of human beings are quite manifestly, as the foregoing analyses showed, far more intricate than the contradictory reaction tendencies which the animal psychologist establishes in his neurotic animals. The demands of social pressure and cultural tradition play no part in the conflict situation of the animal subject. This important difference is not to be overlooked. Nevertheless, the greater simplicity of the animal's conflict situation may make it easier to isolate the essential etiological factors. Such isolation may prove most valuable in aiding our quest for ways of warding off neurotic breakdown.

Before pursuing this quest it might be well to call attention to

[26] Lynd, R. S., *Knowledge For What?*, Princeton University Press, Princeton, 1940, p. 103.

one final difference between neurotic disturbances in human beings and seemingly analogous disturbances in animals. The reaction of the animal is not characterized by elaborate defense mechanisms and compensations. The human neurotic endeavors to circumvent his problem by various dodges: pretending to be sick, blaming others for his troubles, refusing to admit the existence of some personal defect or weakness, exaggerating the weakness or unfairness of his opponents, playing up his own assets and virtues, indulging in daydreams of heroic conquest, and distorting the factors responsible for his difficulties by other self-deceptive evasions. Self-deception of this kind is very likely not a constituent feature of the clinical picture of the neurotic rat or dog or sheep. Both intentional as well as unintentional bluffing requires more thinking ability than the infra-human animal possesses. In this sense the neurotic disturbance of the animal is not warped and concealed by a network of compensatory reactions, artful rationalizations, and other products of self-protective strategy. In this respect the animal subject may be thought of as exhibiting the core of neurotic difficulty undisguised and uncomplicated by the psychological camouflage of which the human subject avails himself. For this reason too it may thus be easier to detect our mental hygiene clues in the animal laboratory than in the consulting room. However, the absence of the complicating social factors as well as the absence of the camouflage means that these clues will have to be supplemented by those which are unique to the consulting room.

SOME MENTAL HYGIENE CLUES

There can be no doubt that the animal subjects are emotionally agitated by the conflict situations with which they have to cope. Their tensions and visceral disturbances parallel those of human neurotics. Since our understanding of their upset is based entirely on observation of their behavior and our knowledge of the stimulus situation, there is no way of getting at their own possible inner orientation to their difficulties. For clues of this sort we have to rely on the testimony of human subjects. The absence of such verbal descriptions must not be minimized in evaluating the mental hygiene significance of the work with animals. It is probably unwise to transfer the diagnostic vocabulary developed in connection with human neuroses to these animal cases. In other words, without evidence of what is " going on in the mind of the patient " one cannot speak of psychasthenia or hysteria or anxiety neurosis. As a consequence, it might be somewhat fanciful to speak of psychasthenic rats, or neurasthenic dogs, or hysterical sheep. The best one can do is to perceive certain resemblances between some of the symptoms of neurotic behavior in the animal and the conventional pictures of " typical " clinical cases of neuroses among people.

Probably the most valuable clue furnished the mental hygienist by these animal studies has to do with what has already been referred to as the essential feature of the experimental situation: the animal is trapped by its ambivalent reaction tendencies. It is baffled by ambiguous stimulus cards. It is unable to determine whether a given card is the signal for reward or the signal for punishment. The same card attracts and repels, arouses desire and aversion, or instigates contradictory impulses. Translated into human terms this means doubt, indecision, uncertainty, or the ideational impasse accompanying the emotional state of anxiety. If the *ideational* factor — the doubt and the insistent preoccupation with thoughts of acting first in one way and then in an opposite way — be segregated for special emphasis, one perceives the outline of the psychasthenic or obsessive-compulsive neurotic syndrome. On the other hand, if the *emotional* factor — the anxiety — be regarded as the most conspicuous factor, then the concept of anxiety neurosis may seem more applicable. Furthermore, if the animal's *loss of functional control* — the insensitivity to light, sound, and touch along with the tremors, contractures, or paralyses of the musculature — be singled out as the most noteworthy symptoms, then the concept of hysteria may seem more relevant.

In some such fashion as this it may be possible to bridge the gap between the experimental neuroses produced in the animal laboratory and the symptoms observed by the student of human neuroses. However, the rather crude nature of the analogies involved should not be overlooked. Their value is chiefly pedagogical in that they may remind us of the complexities of neurotic manifestations among human beings. Only in a somewhat tenuous manner can one see a linkage between the varied nature of human neuroses and the less complicated difficulties of the neurotic animal. The analogies in question are akin to the biologist's procedure when he calls attention to the fact that ingestion, digestion, assimilation, irritability, motility, and reproduction can be observed in the amoeba as well as in man. He does not mean that the mechanism of digestion, for example, is the same in one-celled animals as in mammals. Similarly, we do not mean that the process by which the rat loses control of its muscles is necessarily the same as that which produces an hysterical paralysis in the human subject.

After this slight digression we may resume our discussion of the mental hygiene implications of the animal experiments. Of what aid are they in enabling us to prevent neurotic disabilities among human beings? After all, it might be said, people are not likely to be seriously distressed by ambiguous stimulus cards. Even the person ignorant of French can succeed in solving the problem of getting a good meal despite his inability to understand the signals on the French menu card. But to argue this way is to miss the point of the experiments. The central factor is the factor of ambivalence and what we have to look for is everyday situations calculated to arouse ambivalent attitudes among people. Parents who are *inconsistent* in their discipline of the children by permitting mood and impulse to govern manifestations of approval or disapproval, may unwittingly be laying the groundwork for ambivalent attitudes in the youngsters. Such inconsistency may be exemplified in countless ways: going to a movie without permission results in a severe scolding on one occasion, but hardly more than a resigned sigh on another. Slovenly table manners provoke a stern rebuke sometimes and an indulgent reference to what " a healthy appetite does to a boy's manners " at other times — especially when company is present. In fact any explosive departure from a settled routine of dealing with children may be regarded as a generalized parallel to the laboratory man's use of ambiguous stimulus cards. If a given item of behavior provokes enraged parental protest on some occasions and is altogether ignored on other occasions, then the child's attitude toward the behavior in question may not be very different from that of the animal baffled by a stimulus situation which may signalize either the reward of food or the punishment of a bumped nose.

The mental hygienist is particularly interested in these parent-child relationships. A good portion of the ensuing chapters will be concerned with their elaboration. In the present context, however, it is important to note the way in which these relationships may be jeopardized by the unwitting establishment of ambivalent attitudes. It is not at all uncommon for a child to be uncertain of the dependability of parental devotion. Along with overt demonstrations of affection for the youngster there are equally overt demonstrations of being overburdened and irritated by the youngster. Sometimes he is called " mother's little darling " and sometimes he is yelled at and learns that he " makes mother sick and tired." Sometimes he is told how " precious " he is and at other times he hears grumbling over the need for buying him new shoes or over the cost of having his teeth straightened. Under the circumstances the child may have trouble deciding whether his mother regards him as a blessing or a burden — whether her solicitude for him is an expression of genuine love or of a grim, unwelcome obligation. Incidentally, in many instances mother herself may have the same kind of trouble; for her own attitude toward the child may also be ambivalent. This is especially apt to be the case if his advent interfered with the prosecution of her career as business woman, actress, writer, physician, or dancer. It may also be the case if the child's looks should happen to resemble those of some despised " in-law." In the latter instance there may be unconscious antipathy in line with the concept of redintegration or the principle of conditioning. At all events it should be obvious that opportunities for the emergence of ambivalent attitudes within the home are legion: both on the part of parents as well as on that of children. Their prevention and control comes within the scope of the mental hygienist's program.

Another common exhibition of parental inconsistency making for emotional ambivalence in the children merits separate mention because of its frequency of occurrence as well as its bearing on the prevention of neurotic tendencies. This has to do with conflicting philosophies of child rearing. The conflict is by no means restricted to the home: it is evident in many classrooms. It is a consequence of divergent attitudes toward the nature of children and the roles of parents and teachers in dealing with that nature.

According to one attitude implicit in our cultural tradition children are selfish little parasites who will grow up into brutish big parasites unless they are taught to be otherwise by means of rigid discipline. This attitude reflects the belief in " infant damnation " so prevalent a few generations ago. It is in line with such proverbs as " spare the rod and spoil the child " or " children should be seen and not heard." It suggests rule by force and the appeal to fear as a device for securing obedience. It implies a state of constant tension between parent and child and teacher and pupil. It is associated with the notion of necessary and inevitable antagonism between warring factions. Gripped by such an attitude, both parent and teacher will conceive of their respective roles as akin to that of an army drillmaster, a dictatorial boss, or benevolent despot. Discipline, order, unquestioning obedience, and regimented compliance with regulations dominate home and classroom where such an attitude is made to prevail.

Opposed to the foregoing view is the notion of the inherent goodness of children. Instead of " infant depravity " it extols the " sweet innocence " of childhood. According to this belief, there are no " bad children," but only misunderstood or mishandled or repressed children. Every child is potentially kind and lovable and cooperative. All that is required is kind and lovable and cooperative guidance. Corporal punishment is tabooed. So is appeal to fear or recourse to threats. Patient explanation and sympathetic reasoning with the child is urged as a substitute for the do-it-because-mother-tells-you command. The youngster is to be encouraged to have his say, to express himself, and to " stand up for his rights." Father and mother are urged to make chums and companions of their children. Love and mutual solicitude are to usurp the place of fear and discipline in home and school management. The teacher is to be friend and adored guide rather than the feared, arbitrary taskmaster. Instead of antagonism and friction within home and classroom one should have harmony, enthusiastic cooperation, and an atmosphere of healthy teamwork. This, in brief, serves to indicate the general drift of the other philosophy of child-rearing.

Most individuals are exposed to both of these philosophies [27]

[27] These two philosophies of child-rearing may be viewed as specialized applications of two antithetic theories of social control: control by power versus control by love. In this connection it might be pertinent to add that Will Durant in his brilliant popularization of the history of philosophy devotes a little space to these antithetic theories by way of demonstrating Spinoza's endeavor to reconcile the opposition. As Durant puts it, there are ultimately " but three systems of ethics, three conceptions of the ideal character and the moral life." Buddha and Jesus with their emphasis on the desirability of returning good for evil, of

in the course of their reading, observation, and personal experience. As a consequence many parents and teachers have unconsciously absorbed both attitudes by the time they are called upon to take charge of the rearing and training of children. Depending on mood and circumstance they veer from one attitude to the other with arbitrary impulsiveness. A child exposed to such impulsiveness is consequently likely to develop ambivalent feelings toward his adult mentor. When the latter plays the role of friendly companion and protector, the child is emotionally oriented in one direction; but with the shift to the role of masterful domination, the youngster's emotional orientation swerves in an opposite direction. Opposed emotional attitudes thus come to be associated with the same adult. One detects attraction and repulsion, friendliness and hostility, trust and distrust, or love and hate as constituent features of the child's reactions toward such an adult. If we think of this adult — this teacher or parent — as a social stimulus, then the child's emotional reactions are comparable to those of the experimental animal baffled by the ambiguous stimulus which arouses both positive and negative reaction tendencies simultaneously. In this sense the parent or teacher functions as an ambiguous stimulus for the child.

The resulting conflict in reaction tendencies may mark the initiation of a neurotic trend. To prevent such a trend it would be desirable — provided this analysis is sound — for parents and

---

being solicitous for the welfare of the obscure and the downtrodden, of being kind and forgiving and merciful and charitable to all exemplify one system. As a political system this points to democracy without restriction. The second system is symbolized by Machiavelli and Nietzsche. It stresses the glory of combat, the struggle for domination, the right of the stronger to exploit the weaker and identifies right with might. Politically it approves of an hereditary aristocracy: continued rule of the weak by the strong. In the ethic of Socrates, Plato, and Aristotle Durant perceives the third system. These Greek philosophers, identifying virtue with intelligence, spurned the universal value of either love or power. In their opinion recourse to either attitude would be a function of circumstances. Depending on the objective to be attained and the barriers to its attainment one would have to judge whether to flash a gun or a friendly smile. This calls for maturity of judgment and intelligent insight; hence in the sphere of government the system would call for an aristo-democracy. In Spinoza's system these three approaches were woven together in a system too complex to be adequately described within the compass of a single footnote. For our purposes it is sufficient to note that neither of the opposed philosophies of child-rearing merits the unreserved approval of the mental hygienist. Domination of the child by the parent is an evil; but so is domination of the parent by the child. (Cf. Durant, W., *The Story of Philosophy*, New York, Simon & Schuster, Inc., 1926, pp. 197–205.)

teachers to ask themselves this question: " What kind of a social stimulus am I making of myself in the eyes of the children whose welfare has been entrusted to me? " Or, to stress the possible mental hygiene value of the animal experiments, the question might be put in terms of this self-explanatory metaphor: " Do the children think of me as a benevolent, protecting *circle* or a hostile, ensnaring *ellipse* or is my behavior so inconsistent, so impulsive, so fluctuating that it leaves them emotionally trapped by making it impossible for them to decide? "

NEUROSES AND THE WAR AND MORALE

It was just pointed out that the mental health of the child is intimately related to his reaction to parents and teachers as social stimuli. This point is not a mere academic inference from the results of the laboratory studies of neurotic animal behavior. It is based on direct clinical study of neurotic people. It is also based on even more recent studies of the effects of " total war " on the mental stability of its victims. One can secure deepened insight into the problem of preventing neuroses by examining some of these studies. British psychiatrists and psychologists have published various reports of their observations of what bombing, threat of air-raids, disruption of family life, being evacuated from home, and witnessing death and destruction have done to the mental health of children, youths, and adults. Two American psychologists, Pritchard and Rosenzweig,[28] have gone over the bulk of these reports and written a very convenient summary and stimulating interpretation of the general drift of the British observations. Unless otherwise noted, the ensuing discussion is based upon their article.

In general, the impact of modern war upon the child involves the hazard of air-raids on the one hand and the threat to its inner security on the other. Contrary to the expectation of many, the former hazard has not proven nearly as serious as the latter threat. Many of the older children have actually been seen to view air-raids as a thrilling experience. However, it is significant to note that such heroic adaptation to danger occurs " only in cases where the adults in contact with children have behaved with self-con-

[28] Pritchard, R., and Rosenzweig, S., " The Effects of War Stress upon Childhood and Youth," *J. of Abnor. and Soc. Psychol.*, 1942, *37*, pp. 329–344.

trol." Panicky adults tend to arouse panicky behavior in their children.

Paradoxically, people who show most anxiety when an air-raid is in progress are not necessarily those who were injured in some previous raid. It is as if the fantasied anticipation of being bombed can be more terrifying than the experience itself. In this connection it may be of interest to cite an observation made by Anna Freud at the nursery home directed by her in London. The most nervous child there was a boy not quite five years old who had never been exposed to bombing. A playmate of his was a little girl some months younger whose life had been in jeopardy when a bomb struck the roof of her house. It was she who ventured to comfort the boy and to tell him " to pull the bed clothes over his head when the guns got noisy."

One should not draw the conclusion that air-raids are altogether devoid of adverse psychological effects on those who have been buried under wreckage, caught in burning buildings, or otherwise directly involved in acute danger. Emotional depression, anxiety, and even some cases of hysteria have followed such experiences. But the human organism seems capable of adjusting to such shock; for unless " there was a predisposing neurotic tendency " or the death of some member of the family, the neurotic symptoms " usually cleared up very quickly." In fact, the authors state that " there is a consensus of opinion that children show great adaptability and recover quickly from air-raid effects if simple and sensible measures are taken." [29]

Disruption of the child's emotional security by being suddenly evacuated from its home to strange surroundings or by the sudden loss of its mother resulted in more serious effects than those produced by the falling bombs. Neurotic disorders are more likely to be precipitated by separating the child from its emotional moorings. Exposure to physical danger is more apt to result in such behavior difficulties as troublesome aggressiveness, pilfering, and unruliness. In the experience of Miss Alcock, one of the British psychologists who worked with many of these cases, it is easier to rectify such behavior difficulties than it is to undo the psychological effects of separation. Interestingly enough, in some of her neurotic cases she found that a complicating factor was a feeling of

[29] *Op. cit.*, p. 331.

guilt on the part of the child because he had left a beloved parent in a zone of danger.

The chief finding emerging from these studies centers on these parent-child relationships as " the most crucial factor regarding the security of children and adolescents." As will be brought out in the remaining chapters, the entire program of meliorative mental hygiene may be regarded as an elaboration of this insight. Emotional security in terms of inter-personal relations seems to be the pivot of mental health. The roots of this security are embedded within the life of home and family. To a large extent, if this insight be valid, the prevention of neurotic disability thus turns out to be a matter of bringing children up in homes whose psychological atmosphere promotes the trust, the confidence, and the belief in the worthwhileness of life that goes with high morale. Achievement of such morale — both in peace as well as in war — is a matter of training, parental example, and a host of subtle factors that shape the young child's basic attitudes toward life.

Sound morale — the kind calculated to ward off neurotic breakdown — is the resultant of a large number of determinants. As a recent analysis [30] shows, " morale is a complex of basic physical and mental states and tendencies, and of attitudes " that has its foundations in bodily vigor, certain mental characteristics, a modicum of economic security, and stimulating ethico-religious ideals. More specifically, these foundations reveal the importance of such varied factors as zestful attitudes toward work to be accomplished, of the " ability to stand unpleasant tension," of the willingness to fight harder when threatened with failure, and of the cultivation of a purpose in life. Being endowed with a sense of humor is another important factor. Nor can morale be sustained without an adequate income to support life and health. The nature of one's job is not to be overlooked as another significant factor; for without " self-respecting status in employment " or the " hope that this may be achieved " there can be no healthy morale. Achievement of morale thus goes beyond the field of control of individual psychiatrist and individual psychologist and into that of the complex field of social control of the factors making for job availability, job security, and job dignity. The fields of ethics and religion also have

[30] Sanford, F. H., and Holt, R. R., " Psychological Determinants of Morale," *J. of Abnor. and Soc. Psychol.*, 1943, *38*, pp. 93–95.

contributions to make; since acceptance of individually congenial religious teachings may supply the believer with an anchorage and an inspiration in terms of which he can be more resolute in facing life's adversities just as acceptance of " high moral standards and ethical ideals " can play an effective role in disposing of conflicts, shaping decisions, and guiding action. And running through the warp and woof of the fabric of which morale is composed are the psychological threads that tie the individual to his family group. Unsatisfactory family ties jeopardize morale. They disrupt what we called the " pivot of mental health " in the preceding paragraph. How to erect such a " pivot " and just what it implies for the prevention of *neurotic* disabilities and what it means in terms of all the other factors involved in the concept of morale are questions that belong to the field of meliorative rather than prophylactic mental hygiene. To find the answers, in other words, we must shift our orientation and begin the quest for factors that safeguard individual and group morale — those factors which, while possibly not directly related to the task of preventing actual *psychotic* [31] breakdown, are nevertheless of incalculable mental hygiene significance because of their intimate bearing on the promotion of mental health.

[31] This qualification is due to the belief — the evidence is not strong enough to make it a conviction — that the role of constitutional factors may be more prominent in the etiology of psychoses than in the neuroses. The basic difference between these two sets of functional disorders may be a difference in kind as opposed to a difference of degree. Apart from the evidence of general clinical impression there is the statistical evidence submitted by Ross. He followed up almost 1,200 cases of neurotic illness for varying periods (the range was from 2 to 12 years) and discovered that only about 5 per cent of these patients became psychotic. (Cf. Ross, T. A., *An Enquiry into Prognosis in the Neuroses*, Cambridge, The Cambridge University Press, 1936.)

In a discussion of Ross's finding Gillespie (*op. cit.*, p. 41) interprets the percentage in question to mean " that some psychotic reactions start with symptoms of psychoneurotic form." However, he holds that the " essential differentiating factor " is a pathological one: neuroses involving " a psychopathology of personal relationships " and psychoses involving " a pathology of the body."

PART FOUR

PROMOTING MENTAL HEALTH

10... *HOME AND THE BALANCED PERSONALITY*

A T THE CLOSE OF THE LAST CHAPTER IT WAS POINTED OUT THAT the pivot of mental health seems to be a function of emotional security and that the roots of this security are embedded within the life of home and family. From now on our task will be to develop the implications of this view in terms of its bearing on a program of meliorative mental hygiene. In thus shifting our attention away from the prophylactic aspects we shall be less concerned with warding off particular psychotic or neurotic reactions and more concerned with safeguarding and promoting morale. It should be remembered, in other words, as has already been pointed out from time to time in the preceding chapters, that the adequacy of a program of meliorative mental hygiene is not to be appraised in terms of the extent to which it reduces the incidence of mental disease, but rather in terms of the extent to which it helps people lead richer and more zestful lives. If such a program should also result in a diminution of the annual toll of first admissions to mental hospitals, so much the better; but — and this should be stressed again — failure to achieve such diminution is not to be construed as failure of the program. Our hope, of course, is that eventually it will be possible to demonstrate statistically that such a program is not merely helping people to bring up their children more wisely, but is also causing fewer of those children to grow up into psychotic adults. Such statistical proof is not yet available. However, on theoretic grounds, particularly if the conflict theory should prove closer to fact than the constitutional theory, one might be justified in expecting the future to reveal statistical proof of this kind, once the teachings of meliorative mental hygiene are carried into practice by all segments of society.

These teachings derive not only from the insights of psychiatrists working with troubled souls in clinic and consulting room. Many of them have long been implicit in the wisdom of the race. Many of them are products of the experiences of social workers and sociologists. Many of them are products of common-sense reflection upon the nature of everyday troubles of everyday people. In brief, no one group of specialists has a monopoly on the kind of wisdom necessary to build up a stimulating philosophy of life which would enable one to handle personal difficulties bravely and intelligently. What the mental hygienist has endeavored to do in drawing up a program of meliorative mental hygiene — a program calculated to promote the morale of individuals and families and communities — can thus be envisioned as the product of a joint undertaking. A more definite statement would be that many fields of study have contributed to the teachings upon which such a program is based. Sociology, anthropology, religion, psychology, philosophy, psychiatry, and all the others mentioned in our first chapter have had a share in this phase of the mental hygienist's work. This will become increasingly manifest as succeeding chapters discuss the nature of this work.

In the present chapter we shall be restricting our perspective to the tremendous role played by home and family in shaping the individual's personality and consequently in laying the foundations for his mental health. In fact, evidence converging from all of the aforementioned fields points to the home as the matrix of the individual's personal traits.

How he was treated as a child by his parents, by his brothers or sisters, and by other relatives may serve to account for his present shyness or boldness or nervousness. One of the first matters a mental hygienist checks on when studying a new case is the past and present family background. He deems it important to find out whether the individual was pampered as a child, whether his parents were too severe with him, whether he respected or loved or hated one or both parents. In other words, a person's attitudes toward his family and their attitudes toward him are of crucial importance for understanding the human personality.

Whether or not a man has confidence in himself may be an outgrowth of the way his father treated him. His distrust of Negroes may be a reflection of prejudiced opinions he gleaned within the family circle as a small child. His belief in a literal hell or his distrust of all preachers or his credulous confidence in miracles may be consequences of childhood theological discussions around the supper table. If he irritates others by his air of superiority, it may be because his parents, almost without themselves realizing it, taught him to think of himself as made of better than common clay. His distrust of marriage may hark back to early impressions made on his mind by scenes he witnessed as a small youngster when his parents indulged in vituperative domestic squabbles. All along, the daily experiences that were his as he was growing up kept shaping his beliefs, attitudes, and ideals. It is not astonishing that some psychiatrists think of childhood as the golden age for effective mental hygiene.

EMOTIONAL SECURITY AND THE ACQUISITION OF POISE

The mentally healthy individual radiates poise and confidence. How to endow a child with these attributes constitutes a major problem of education within the home. A good portion of what the mental hygienist has to say about solving this problem is so obvious that it has long been known to intelligent parents. They may never have reduced their knowledge to verbal form, but their exemplary family life suggests the existence of the requisite knowledge and insight at least implicitly. The job of the modern mental hygienist is to render explicit this implicit understanding of intelligent parents. Observing such parents dealing with their children ought to furnish the astute observer with valuable mental hygiene clues. One of the first things he is likely to notice is that the home atmosphere is one of mutual trust and considerateness. This initial impression is apt to be followed by the realization that even the very young children are treated as *persons* and not as impersonal, troublesome organic creatures. What the parents seem to be doing is to make the youngsters feel secure. And this might strike him as the most valuable clue of all. Let us see why.

It is obvious in the first place that, to put it negatively, feelings of insecurity are not conducive to poise and serenity. To be poised and serene implies an inner world of self-assurance and security. This holds true for adults as well as for children. Whatever adds to one's feelings of security aids mental hygiene. In terms of its origin the word *secure* means to be without care (from the Latin *se*, without, and *cura*, care). If the child is to be secure, to be without cares from the mental hygiene viewpoint, there are certain basic needs that have to be gratified in dependable fashion. Possibly the most important need is the affectionate devotion of his parents. The child has to be able to count on their support. He has to feel that he is wanted in the home. He has to feel that his parents take care of him not because of the pressure of parental duty imposed by a critical public opinion, but because they genuinely care for him. As every experienced mental hygienist knows, the child who feels himself unwanted or rejected by one or both parents is likely to need the services of a psychological trouble-shooter. He grows up wondering why people seem not to like him or at least uncertain whether they will find him acceptable. He is often the victim of feelings of inferiority. Because of his insecurity he is not at ease when he meets people. This may show itself either in terms of extreme shyness or the opposite extreme of irritating aggressiveness. It is not a mere play on words to say that because his parents failed to make him feel at home in the parental household he subsequently has trouble feeling at home in other households.

The psychological importance of these feelings of security as they are built up within the family circle can hardly be overstressed. That is why the late Sigmund Freud deemed it necessary to learn about the early childhood experiences of his adult patients in order to understand their mental difficulties. Much of Freud's teaching has been misunderstood as a result of the highly figurative descriptive vocabulary which he introduced. However, after allowing for rhetorical exaggerations, his basic insights are not to be waved aside in cavalier fashion. Stripped of its somewhat forbidding use of names borrowed from Greek mythology, these insights are seen to refer to the child's concern about his status in the family set-up.

All sorts of rivalries, jealousies, or preferences may threaten the security of the youngster's position in the constellation of family affection. Very early in the baby's life the significance of parental approval comes to be a factor in its developing mental life. The helplessness of the infant endows the parents with relative omnipotence. He is altogether at their mercy when it comes to being fed, washed, aired, picked up, put to bed, dressed, rocked, soothed, and scolded. In technical language, parents come to possess colossal stimulus value for the child. His welfare is contingent on their good will: they reward and punish. As he grows older, this becomes more and more evident to him. If they approve of his actions, it means rewards in the ways of praise, toys, and good things to eat. Disapproval is registered by means of slaps, being put to bed without dessert, being yelled at, being ignored, or being forced to withdraw from the family circle by going to one's room or standing in the corner. The latter procedure is the equivalent of temporary ostracism. It is like telling the child, " you can't belong to us if you do these things." It thus becomes of supreme importance to the child to see to it that he does belong. What the adult calls *family pride* has its roots in these childhood experiences. The psychological direction of the tree of adult personality depends on the way parents bend the twigs of budding personality. If they twist it by means of devastating apprehension of loss of parental affection, the consequence is apt to be a twisted or poorly balanced adult. In broad outline this constitutes the core of Freud's teaching. It might be well, however, to fill in some of the details of the outline and to consider some of its implications.

To feel safe means to feel at home — providing our own experience with home gave us a feeling of affectionate security. As has already been stated, the mentally healthy individual is one who feels at home in the world at large. What Freud has taught us is that the person who never learned to feel at home in his childhood home is apt to have trouble with his mental health in later years. The family is the child's first psychological laboratory. What he learns there about other people and about himself is likely to color his subsequent interpretations of human nature. His eventual thoughts on the meaning of marriage, on how one ought to bring up children, on the place of a father in the home, on the role of the mother may be given shape and substance by what he notices in this early domestic psychological laboratory. This is an " obvious " truth tragically overlooked by tyrannical fathers, shrewish wives, overindulgent parents, jealous husbands, and selfish mothers. They fail to realize that the child may come to worry whether he means as much to them as they mean to each other. Put more bluntly, he may worry whether mother loves him as much as she loves daddy. He may worry whether they love him as much as the new baby they fuss over so much. These threats to his inner security may assert themselves in the form of feelings

of jealousy, attitudes of infantile belligerence, negativism or unwillingness to cooperate with others, and even wishes that harm
may come to those who are his rivals in the struggle for affection.

Building up a child's feeling of security is thus a chief parental
responsibility. It demands intelligent handling of the youngster's
needs. There are certain self-evident precautions to be observed
in the way of not playing favorites by being more generous with
one child than with another. Every intelligent parent, like every
intelligent teacher, knows the psychological danger of playing
favorites. " Teacher has a grudge against me " is the schoolroom
equivalent of " Mother, you pick on me more than you do on
Brother." Equality of opportunity and treatment for *all* the children is a good mental hygiene principle both in school and home.
It is far easier, though, to pay lip service to such a principle than
to make it a living reality. Some youngsters are more tractable
than others. Some have irritating mannerisms like fidgeting, nail-
biting, or thumb-sucking. Some are physically more attractive
than others. The ugly duckling still makes its appearance on
domestic and academic horizons. A homely youngster, one with a
harelip and pock-marked face, is not as immediately appealing to
mother or teacher as his handsome brother. Although a deliberate
effort may be made to conceal such spontaneous esthetic preferences, the sensitive youngster can often detect the effort involved.
He will realize, as a consequence, that even though he may be
getting the same kind of treatment as his brother he is not getting
it as a free-will offering. The very fact of its being forced may
cause him to question its sincerity and thus come to jeopardize
his feeling of security.

Furthermore, living up to this principle of equality of treatment
is by no means restricted in its difficulty of application to matters
of differences in looks. Other inveterate differences come to plague
the conscientious parent. A bright child will require less help with
his lessons than a dull brother. Will this involve a violation of the
principle? Older children require less sleep than younger ones;
but this does not prevent the latter from protesting when they are
not permitted to stay up as late as the former. It requires a tactful
parent to adjust children to such differences in treatment so as to
avoid feelings of resentment against what the youngster is apt to
regard as unfair and discriminatory and anything but *equal* treat-

ment. Possibly even more important than tact is the existence of genuine equality of solicitude for the welfare of each child. Where emotions are genuine and sincere, there are no shams for a suspicious child to detect. Unfortunately, emotional preferences cannot be legislated out of existence by any acts of mental hygienists in convention assembled; hence the need for tact and adroit human engineering.

DANGERS OF OVER-SOLICITUDE

There are still other reasons for elevating parental tact and keen judgment to a position of central importance. The enterprise of so administering family affairs as to produce well-balanced personalities is really a complex art. The goals to be reached are not always easy to define. We have spoken of inner security as one of these goals. And yet there is danger of overshooting the mark. The conventional picture of the spoiled brat is a good example of the psychological consequences of such poor marksmanship.

In his otherwise laudable efforts to avoid the evils of rejecting the child, the parent sometimes goes to the other extreme of over-solicitude. Disciplinary measures are dodged for fear of arousing antagonism. Initiative is balked by anticipating wants. By making the child the center of the family, the welfare of the family as well as of the child is subject to interference. Ideal family life calls for cooperative living: achieving the delicate balance between individual rights and group rights. Spoiling a child by over-solicitude upsets this balance by inducing the child to regard its own welfare as paramount and that of the family as either secondary or nonexistent. It is poor preparation for socialized living. It augurs trouble for the future in the way of shirking responsibility, weakness of self-control, and an individualism so pronounced that adjustment to the reasonable expectations of others becomes a chronic personality difficulty. People who are products of this kind of over-solicitude may be among the ones who feel constrained to read books purporting to tell them how to win friends. Friendship calls for *mutual* solicitude and this is precisely what the spoiled child fails to learn as a result of parental over-solicitude. He learns to be an insatiable receiver and a niggardly giver.

The selfishness of the victim of over-solicitude may have other untoward psychological consequences. In her blind devotion to the child, the mother may become too zealous about matters of health, manners, character, language, and other areas of training. Too much talk of vitamins, germ-laden fingers, the dangers of wet feet, and the prophylactic blessings of clean teeth and spotless skin may result in a nagging atmosphere. What is more, it may cramp the child's spontaneity of play. This inevitably makes for feelings of frustration. Constant nagging and needless frustration are among the leading mental hygiene taboos. They are tabooed because they engender antagonisms and tensions which make the child veer either to the extreme of angered rebellion or the extreme of meekly melancholy surrender. Among other things such extremes defeat the very purposes of the mother's admonitions which called them into existence. Anger or sadness and a healthy digestion do not go together. As an ancient, Biblical mental hygienist observed: " Better is a dinner of herbs where love is, than a stalled ox and hatred therewith."

Another possible consequence of too much talk about health, diet, hygiene, germs, and regular elimination is that the child may become too preoccupied with the subject of disease symptoms. The emotional effect may be an almost morbid anxiety about every trivial departure from parental standards of ideal bodily functioning. The clinical thermometer and the enema bag may be put to work at the slightest provocation. Every scratch is viewed as potential lockjaw and every cold as a threat of pneumonia. In other words, such over-solicitude may be preparation for that common nuisance, the hypochrondriacal health faddist. He becomes a nuisance not only to his ever-changing " favorite " physician, whose time and patience he taxes by tedious descriptions of petty and imaginary symptoms, but also to his friends and sometimes to the public. He may be a fresh-air fiend or a vitamin votary or a drink-at-least-a-gallon-of-water-a-day devotee. For him cigarettes may be coffin nails and cocktails toxic potions. As a result of his morbid obsession with the subject of health, he thinks of a single puff or a single sip as sufficient to " put the skids under " an otherwise robust physique. It requires almost no persuasion to get him to join a vegetarian club, a sun-tan society, an anti-tobacco organization or even some obscure eat-raw-meat cult. It is obvious, of course that such a fanatic is taking both himself and the subject of health too seriously.

Excess of solicitude about a child's health need not result in hypochondria and fanaticism. It may have an opposite effect. The child may grow up to be too careless and indifferent about ordinary hygienic and dietary precautions. This is especially apt to be the case if the overcautious mother overstates the case by predicting that illness is bound to occur with every violation of such precautions. The youngster gets wet feet and no cold develops. He puts dirty fingers in his mouth without getting sick as mother predicted. During the flu epidemic he is forbidden to go to the movies while his cousin goes twice a week. If, as sometimes happens, *he* develops a case of flu and the cousin escapes, it is not to be wondered at if the youngster gets skeptical about the wisdom of all this health talk. The dire predictions fail to materialize. Why all the fuss about plenty of sleep, regular habits of brushing teeth, no eating between meals, and only small amounts of candy, when your everyday experience shows that these injunctions can be violated without inevitable and immediate catastrophe? Since too harsh an insistence on rigid conformity with respect to these matters usually arouses antagonism and frustration, skepticism regarding them is more likely to be welcomed than spurned. If what mother says the doctor told her will happen, fails to happen, why bother with the whole business? It all seems to be foolishness and irritating superstition. In this way an attitude of self-conscious, blatant nonconformity may assert itself in the course of time. It is a nihilistic attitude: nobody knows anything about diet, exercise, health, and hygiene. The logic back of this position seems to be that because not everything is known and little with complete certainty, therefore nothing is known. If almost nothing is known with assurance, then the person who pretends to know must be a charlatan. The result is a neat logical justification for doing pretty much as one pleases with serene indifference to official medical admonitions. By such specious argument the disgruntled nihilist finds it wise in his own eyes to substitute physiological impulsiveness for hygienic control.

The wise parent has to learn to strike a balance between this attitude of dangerous indifference to health on the one hand and the equally extreme attitude of anxious apprehension on the other. To achieve this is not at all easy. Nor is it easy to specify just where the golden mean between these extremes is to be located.

It may be helpful though to know what kind of extremes to avoid. By keeping the child from veering to either extreme the chances of locating the mean are increased. Actually, of course, the child in the course of his development will have to locate his own mean. His task will be rendered less arduous, however, if parental precept and example has already suggested to him that avoidance of extremes is one way to approximate the mental hygienist's dream of a perfectly balanced personality.

What the concept of a balanced personality implies

It may be profitable to pursue this clue to understanding the meaning of the concept of a balanced personality. We have suggested that the key word *balanced* refers to an avoidance of extremes, to finding the happy medium. As applied to dress and personal appearance it calls for building up standards of " good taste " allegiance to which will protect the individual from being catalogued either as an overfastidious, perfumed fop or as an unkempt, slovenly hobo. Neither the fop nor the hobo represent sartorial balance. As applied to learning the concept involves steering a middle course between crass, shocking, self-satisfied ignorance at one extreme and opinionated, painfully detailed, complacent pedantry at the other. The pedant is unable to see the wood for the trees and the ignoramus sees neither the wood nor the trees — and both are unaware of this intellectual blindness. With respect to sex the concept implies adoption of an attitude of enlightened self-control that will enable its possessor to escape the difficulties of the overinhibited, squeamish prude as well as the dangers of the overindulgent, prurient libertine. Both the prude and the libertine symbolize divergently extreme failures to achieve a balanced sex life. The prude is so afraid of sex that ignorant fear prevents appreciation of its beauty, while the libertine is so engulfed by lust that the beauty of sex is never cultivated. The one has too many inhibitions and the other not enough; hence both are off balance. Similarly, in connection with monetary matters balance suggests avoidance of both the Scylla of stinginess and the Charybdis of extravagance; for the miser's potential spending impulses are crushed by powerful inhibitions, while the potential saving habits of the spendthrift are never born because he is unable to curb the impulse to spend.

Almost every aspect of personality reveals such distortion by failure to achieve optimal balance between the extremes of over-development on the one hand and under-development on the other. The aspect of religion furnishes the extremes of the smug, uncritical, supercilious, pietistic bigot along with his antithetic brother of the left: the self-satisfied, stridently dogmatic, atheistic scoffer. A glance at the aspect of patriotism reminds us that a personality can be so fervently and chauvinistically patriotic that his country appears to him to be the apotheosis of all national virtue or, contrariwise, a personality can be so hypercritical of his country that he magnifies its vices and is blind to its virtues. Neither the jingo nor the " copperhead " is an ideal patriot. If we turn to the aspects of communicativeness, we find both garrulous and taciturn individuals. The former are such chatterboxes that they bore others by their ceaseless stream of talk, while the latter are so silent as to make ordinary conversation a laborious undertaking. Here, too, there is a golden mean between saying too much and saying too little, just as there is between talking too loud and not talking loud enough or too rapidly and not rapidly enough. In analogous fashion personalities can be too aggressive or too meek, too excitable or too phlegmatic, too serious or too flippant, too ambitious or too apathetic. Even in terms of the personality's evaluation of itself the need for balance can be detected. The conceited egotist exemplifies an exaggerated evaluation while the discouraged victim of acute feelings of inferiority exemplifies the other extreme. What we ordinarily call *self-esteem* refers to an optimal balance between these extremes.

The balanced personality is poised. A little reflection will demonstrate that this is a tautological statement; for to be poised means to be balanced. (The word *avoirdupois* comes from the Latin word *pensum,* meaning weight.) We have deliberately introduced this tautology in order to reveal a basic relationship between the implications of the concept of a balanced personality as just discussed and the concept of a poised, confident, secure personality with which we started this chapter.

The Art of Mental Hygiene

Parents who succeed in bringing up their children in conformity with the principle of mental balance will tend to see the youngsters develop into poised adults. However, to accomplish this is an *art* rather than a science. It is actually the art of living gracefully and efficiently. No mental hygienist can teach this to a parent in the way in which an instructor can teach French vocabulary, or chemical formulas, or a military salute. It is much too complex to be learned by drill or rote memory. It is too complex to be reduced to a series of rules like the rules of grammar. Most of the learning has to be self-learning in the give and take of everyday living. Most of the teaching, so far as the growing child is concerned, has to be more by casual parental example than by verbal precept. Furthermore, as has already been suggested, the child's learning in the last analysis is also reducible to self-learning. Through the years he must decide for himself what point between given extremes affords him the most congenial balance. How much stress to give to matters of health, how much to study and learning, how much to recreation, or how much to cultivating friendships cannot be specified by any mental hygienist in the way in which a cook can specify how much flour or sugar to use. The mental hygienist can warn against the dangers of too much or too little, but must leave it to the good sense and ingenuity of his client to stumble on the optimal dosage.

Some people are apt to be disappointed upon learning that so much of mental hygiene is an art rather than a science. The fact that the word *hygiene* ordinarily connotes men in white and disinfectants of measured potency possibly suggests that mental hygiene ought also to deal with the capital-S kind of Science. People of this sort expect the mental hygienist to have the psychological equivalent of the physician's *materia medica*. They hope to get sure-fire mental prescriptions. If the child has a temper tantrum, they'd like the mental hygienist to prescribe for such an emotional flare-up with the definiteness and speed with which the physician prescribes for a flare-up of malarial fever. If the child is painfully shy, they'd like to administer some quick-acting treatment that would work like magic anti-shyness pills. If they believe in corporal punishment for naughtiness, they'd like to have the omniscient mental hygienist tell them how to go about this "scientifically." Possibly they believe such a specialist carries a little black book with him in which he has a list of different kinds of naughtiness, each with its appropriate punishment. Mild impertinence,

so they believe, ought to be punished differently from " impertinence with profanity," and the triple offense of " impertinence plus
profanity plus lying " still differently. For each offense they expect
the little book to tell how many licks to give the child with the
dosage neatly tabulated to suit the variables of age, sex, and
weight. Accordingly, all that the specialist would be expected to do
would be to learn the precise nature of the offense and then find
the appropriate line in his " Table of Scientific Punishments." The
troubled parent would then get a " shake-well-before-abusing "
kind of psychological prescription.

We have deliberately exaggerated this sort of expectation in
order to reveal its absurdity. Anybody uninformed enough to expect this kind of applied science from mental hygiene, deserves
to be disappointed. If this is too harsh a verdict, it might be sof-
tened by saying that such a person ought to acquire a better grasp
of the meaning of the word *art* as employed in the phrase the " art
of mental hygiene."

A beginning might be made as soon as the worried or irate parent
asks, " What shall I do to this child? " The first answer a mental
hygienist might suggest is " Change your preposition." A cryptic
answer like this is for the purpose of driving home the vast psychological difference between asking, " What shall I do *to* this child? "
and asking " What shall I do *for* this child? " The first formulation indicates an underlying attitude of hostility to the child. We
do things *to* our enemies but *for* our friends. Enemies are treated
harshly and friends solicitously. It may not be irrelevant in the
present context, therefore, to point out that we may speak of a
science of warfare, but not of a *science* of friendship. Making
friends is an *art* rather than a science. And keeping friends is a
particularly fine art. It calls for the cultivation of that mental
hygiene atmosphere which makes a home a home and not just a
dwelling place: an atmosphere of mutual trust and tolerance and
security and understanding. Where such an atmosphere prevails,
the members of the family, paradoxical as it may sound, will be
induced to behave like friends and not like mere relatives.

The art of rearing balanced personalities thus calls for this kind
of home atmosphere. In addition, though, the concept of art has
some wider mental hygiene implications. It was noted that, although the general idea back of the concept of a balanced per-

sonality could be explained, this did not mean that the mental hygienist was ready to prescribe rigid formulas for specific individuals. The point was made that, in the last analysis, each developing personality would have to work out its own uniquely applicable formula. In this connection mental hygiene was described as more art than science. However, it remains to be demonstrated that this is not necessarily a confession of weakness or impotence. As will soon be evident, it is bound up with the very nature of artistic experience.

To ask a mental hygienist to prescribe a definite personality formula for a given child is like asking the musical expert to furnish an inventory of musical tastes the child " ought " to have. Even if the expert consulted happens to prefer Bach to Beethoven, he would hesitate to insist that all cultivated musical minds must endorse his preference. There is no stereotyped pattern of fixed musical preferences upon which all competent experts would agree. Suppose, though, that the mother, anxious to build up the musical aspect of her child's personality, persists in her quest by pleading with the expert to give her some positive help, what might he do? He might suggest the desirability of having the child learn to read music and to play an instrument so as to acquire at least a dim appreciation of what outstanding performance demands in the way of skill, control, and interpretation. He is even more likely to recommend affording the child frequent opportunity to listen to outstanding performances. If the concert hall is not accessible, then the radio and the phonograph may be suggested as substitutes. However, if mother wants a definite list of the " ten best symphonies," the expert is apt to balk. He is likely to urge the mother to permit the child to listen to a fairly representative sample of " good music " as it is broadcast and to base the collection of records in terms of what seems to be appealing to the child. With increasing maturity and deepened appreciation the child will exhibit new and different likes and dislikes. Such appreciation must develop from and with the child's musical experience and is not to be forced on a child. If it is to be genuine appreciation, it must be an expression of what the youngster likes and not an automatic echo of mother's musical convictions. Insincerity and sham are not stepping stones to a wholesome personality. To be inwardly genuine is more important than to be outwardly orthodox.

What has just been stated should not be construed to mean that mother ought to conceal her own musical preferences for fear of jeopardizing the spontaneity of the youngster's preferences. As a matter of fact, if mother is herself sincere, her likes are bound to assert themselves. The child will become aware of her standards with respect to music just as he becomes aware of her standards with respect to morals, literature, diction, religion, philanthropy, interior decorating, and politics. She and the father will make such standards evident by the books they read, the magazines they purchase, the radio programs they listen to, the table conversation they initiate, the friends they cultivate, the furniture they purchase, the charities they support, and the gossip they taboo or encourage. All this is of the very life and substance of growing up in a family and being in a home.

The mental hygienist is thus not concerned about a child's being kept in ignorance of parental standards. He is more concerned about the nature of some of these standards and still more about having them foisted upon the child with authoritarian disregard of the child's own needs and preferences. He is concerned because such regimentation thwarts self-development, initiative, independence of thought, and the emergence of that uniqueness which makes one personality, even within the same family, refreshingly different from the others. To regiment children is to produce robots and not personalities. For children being prepared for participation in democratic living it is especially important that parents sedulously avoid brutally arbitrary imposition of inflexible standards. A concentration camp can never be a home.

WHAT DOMINATION MAY DO TO CHILDREN

Our concern with the influence of parental domination on the personality development of children is not merely the result of common-sense analysis and clinical experience, but also a reflection of the outcome of several experiments undertaken in recent years. Understanding of some of the psychological issues involved may be heightened by a review of these experiments.

The psychologist Mowrer [1] was interested in making controlled observations on the behavior of children when given no voice in the

---

[1] Mowrer, O. H., "Authoritarianism versus Self-Government in the Management of Children's Aggressive Reactions as Preparation for Citizenship in Democracy," *J. of Soc. Psychol.*, 1939, *10*, pp. 121–126.

management of their affairs as opposed to their behavior under conditions resembling democratic self-participation. He worked with a group of youngsters living in a cottage at the New Haven Community Center. At this place the customary official rules more or less arbitrarily imposed by the adults in charge constituted the framework of social control of the group's conduct. The adults decided what constituted an infraction of the rules and meted out what they deemed to be appropriate punishment. Under the circumstances the children were the passive recipients of the consequences of externally imposed regulations. The atmosphere was non-democratic and might be described as one of benevolent authoritarianism. Under Mowrer's supervision this atmosphere was changed by the introduction of a form of self-government. Under the supervision of adults the children in the cottage were encouraged to make their own rules. Furthermore, violators of the rules were tried and disciplined by the children themselves. The adults intervened only when the action of the youthful judges seemed to be too severe. Incidentally, there was a tendency for the children to manifest more indignation with respect to transgression of a given rule than the adults might have experienced had they been playing the role of judges. When it became necessary for adult intervention to take place, care was exercised not to do so arbitrarily. The need for it in terms of the genuine welfare of the children themselves was pointed out. For example, the malicious or mischievous destruction of window screening, which some of the children viewed as a relatively minor and somewhat personal offense, was given a different judicial setting by enabling the youngsters to grasp its social consequences not so much as a matter of property damage as a matter of annoyance to the entire group; for the influx of mosquitoes affected everybody.

There were at least three important consequences noted by Mowrer in comparing the behavior of his subjects under the two regimes. In the first place the democratic regime made for a reduction in the amount of fighting. There was also a definite increase in the amount of cooperative behavior and, finally, there were fewer violations of the rules. In short, the older authoritarian regime seemingly resulted in more frustration and this in turn made for more hostility within the group. Antagonisms that cannot vent themselves against " powerful oppressors " are apt to find vicarious outlets. This is the psychology of the scapegoat mechanism.

Reaction to dominating authority is by no means limited to aggressive counter-measures directed against the " tyrant " or some innocent scapegoat. Antagonism may be active or passive. In the case of a " strong-willed," self-assertive, rebellious individual active antagonism is to be expected. A policy of ruthless brutality may " break the will " of such a person and his subsequent conduct may be characterized by submissive, unenthusiastic compliance with orders. Hatred of the oppressor is still present, but the will to resist is gone. This sort of meek, listless obedience is what we mean by passive antagonism. Both the active and the passive kind is being revealed by reports coming from the occupied countries of Europe. In less dramatic form the same reactions can be observed in children subjected to dictatorial domination at home, in school, or on the playground. A group of psychologists [2] studied such variations in the aggressive behavior of children by a more elaborate modification of the experimental conditions introduced by Mowrer.

In some respects the conditions arranged by these investigators may be regarded as rough approximations of three techniques of government or social control. Rearing a family and training children is also a matter of social control, so that these techniques are not devoid of mental hygiene implications. Parents can venture to " govern " their offspring by creating an authoritative or a democratic or a laissez-faire home atmosphere. These were the three experimental conditions investigated and it will be necessary to understand these conditions in order to appreciate the findings. Although the work was not done with family groups, the psychological factors involved are readily recognizable in family situations.

The three techniques of control were studied by modifying the administrative organization of clubs for boys. Of course the boys were not informed of the purpose of the experiment. No coercion was used to get them to join a particular club. They were free to participate in what they took to be a scheme to teach them such

---

[2] Lewin, K., Lippitt, R., and White, R. K., " Patterns of Aggressive Behavior in Experimentally Created ' Social Climates,' " *J. of Soc. Psychol.*, 1939, *10*, pp. 271–299.

skills as carving, painting, toy airplane building, etc. To achieve greater homogeneity membership in the four clubs was limited to 10-year-old boys, and an effort was made to arrange the groups so as to have approximate equality with respect to range of intelligence, social attributes, and economic status. Over a period of six weeks each of these four clubs met once a week under a given leader. At the end of this period each club received a different leader. When the leadership was changed the technique of club administration was also changed. The experimenters described this as a change in " social climate." The " democratic " leader would take charge of a club that had just been under " authoritarian " leadership and the director of the latter group would shift his dictatorial role to the former group. In this way each club was subjected to both kinds of leadership. To check on the results of such changes in " social climate " observers were stationed behind a transluscent cloth screen in a darkened part of the club room.

When a group was under the aegis of an " autocratic " leader, individual initiative was reduced to a minimum. The leader determined each step of a given project item by item so that there was an atmosphere of uncertainty concerning the next step. He also farmed out particular jobs to given boys in dictatorial fashion. Very often he specified just which boys were to work together thus depriving them of the privilege of selecting their own more congenial friends as work companions. His general attitude toward the boys was not so much one of open hostility as of detached neutrality or impersonal aloofness. He became personal only when the work of individual members called for words of praise or censure.

A more " democratic " social climate was created by having the leader permit discussion of issues of concern to the club with a view to having governing policies an outcome of group decision. In the first " democratic " meeting the full nature of the activity was outlined to give the boys intelligent comprehension of the tasks upon which they were about to engage. Instead of arbitrary imposition of particular assignments the boys were permitted to choose from among several possibilities suggested by the leader. As might be expected, the boys were also free to select their own partners for given tasks. In accord with the spirit of democracy the leader tried to identify himself with the group. He refrained from personal jibes if the work went awry, contenting himself with a factual comment about the work itself. Although he did not do much of the work, he tried to help by being with the boys as they were working and giving them the benefit of his friendly counsel. In this social climate there was relative group freedom under friendly guidance; for democracy does not necessarily imply absence of all guidance by those competent to guide.

For the purpose of noting the influence of complete group freedom on the club's activities, the laissez-faire type of organization was introduced. Under these conditions the leader refused to lead, permitting the boys to work out their problems in their own way. As he handed out the supplies for the work, he let it be known that no information or advice could be expected from him unless it was specifically requested. Accordingly, the leader kept himself as much in the background as possible and refrained from comment regarding the progress of the work except when questioned by an individual member.

The screened observers made notes of all aggressive actions in the way of actual fighting or angry comments or hostile joking. In the laissez-faire "social climate" there was a larger number of such signs of aggressiveness than in the other two. Leaving children altogether to their own devices, as every experienced teacher knows, is evidently not conducive to the general peace. The democratic regime resulted in a moderate amount of aggressive behavior. From the mental hygiene viewpoint the results for the autocratic regimes are especially interesting. In line with what has already been said concerning passive and active antagonism there were two kinds of group reactions to the "dictatorial" leadership. In one club there was a large amount of aggressive antagonism, more than when this club was governed democratically; but in other clubs the amount of overt aggressiveness was very much reduced. However, under these circumstances the observers noted the occurrence of passive antagonism in the form of apathy. Such apathy was not observed either in the laissez-faire or democratic "climates." It was characterized by lack of enthusiasm for the work, a disinclination to smile, absence of contentment, and other indications of repression interfering with joyous activity. This apathetic behavior tended to disappear when the autocratic leader left the club room. What is more, when the apathetic boys were shifted to one of the non-autocratic " climates " they often cut loose with aggressive behavior. In other words, the dictatorial leadership tended to preserve the peace, but only at the cost of numerous inner tensions. The boys were practically unanimous, upon being interviewed, in their expressions of dislike for this kind of leader. Of 20 boys 19 reported liking the democratic leader better than the autocratic and 7 out of 10 preferred the laissez-faire leader to the autocratic.

As applied to the home, the results of both the Mowrer and this other investigation are in line with what we have already suggested as an optimal home atmosphere. The dominating parent may secure outward obedience, but may be jeopardizing the child's emotional welfare in the process. Without realizing it, such a parent may be paving the way for either undesirable aggressive attitudes or equally undesirable apathetic attitudes. And what is of still greater moment to the parent himself, insistence on unquestioning obedience, as these experimental results suggest, is very apt to alienate the child from the domineering parent. The latter conclusion seems to apply both to those cases in which the attempt to dominate produces rebellious aggressiveness as well as to those in which it results in apathetic conformity.

To help children grow up to be adults capable of judicious self-direction and capable of intelligent, sympathetic participation in the responsibilities of democratic citizenship, the " domestic climate " must veer away from the extreme of authoritarian parental domination on the one hand and the opposite extreme of laissez-faire, parental indifference on the other. The " domestic climate " should reflect the larger " social climate " in which the child, when he is grown, will be expected to live, move, and have his being. His home must supply him with a suitable psychological framework by means of which he can learn the art of living in a democratic society.

From parental guidance to self-guidance

In terms of the framework of standards, tastes, and ideals reflected by the parents, the child should consequently be given increasing opportunity to foster his own interpretation of the meaning of this framework for his developing self. It is sound mental hygiene to permit the child some voice in the management of affairs that concern him directly. The ornaments in his room, the ties on his rack, the books on his table should, as he grows older, be more and more an outcome of his own choice. Even an occasional blunder on his part is a negligible price to pay for the self-direction and independence of judgment which such gradually increasing freedom places at his disposal.

The change from helpless, dependent infancy to the controlled maturity of the self-disciplined adult is to be achieved, not by sudden jumps, but by gradual transitions. It is unwise to regulate a child's life by the calendar and promise certain privileges at age 6, certain others at age 10, and still others at age 18 without enabling the child to anticipate new responsibilities by growth in the exercise of old ones. Where this is done, the calendar will be superfluous. Instead of fixed chronological ages, given levels of attainment will mark the child's readiness for personal control of ever-widening areas of its life. Many parents are aware of this as it applies to early childhood, but lose sight of it later. They do not set a fixed year or month when the baby is to be permitted to dress itself, a different one for self-feeding, and a third one for riding a kiddie-car. All along the baby is encouraged to try things for itself so as to prepare it for the complex maneuvers involved in manipulating buttons, shoelaces, spoons, and zippers. Given adequate opportunity for such learning the baby sets its own pace and as a result acquires emancipation from infantile dependence much sooner than a baby deprived of such opportunity.

It is the *continued* need for more and more emancipation which merits explicit emphasis, because parents are so frequently blind to this need as the years of childhood and adolescence loom on the familial horizon. They fail to realize that without such progressive emancipation they are apt to fail as parents; for the chief business of parents is to make children into adults, and full-fledged adults are capable of standing on their own feet without leaning on *their* parents. In fact, when the leaning obtrudes itself by being too pronounced, the mental hygienist is apt to stigmatize it by calling it *mother-fixation* or *father-fixation*. Translated into everyday speech, this simply means excessive dependence on parental guidance; it also suggests inadequate preparation for adult living due to lack of trained capacity for intelligent self-direction. It should be evident that more than one kind of umbilical cord has to be cut if such fixation is to be avoided. A child is handicapped by being tied to its parents longer than is necessary or more tightly than is necessary. The ideal parent is one who succeeds in giving the child gentle pushes by virtue of which the clinging, utterly dependent infant becomes transformed into an upstanding, independent grown-up. This transformation calls for a continuous drift from parental discipline to self-discipline, from parental guidance to self-guidance, and from the impulsiveness of the baby to the self-control of the emotionally mature adult.

11... THE DYNAMICS OF CONSCIENCE

A TROUBLED CONSCIENCE ALWAYS MEANS A TROUBLED MIND. THE poise, serenity, and self-confidence characteristic of the buoyantly healthy mind are conspicuously absent in the conscience-stricken individual. He complains of being low in spirit and shows it. His posture and gait suggest depression. There is a marked loss of appetite. Insomnia is another frequent symptom. In fact, a detailed catalogue of the symptoms of an acute case reminds one of the lugubrious advertising copy distributed by high-pressure patent medicine vendors. The victim is " miserably wretched, has indigestion and other visceral disturbances, lacks pep and go, is nervous and tired out but can't sleep, keeps hearing voices, and sometimes has thoughts of suicide." Of course the sophisticated person, aware of the relationship between such symptoms and his moral lapse, will recognize them as what he ordinarily classifies as *guilt feelings*. To him they signify that all is not well with his " conscience."

The case book of every veteran mental hygienist is replete with histories of patients whose difficulties involved a sick conscience. This is true even if the word *conscience* never appears in the book; for many such veterans prefer to employ a Freudian term like *super-ego* to designate the same process. However, there is no need to argue about suitable terminology at this point. It would be better to devote space to more revealing considerations.

OUTLINE OF THE PROBLEM

Most people take the fact of conscience for granted. If asked to explain what they mean by it, they are sometimes slightly baffled at first but after momentary reflection decide that " conscience is an inner voice telling you the difference between right and wrong." Just where this " inner voice " comes from and what is the source of its authority are left a mystery. It is hard to find a person willing to admit his lack of a conscience. A little deft questioning of one's friends will soon reveal that some of them are very confident of the existence of conscience and very muddled regarding its nature. They may tend to regard it as verging on the supernatural, almost like God whispering to man. Although they hesitate to be dogmatic on the subject, these friends will leave one with the impression that, in their opinion, a mystical halo surrounds the subject of conscience, a condition which makes ordinary scientific probing of the matter a little irreverent and very likely futile. It is almost as if ordinary psychological principles are not to be applied to the problem, because these principles have to do with the ordinary and the natural and conscience seems to involve something extraordinary and supernatural.

People holding views like this may even venture to support them by consulting numerous textbooks of academic psychology. They will find it easy to gather an impressive list of such books in which the word *conscience* is not even mentioned in the index. When it is mentioned the topic may be glossed over in a sentence or two as if the writer were reluctant to devote more space to problems so essentially inscrutable. The advocates of mystical interpretations of conscience can use this silence or fragmentary comment of official psychologists to support their mysticism by saying: " Professors of psychology can't explain conscience. They write long chapters on motivation and yet say nothing about the strong motives of conscience. They tell all about the hunger motive and the sex motive and learning mazes but nothing about the hunger for righteousness and learning the difference between good and evil. They tell us all about the nervous system and show how the brain cortex has to do with intelligence and the thalamus with emotion, but they don't tell us what part of the brain is used by conscience. This shows that psychology can't account for it. It's too much for science because when you come right down to it, it's a mysterious business."

A challenge of this kind merits respectful consideration. So long as so many people are confident their behavior is governed by conscience, it is fitting that those who profess to be specialists in human behavior say something intelligible about the subject. If *all* human conduct is to be explained naturalistically, it would be inconsistent to relegate the facts of conscience to the limbo of a supernaturalistic sanctuary. Furthermore, it is especially important for psychologists working in the field of mental hygiene to come to grips with the topic; because, as has already been stated, so much of man's trouble is rooted in a troubled conscience. It is as important for the mental hygienist to understand the workings of conscience as it is for a garage mechanic to understand the mechanism of the carburetor.

An inventory of the customary equipment of a fully developed conscience might be a valuable point of departure. In other words, what are the recognizable features of a high-powered conscience? The " still small voice " has already been mentioned. The widespread visceral distresses have also been referred to by way of introduction. These might be related to what people often call the " pangs of conscience." There is also an impulsive aspect which ought not to be overlooked: something keeps driving the conscience-stricken individual to do something. He experiences an impulse to seek forgiveness, to humble himself, to make amends, to undo the wrong, to straighten things out, to " take his punishment and get it over with." If no wrong has yet been committed and the temptation, nevertheless, be strong and insistent, he will experience the impulsive aspect very keenly. Its dynamic insistence may even induce him to speak of " wrestling with his conscience." Should he be successful in overpowering the temptation, he is apt to register self-satisfaction. He may report a thrill of pride in a personal victory over a tough antagonist. A theologically minded witness might describe this thrill as the " glow of righteousness." Accordingly, in terms of traditional vocabulary, there are four symptoms of conscience to be explained: the " still small voice," the " pangs," the " wrestling," and the " glow of righteousness." There is no need to draw on mystical beliefs in order to achieve a satisfactory explanation. However, there will be a need to revive some elementary teachings of psychology regarding emotion and motivation.

A SCIENTIFIC VIEW OF CONSCIENCE

Before describing such a naturalistic theory of conscience, it might be well to point out that such a theory does not assume any *inborn* mental mechanism by means of which a baby differentiates right from wrong. To attribute conscience to an innate moral sense or to an instinct for righteousness is to beg the question. It is the equivalent of assuming the prior existence of that which one is called upon to explain. It is like accounting for a great engineer by assuming that he was born with an engineering instinct or a great baseball player by endowing him with fielding and home-run-hitting instincts. Using the concept of instinct this way does not make for intellectual enlightenment. It gives a label to ignorance in the guise of knowledge. In the present context use of such a concept is particularly misleading. Not only is it poor logic because of its question-begging implications, but it is also very dubious biology and equally dubious psychology. A baby can no more be born with a conscience than it can be born with a knowledge of Greek syntax.

By denying that conscience is innate we are affirming that it is a product of learning and training. The initial urges of the new-born child or neonate, as it is called technically, are all functions of organic needs. Motivation in general and conscience in particular go back to these needs. It will be profitable to enumerate these basic needs in order to demonstrate how they are enlisted in the service of adults for the purpose of *teaching* the baby to be " mindful of the rights of others " and not be " a selfish little animal."

These needs have to do with matters of physiology. They include a dry pharynx and the distress of thirst; an empty, contracting stomach and the distress of hunger; a clogged respiratory tract and the distress of choking; a tired body and the distress of fatigue. Tensions arising from distended bladder and bowel, giving rise to eliminative needs, should also be incorporated in this list. Furthermore, other pelvic tensions that eventually come to be recognized as sex tensions are not to be overlooked in this inventory. The need for exercising rested muscles, or the beginnings of the play impulse, should be added. Are there any more needs revealed by the newborn child? What about the distress occasioned by being too hot or too cold or having a clumsy nurse jab a pin into the skin? Evidently the baby requires avoidance of extremes of heat and cold as well as a skin surface free from irritation or pain. The latter may be called the need for cutaneous comfort and the former may be designated as the thermal need. All these needs the human infant shares with every other mammal. For the most part they constitute visceral or internal needs and for purposes of descriptive economy may be summarized as the nutritional, eliminative, genital, respiratory, play or activity, sleep, thermal, and comfort needs of the organism.

The genesis of motivation lies in the dynamics of these needs. They are the various urges, impulses, cravings, tensions, or drives with which the individual organism starts its extra-uterine existence. As such they are unlearned. They are functions of the autonomic nervous system as it influences digestive, circulatory, respiratory, excretory, gonadal, and other smooth muscle tensions. They are the background of those biological processes the Freudians sometimes call the *id* impulses. In one sense they may be regarded as the equivalent of what Freud himself designated as the *libido*; for they not only serve to sustain the life of the organism, but their gratification is ordinarily pleasurable. It should also be noted that for the baby as well as for the kitten or puppy there are no ethical questions involved in this kind of gratification. To eat when hungry, to sleep when tired, to drink when thirsty are amoral acts to the untutored animal. There is no question of right and wrong: just crudely imperious body craving getting in its spontaneous demands. The Freudians are correct when they describe the *id* as blind impulsiveness, altogether selfish, and devoid of any trace of ethical sensitivity.

However, it is around these *id* impulses — these basic, biological needs — that the child's emotional attitudes, likes, aversions, and ideals of conduct develop. Character-training may be described as the technique of utilizing the motive force of these biological drives for the purpose of establishing specific habits of reaction in line with socially commendable ends. A clear understanding of the way this is accomplished will render the problem of conscience less difficult. By way of illustration, a single system of habits, such as the one pertaining to property rights and stealing, may be considered. Stated more concretely, where and how does our " conscience " learn that it is wrong and sinful to steal? How do parents train children to be honest? How do youngsters acquire a code of honor, allegiance to which renders it impossible for them to pick a stranger's pocket, to cheat at cards, to embezzle funds of a school club, and to steal answers by copying during examinations?

Among the early habits of reaction in an infant's life those involving the parent or nurse loom up large. It is the mother who usually caters to the impulses of the *id*, the unlearned physiological needs. After several hours of fasting, gastric contractions set in and the baby cries and squirms and manifests other symptoms of the visceral distress called hunger. By supplying milk the mother alleviates this distress. She thus functions as an indispensable accessory instrument to produce gratification. By the learning process variously called associative memory or conditioning, the *sight* of the mother soon suffices to produce a joyful reaction in the child just as the sight of the nursing bottle does. She is the means of catering to all of the basic cravings: cutaneous comfort; sleep, play, fresh air, warmth, as well as food and water. By a further extension of this conditioning process, other human beings in the baby's world come to serve as agents of rescue from various kinds of organic distress.

The point to be stressed in this connection is that long before anything in the way of ethical discrimination, logical reasoning, or conduct motivated by conscience is in evidence, human beings have come to occupy a position of vital significance for the baby. To put this technically: the *stimulus value* of people has been very much enhanced. There is thus no need to posit a specific gregarious instinct to account for such enhancement. The baby's desire to be with people is a product of learning. Had he been brought up by a pack of wolves like Romulus and Remus he would have developed a craving for the society of wolves rather than members of his own biological species. Human beings come to be important in the life of the child because his bodily comfort is so largely contingent on their services. A little later his bodily discomfort is similarly contingent on their disservices. Such disservices are conventionally called punishments. They involve the cutaneous discomfort of being slapped or spanked, the continuation of gastric distress by being sent to bed without supper, the frustration of the activity motive by not being allowed to go out and play, and similar interferences with the gratification of aroused desires. It is because of the all-powerful role played by adults in acting as conditioning agents with respect to the satisfaction of such bodily cravings that the desire for *prestige* is born. Human approval comes to stand for an almost necessary means of alleviating visceral distress. Contrariwise, human disapproval comes to symbolize a continuance or even an intensification of such distress. Even in the case of a very young child such distress is regarded as an *emotional* condition. In everyday speech we employ various phrases to describe such emotional episodes. The child is said to be " all upset," " in a tantrum," " terrified," " sulking," or " dreadfully sad." Sometimes the condition is merely attributed to a " bad mood."

Like the emotionally aroused adult, the emotionally disturbed youngster is thrown into a state of *excitement*. To appreciate what this means for the eventual development of conscience it is well to be reminded of some of the bodily characteristics of excitement. Casual observation as well as laboratory studies indicate involvement of the entire autonomic system. There are changes in heart and blood vessels. The novelists have suggested this by such dramatic phrases as " pale with excitement " and " heart pounding in excitement." Sometimes they describe the " red countenance " of the excited man. These references to changes in complexion point to changes in the diameter of the arteries and capillaries: widening of the latter results in engorgement and narrowing results in exsanguination. In addition to such blood pressure and blood volume changes there are widespread modifications of the tonus of the digestive tube. There may be a " lump in the throat " as the smooth muscles of the gullet tighten. There may be sudden loss of appetite and abdominal distress variously described as " burning sensations " and " sinking feelings " or " pressure at the pit of the stomach." Breathing is affected. In extreme cases the muscles regulating the organs of elimination elude the victim's control so that involuntary excretory action is by no means uncommon. Even the little muscles governing the pupil of the eye fail to escape the consequences of a " wave of excitement." This is the physiological basis for the familiar phrase, " wide-eyed with excitement." Many of the glands are also affected; hence palms may be moist, perspiration may gather on the brow, and the mouth may get dry. Physiologists also report action of the ductless glands. Furthermore, there are drastic changes in energy output. Sometimes the excited person has more energy at his disposal than he can employ so that it spills over into his muscles and they get so taut as to tremble. At other times or for other individuals an opposite result may be observed: a panic-like weakness sets in and the musculature wilts as the victim either flops into a chair or actually faints. There are still more changes; but there is no need to list them. For our purposes it is enough to note the catastrophic and diffuse nature of the bodily upheaval occasioned by excitement. It may be regarded as a physiological panic or a visceral turmoil.

Such a visceral turmoil involves action of the smooth muscles. Smooth muscle action is much slower than the kind of striped muscle action which enables a pianist's fingers to fly over the keyboard. In fact, it is this sluggishness of visceral action which accounts for the persistence of excitement after the occasion for it has vanished. The " emotionality " of excitement experienced early in the morning may color one's entire day. It is this persistence of the bodily set involved in emotion which is responsible for " spoiling the entire day " if the maid starts the fire with today's newspaper and places yesterday's on, say, the banker's breakfast table. Persistence of this kind is what is ordinarily called a *mood*. The banker's stenographer would recognize his " grouchy mood " as soon as he walks into the office. A mood may consequently be defined as a protracted, sub-acute emotion. Usually when moods are pleasant the visceral activity associated with healthy digestion is the dominant one. Should this visceral activity be thrown out of gear by the consequences of excitement or strong emotion, the resulting mood is more apt to be an unpleasant one. The term *complacency* may be used to designate the condition of adequate fulfillment of all visceral needs and the term *distress* to the opposite condition. A healthy cow chewing its cud on a balmy summer afternoon in a peaceful meadow is a good picture of complacency. Distress is too well known to require a separate picture.

By this time our hypothetical child waiting to be equipped with a conscience has gotten sufficient rest to fortify him against the necessary psychological treatment. By way of summary it might be well to review the equipment the child already possesses. He has a complex array of motivating mechanisms mainly visceral in nature along with the beginnings of a desire to be approved of by his fellow human beings. This desire is the result of conditioning incident to the daily ministrations of his mother and other people serving as instruments to satisfy the recurring bodily needs. The attainment of this bodily satisfaction makes for complacency while interference with it in any way makes for distress. The distress should be thought of as a more or less widespread condition of organic excitement, emotional upheaval, or energy release. All we have to do now is to add a few spare parts and conscience as a going machine will make its magical appearance.

Let us assume that the child is taken to visit a neighbor. While its mother is busy retailing community gossip, the youngster wanders into the kitchen and helps himself to an apple. He returns to the living room with bulging cheeks and complacent demeanor. Immediately his mother, because of the training or conditioning she has received, proceeds to register shocked amazement. The still retrievable portion of the apple is taken away from the infantile thief. Possibly the offending hand is given a smart rap while in firm and dogmatic tones the boy is assured, " God punishes little children who take things. Mother and Daddy don't want their boy to be a thief. You must never, never touch anything that belongs to another person. Only bad boys do such things. It's a terrible sin. Now go over at once and tell the lady you're sorry and that you'll never do it again." A verbal barrage of this sort is usually indulged in on such occasions. It will pay us to consider such an episode a little more carefully.

Being deprived of the apple produces distress in the boy. Having his knuckles rapped adds a little cutaneous insult to the injury. To have his mother scold and look at him that way completes the visceral havoc. In other words, the lad is emotionally aroused, which means a surplus of energy is suddenly released. This release may be manifested by his screaming, sobbing, throwing himself on the floor and kicking vigorously, or (if he has already been differently trained) in more restrained behavior which will be limited more to catastrophic inner changes such as a pounding of the heart, trembling of the muscles, and weeping.

Suppose a situation of this sort takes place two or three times. If the conditioning has been effective, the child's conscience with reference to stealing apples will have been established. That is, he is motivated in the direction of responding negatively to the sight of an apple belonging to someone else. If the learning is only partially effective, he may still steal the fruit but his conscience will bother him. When this happens, the experience that was his during the conditioning procedure will tend to be rearoused. His visceral complacency will give way to visceral distress. A " voice " will keep reiterating, " You're a little thief. God will punish you. If mother finds out she'll scold and won't love you any more." The inner turmoil with the vague aches and burnings and tensions within the trunk are the conventional " pangs " of conscience. The latter along with the modified heart action may be regarded as the physiological correlate of the " feeling of guilt." *Conscience thus represents a conditioned emotional reaction to situations involving moral disapproval.* Taking the apple touches off the visceral changes which followed such purloinings in the past. When conscience impels or motivates us to right a wrong, the motivating energy comes from the aroused emotion. In terms of our example, at the time the excitement was precipitated the boy was compelled to act in a specific way to obtain the forgiveness of the owner of the apple. Not until this was done did mother consent to smile at him and thus restore his disturbed visceral equilibrium. Had mother insisted on taking part of the boy's spending money and compelling him to purchase another apple to replace the stolen one, our picture of the way in which this available energy is *organized* into socially approved habits of conduct would be even more complete.

One other phase of this illustration should be considered and that is the positive as opposed to the negative side of conscience. Let us assume that shortly after the boy's disastrous experience with the purloined apple, the opportunity of helping himself to forbidden fruit again presents itself. On this occasion he permits the opportunity to knock without answering it. When his mother notes his " self-control," as she might call his failure to help himself to the fruit, she commends him for it. The verbal barrage now takes the following form: " You're just a fine boy. Mother is proud of you for resisting temptation. God loves little boys who do right this way. Tonight I'm going to tell daddy what a fine boy you've been. And just because you didn't take the apple, I'm going to give you an extra portion of dessert."

We have already pointed out how the approval of the parents is conditioned on the bodily process making for the satisfaction of the original mechanisms of motivation. With this in mind, it should be clear that such an endearing approach as the foregoing serves to elicit those visceral changes we have designated as making for complacency. The pleasure the child experiences now is similar in mechanism to what he experienced a few years earlier when mother said, " I'm bringing you your bottle of milk." On subsequent occasions, even in adult life, the successful inhibition of temptation makes for a visceral condition we label an " inner thrill," or what the professional moralists call the " glow of right-eousness."

Conscience is thus no new, mysterious psychic process different in kind from the mental mechanisms utilized in other daily situations. It is a name given to emotionally toned habits of adjustment to situations involving the rights of others. It is not a thing or an entity, but a manner of responding to a given group of social stimuli. *The highly developed conscience is nothing more than a highly integrated system of social habits.* When the habits deal with municipal or governmental problems, we speak of " the civic conscience." In the same manner we refer to other habit systems as a man's " religious conscience " or his " political conscience " or even his " artistic conscience " if he has acquired such habits.

ETHICS AND ETIQUETTE

In terms of the mechanisms involved, the essential characteristics of conscience are met with in situations not ordinarily regarded as involving ethical values. Consider the embarrassing experience of unwittingly appearing at a social function in a sack suit or house dress when all the other guests are wearing impeccably correct formal attire. The victim of such sartorial negligence undergoes all the symptoms of an attack of " conscience." A " still small voice " keeps tormenting him with such reminders as " why didn't you find out whether this was a formal affair," " maybe you can rush home and change your costume now," " you're making an awful break," " everybody is staring at you," " your social standing is going to be ruined because of this," and similar variations of the same theme. Along with the torture of the " still small voice " we find an internal agony identical with the " pangs " of conscience. Heart action and circulation are affected as revealed by the pounding heart and flushed face. Desire for food may disappear, especially as unpleasant visceral tensions begin to obtrude themselves in the consciousness of the victim. That is one of the reasons the sufferer describes his experience as one of misery. There is often a strong impulse to sneak away and to do something that will " prove to people that one knows better." The admonitions of the

" still small voice " are answered by an inner resolve to avoid a similar breach of etiquette in the future.

The entire experience is parallel to the sufferings undergone in a full-fledged attack of conscience. The parallelism holds both in origin and in terms of the processes involved. Nevertheless, the one experience is usually thought of as " natural " while the other is regarded as " mysterious." A plausible reason for this is to be found in the differences in the training or conditioning. The ethical training of children is surrounded by theological references and religious sanctions. Sacred literature as well as the institutional prestige of the synagogue and the church furnish the background for such training. Parents urge Sunday School attendance in the hope of having ethical loyalties strengthened and home teachings buttressed. Training in matters of etiquette, however, is not usually given any Biblical authority or reenforced by any official body outside of the home. There is no Sunday School to instil knowledge of and respect for the doctrines of Emily Post. The child is taught to regard stealing as a violation of God's commandment and to expect punishment both here and hereafter for breaking the commandment. Standards of courtesy, proper taste in dress, and approved table manners are all drilled into the youngster without any threats of divine punishment. The consequence is that a subsequent ethical breach with its attendant distress is regarded by the child as a manifestation of divine disapproval, while the distress incident to a breach of etiquette is taken in a more matter-of-fact way as being occasioned by mere social disapproval. Incidentally, it may be interesting to note the glow of satisfaction experienced by the person who is conscious of being eminently well dressed at a social gathering. A glow of this sort, from the psychological viewpoint, is probably not very different from the " glow of righteousness."

Furthermore, consideration of the social function of etiquette will indicate a telescoping of this function with that of ethical behavior. It is often hard to decide whether a given item of misbehavior should be classified as exclusively a matter of immorality or of discourtesy. A few concrete instances will reveal this difficulty. How shall we classify the act of reading over the shoulder of a fellow passenger, especially if what is read happens to be a very private letter ? What about listening in on a party line ? What about malicious gossip? What about refusal to help a bewildered blind man who asks for information about a house number? What about the healthy young person who fails to offer his seat on a crowded street car to an old lady on crutches? What about cursing one's parents? What about the unconventional young rebel who embarrasses the guests at a formal dinner party by coming attired in a sweater and shorts?

It should now be clear that much of the ritual of etiquette is for the purpose of lubricating social relationships. By knowing what to do and what to expect in our dealings with others we avoid much needless conflict. A code of etiquette serves to make people feel at home, induces them to behave with solicitous regard for the feelings of others, and renders them mindful of the comfort and welfare of friends and strangers. But these functions, broadly considered, can also be subsumed under the concept of moral purposes or ethical goals. To make guests feel at home, to avoid hurting another's feelings, and to be kind to strangers are all specific ways of showing loyalty to the venerable moral injunction to be one's brother's keeper. In terms of social purposes to be achieved there is thus no basic antithesis between ethics and etiquette. The psychology of conscience merges with the psychology of courtesy.

If this emphasis on the essential similarity between the psychology of conscience and that of etiquette is correct, not only is a good deal of the mystery surrounding the former dissipated, but an old philosophic teaching receives new support. According to some philosophers, esthetics and morality belong in the same category; the beautiful and the good involve the same principles. There is no need to elaborate the details of this ancient and still controversial philosophic problem. To do so would involve too much of a digression and carry the discussion away from the central issues of mental hygiene. A more profitable undertaking would be to show at least in outline form how the latter issues have something to do with esthetics. This relationship has often been overlooked even by some of the professional mental hygienists. And yet a vast portion of everyday mental distress is occasioned by annoyances, irritations, and disappointments having to do with the esthetic sensitivities of everyday people.

Marital bickering may start when the young bride registers very vocal disgust at the sight of the young groom manipulating a toothpick after every meal. Countless mothers have become tense because children substitute sleeves for handkerchiefs. Many a family quarrel has been brought on because a housewife's esthetic need for order prompted her to scold children for leaving skates on the living room floor or clothes on the bedroom floor. This same need is responsible for her irritation when father scatters cigar ashes. Nor are these irritations limited to the home. Concert audiences and performers suffer annoyances when people cough. Some movie goers are disturbed by the unesthetic gum chewer sitting next to them. Thousands of school children were and are subjected to momentary but not uncommon annoyance as chalk and blackboard cooperate to produce an acutely distressing squeak. Blaring radios, honking automobile horns, backfiring motorcycles, scale-practicing amateur musicians, rattling windows, and crying babies are still other examples of common auditory means of disturbing mental peace. Olfactory means of accomplishing this are also well known. Terms like " halitosis " and " B. O." constitute the advertising man's contribution to the psychologist trying to point to such frequent sources of esthetic distress. Glue factories, stockyards, and poorly ventilated locker rooms might also be mentioned in this connection. Cheap perfumes belong in the same category. The very fact that a cosmetic industry exists serves to reenforce this emphasis on the importance of esthetic values to people in our culture. Barbers, beauty parlor operators, dressmakers, jewelers, and florists all owe their very economic existence to the ubiquity of such values. These values are not only ubiquitous but also decidedly personal and crucial for many people. To appreciate this truth it is only necessary to think of the social importance of good looks, a trim figure, and graceful gestures. In the present context it is also relevant to think of the frequency with which the potential social value of a pretty face and an attractive physique is lowered by questionable taste in dress and by crude manners.

Good manners are a product of adequate training in etiquette. Training of this kind calls for more than stereotyped " good morning's " and " thank you's " and " after-you-my-dear-Alphonso's." It embraces all that is connoted by the concept of good breeding. The latter connotation suggests artistic furniture, pleasing costumes, and earnest solicitude about the welfare of friends, guests, and others. It implies both a fine technique of living and thoughtful consideration of other people's feelings. Art and morality need not be altogether independent variables. Good morals and good *taste* may go together. This reference to a gustatory experience is more than a convenient metaphor. In the light of what was said concerning the origin of conscience, it might be taken to indicate that a person with good taste is one whose physiological cravings have been wisely conditioned. One is reminded of the frequency with which disapproval is indicated by words like " nasty," " sour-faced," " nauseating " and contrariwise, approval is registered by words like " sweet " and " appetizing."

The close relationship between the good and the beautiful is further brought out by reflecting upon the ambiguous status of the adjective *nice*. Children are taught that it is " nice " to go to church and " nice " to get dressed up. They learn that people describe swearing, immodest dress, impertinence, ugly pictures and the taste of castor oil as " not nice." They hear their parents refer to the new neighbors as " nice people " and to the new automobile as a " nice car." Ethics and esthetics are thus neatly united in this indiscriminate but not incorrect verbal usage.

In teaching the child the multiple ways in which one has to be " nice " the parent is laying the foundation for acceptance of the ways of the larger social community. The child is acquiring habits of conformity to group standards. These group standards are products of the social tradition of the group. They are the ways " decent folk are expected to behave "; hence it is altogether appropriate to call them *folkways*. They refer to both the realms of ethics and of etiquette. They have to do with matters of dress, language, religious worship, honesty, loyalty, weddings, education, funeral rites, and attitudes toward class and caste — in a word, all that we mean by the culture or civilization of a people. In the sense that a people or a society transcends the ego of the lone individual, regarded as isolated from such a cultural setting, it may be helpful to think of this cultural setting as what Freud has called the *super-ego*. All that the child absorbs as right and proper and " nice " and in accord with the folkways of his culture becomes part of his super-ego. His code of ethics as well as his code of etiquette — his habits of conscience and his habits of courtesy — constitute his supero-ego.

How we learn the meaning of duty

Another way of approaching these aspects of personality is to ask how does the child learn to behave in terms of " I ought " as opposed to his unlearned " I want." Behavior in accord with established principles of conduct as laid down by group tradition and imposed on the child by means of family and school codes has to do with what one *ought* to do under given circumstances. It is what those in authority dignify by such majestic words as *right* and *duty*. In the beginning, as everybody knows and as has already been pointed out, the baby lacks the remotest inkling of rights and duties. His world is a world of sights, sounds, pressures, and visceral distresses. Even the latter may be too strong a term ; for a condition that is ordinarily distressing to the older child need not be for the baby. This is particularly true, for example, with respect to tensions incident to a distended colon or bladder. The baby responds to these tensions so spontaneously, impulsively, and automatically that the distress occasioned by inhibition of the eliminative impulses is nonexistent. Such inhibition comes later after the baby is *taught* self-control.

This is one of its earliest conflicts with its human environment. Adults, from the baby's viewpoint, must have ganged up against a little organism's right to excretory freedom. They *all* agree that one *must* learn to exercise control and that to be soiled is to be guilty of some horrible offense. As a consequence, this is one of the first *duties* the young infant acquires. In fact, some parents employ the word " duty " as a euphemism in the very process of toilet training. It is not at all uncommon for a child just learning to speak to make his inner needs manifest by saying, " Baby wanna make duty." For such a child the concept of duty very likely means little more than controlling the eliminative impulse long enough to get to the place mother specifies as the " right " place. It also suggests, of course, that to get along in one's infantile world it is necessary to curb one's *id* impulses and do what mother commands. At all events this particular and very restricted meaning of the concept of duty is so firmly entrenched and is acquired so early that very few, if any, people ever rebel against it. Even the most ardent advocates of " natural freedom " — those who regard any self-control with respect to sex impulses as a violation of " Nature's orders " — are altogether submissive and acquiescent when it comes to enforcing society's taboos on the " natural," biologically imperious excretory impulses. Parenthetically, it might be illuminating, in the light of what was said regarding the close relationship between codes of ethics and etiquette, to point out that the adult who chances to lose control of his sphincters and finds himself guilty of violating such taboos suffers from an intensity of humiliation and a feeling of disgrace just as if he had been caught violating some moral precept.

During the early days of its training the young child does not suffer any personal humiliation because of inability or unwillingness to govern the sphincter muscles. There can be no humiliation or loss of self-respect without acceptance of duties, principles, or obligations. In the case of such a young child, control is exercised because the child regards it as the *expedient* maneuver. It is as though he were engaged in a contest with his social surroundings: he experiences an impulse and adults demand that it be curbed until conditions *they* have specified are attained. If he complies with these conditions, they praise and reward. Contrariwise, if he behaves impulsively, they scold and punish. This is the kind of social situation he finds himself up against in all of its relentlessly stark reality. His ego — his self — has to come to terms with this reality. This is an example of what Freud called the *reality* principle. It also illustrates what Freud meant by the *ego* in contradistinction to the super-ego. What the young child demands is the relief or gratification experienced by yielding to the visceral tensions in question. Although his ego demands such gratification, reality in the guise of a stern parent interposes barriers to the immediate attainment of the goal. Gratification has to be postponed. The ego has to put up with the distress instead of finding instantaneous relief. It is a case of ego *versus* social demands. This conflict persists during the entire period of training. It ceases to be a conflict as soon as the child comes to substitute self-control for parental control. Another way of putting this is to say that the conflict ends when the child identifies *his* demands with parental demands. This means a change in the early ego demands. What the child now desires for *himself* is the kind of control the parent has been forcing on him for many months. In Freudian terminology, the child's super-ego has taken control of the ego. The youngster has learned to adjust to the reality principle. He has learned to postpone immediate pleasure either in order to avoid the discomfiture of punishment or in order to enjoy the consequences of parental approval. He has been transformed from a creature of biologic impulse to the beginnings of a willing participant in socialized living. The taboos of his social group are now his taboos. He accepts them and approves of them. Conformity is no longer a matter of expediency but a matter of doing what he himself deems to be right.

By this time it ought to be clear why so many modern students of human maladjustment devote a portion of many case histories to inquiries regarding the establishment of sphincter control. They note the age at which such control was established, the technique of training employed by parent or nurse, the child's reactions to such technique and other details that, superficially considered, seem to be far removed from the business of understanding a troubled personality. However, as has already been implied, such details may furnish revealing clues to the investigator. They may serve to show whether it was easy for the youngster to learn to curb his spontaneous physiological impulses and behave in accord with the mores of his group. They may indicate that his early reaction to such training was one of rebellious antagonism. Antagonism of this kind is particularly apt to assert itself if parental training was too harsh or punishment too brutal. It is not inconceivable that *enuresis,* or failure to achieve control of bladder functions, may sometimes be the child's way of retaliating for such brutality. In other words, this early initiation into the ways of civilized living may involve a conflict situation for the child. How this conflict was handled may be revelatory of his later attitudes toward those in authority and toward the codes of ethics and etiquette of his social group.

ACHIEVING PERSONALITY INTEGRATION

In broad outline the dynamics of personality development have now been traced. It might be clarifying to summarize and reformulate these dynamic factors in order to secure a more coherent and better organized grasp of their mutual relations. Since the concepts of Sigmund Freud have influenced the thinking of so many psychologists, psychiatrists, sociologists and others professionally interested in human nature, it was deemed useful to introduce some of these concepts as we discussed problems of conscience and personal conflict. As a consequence, we found it desirable to mention such terms as id, ego, super-ego, and the reality principle. These terms refer to different aspects of the various influences which push and pull the human organism in its traffic with other human beings and as it comes to grips with its physical environment. The *id* influences are those deriving their energy and impulsiveness from such physiological needs as hunger, thirst, sleep and the others catalogued on a previous page. They prompt the organism to respond to the environment seeking for means of gratifying these urges. Failure to get food when hungry or sleep when tired precipitates frustration. This constitutes an early conflict situation. The ego endeavors to find ways of dealing with such situations. In terms of this Freudian usage, the ego prompts the small boy to steal cookies or to snatch forty winks in the classroom by hiding behind the large geography text. All those influences which bring the individual into contact with the world belong to the ego aspect of the personality.

As the word suggests, the ego is concerned with the welfare of the self. It schemes and maneuvers to satisfy its own urges and longings. The rights of others are given only secondary consideration or no consideration whatsoever. Scheming and maneuvering is needed only because *id* impulses so frequently conflict with reality. This *reality principle* asserts itself in a multiplicity of situations: when no money is forthcoming with which to purchase candy; when the new toy fails to work; when fingers fail to clutch the distant object, and whenever the stern parent says " no." These are all phases of the real world with which the child must reckon. They balk the immediate pleasurable experience of gratified id impulses. To circumvent such frustration the child learns to anticipate the conditions making for such interference. If he is a thumb-sucker, he yanks the thumb out of his mouth as soon as he hears Mother's footsteps approaching. Of course, the sound of her receding footsteps is the signal for the thumb's return to the pleasure-seeking exercise. As is obvious, the impulse is curbed not because the child is sensitive to Mother's welfare; but because he deems it expedient to inhibit the impulse in terms of his own welfare. He exercises self-control for the same reason the professional thief refrains from picking the pocket of a sleeping fellow traveler if an alert detective has his eyes glued on the restless fingers. The self-control is the control of *expediency*. There is no question of ethical considerations determining the issue. The latter considerations are not brought into play until the influences we have already mentioned in the discussion of conscience are made a constituent and dynamic phase of the child's personality. These are the influences which render the child sensitive to the rights of others. When they function, the self-control is a consequence of the ethics of *altruism* rather than the ethics of expediency.

A conflict between id and ego is apt to be more acute than one between id and super-ego; for in the former case temptation has to be met by a " can-I-get-away-with-it " type of inner debate, while in the latter case there may be no debate as soon as temptation is recognized as a threatened violation of a moral principle. The person whose loyalty to the super-ego's ideal of honesty has been made an integral factor in the dynamics of his personality does not have to wrestle with his conscience every time a careless house guest leaves his wallet unguarded. Such a person may never experience an impulse to steal the wallet even if detection were altogether out of the question. In the absence of the impulse there can be no temptation. To this extent loyalty to ethical principles may serve to reduce tensions and minimize personal friction. Problems are handled in terms of such principles and once a difficulty is recognized as a special instance of one of the principles to which one is committed the solution of the difficulty is apt to be almost automatic. Consider, for the sake of illustration, the student who comes across a theme written by his older brother years before. This theme will answer the requirements of the student's assignment for English. Should he copy it and turn it in as his own work? Once he realizes that this would constitute plagiarism and that plagiarism is a form of stealing he may find it easy to dispose of the question — especially if his super-ego, his code of honor, renders any form of stealing taboo. Of course, he has to recognize the case as one covered by the principle. This is not always easy for people who restrict the concept of stealing to material possessions. They may be averse to stealing a car or a watch but not to stealing another man's ideas or his wife. However, this merely serves to indicate the need for making the ethical training of children definite enough so as to build up attitudes of sufficient scope to cover a vast number of particular instances to which a given principle of conduct is applicable.

Serviceable principles of conduct aid in the disposition of specific conflict situations just as a scientific formula aids in the solution of specific laboratory problems. Both the formula and the principle are generalizations intended to facilitate the handling of individual cases, to eliminate indecision, and to substitute the efficiency of automatic behavior for effortful blundering. Daily life would be both exhausting and confusing if we had to decide over and over again whether to be rude or courteous, trustworthy or dishonest, vulgar or refined, brutally lustful or wholesomely self-controlled, monogamous or polygamous, criminal or law-abiding. A healthy super-ego reduces inner friction and makes the going smoother with less of the wear and tear incident to doubt, mental conflict, and the fumbling search for a helpful solution.

It should also be recalled that the concept of the super-ego covers not only principles of ethics but also principles of etiquette. This means that knowledge of what the folkways demand in given situations will also serve to make the going smoother for the possessor of such knowledge. To know what kind of garb is called for at a formal church wedding, how to comfort the bereaved, how to behave at a funeral, when to speak and when to keep silent, when to be yielding and when to be aggressive — all such knowledge also serves to make for more efficient everyday living. Ignorance of appropriate dress, demeanor, and deportment is often responsible for needless conflict and the distress of embarrassment. It is akin to trying to drive a car through heavy traffic without being familiar with traffic signals. Conducting oneself through the traffic of ordinary social relations also requires knowledge of conventional social signals and social responses. Persistent violation of such signals stigmatizes the violator as either a boor or an ignoramus. Both the boor and the ignoramus have trouble in getting along with people, and knowing how to get along with people is essential for sound mental health.

The relationship between ego and super-ego is not necessarily an antagonistic one any more than the relationship between individual and society need be antagonistic. Only when there is a conflict does it become ego *versus* super-ego. A helpful analogy for purposes of clarifying this relationship is to be found in the organization of group games. Games like baseball or bridge require the acceptance by all participants of certain conventional rules. Behavior according to the rules is necessary for orderly progress of the game. Knowledge of the rules serves to lubricate the social contacts of the individual players. Without such knowledge, *team* play would be impossible. To the extent that each player knows the rules and abides by them, his super-ego may be said to have been properly developed and educated for team membership. Analogously, to the extent that he finds himself wanting to hog the spotlight by grandstand playing, his ego may be said to be interfering with his usefulness to the team aspect of the game. A second baseman sprinting across the infield to grab the ball trickling to the outstretched hands of the third baseman is a poorly socialized ball player. His ego and super-ego have not learned to cooperate; hence his inadequate adjustment to the exigencies of group play.

The valuable player is one who has learned to subordinate his impulsive desire for ego enhancement to the welfare of his team. Such a player tends to have a minimum of personal conflict because he has identified his welfare with the team's success. Put more technically, his ego impulses have merged with the requirements of group living so that super-ego and ego are working together in unified or *integrated* fashion. It is no longer a question of his prestige *versus* the team's prestige; because his identification with the team renders its success his success and its failure his failure. That is why he may feel chagrined if his pitcher, losing his temper, violates the code of sportsmanship by trying to " bean " an opposing batter; for this code is part of his personality, part of his super-ego. In other words, the ideal of an integrated personality calls for the harmonious functioning of ego impulses in terms of the rules of the game as accepted and understood by the super-ego. When ego and super-ego cooperate like the members of an efficient team, *personality integration* has been achieved.

WHEN CODES ARE WELCOMED

It has just been pointed out that conflict is minimized and unification of impulses furthered by the process of self-identification with group practices. As an example of such identification, affiliation of the individual with *his* baseball team was introduced. However, to reveal some additional aspects of the mental hygiene factors involved some more examples ought to be considered. The rather arbitrary and sometimes logically indefensible nature of many fixed social usages may be taken as a convenient point of departure. Society permits the businessman to purchase advertising space in order to tell others of the fine quality of the product he has to sell and the splendid services he is capable of rendering. A similar privilege is not extended to the young physician or the young lawyer. It is regarded as poor professional etiquette for them to do more than announce to the public that they are licensed to practice and are specializing in given branches. Of course, they may also indicate the location of the office and the time for daily meetings with the public. They may not " sell themselves " to the public by announcing their scale of professional fees, their list of cases " handled successfully," or the number of courses passed with distinction or of books and articles published. In other words, their professional code of conduct taboos any such effort to enlighten the public with respect to their superior competence over rival professional men. The young army officer must also learn to respect the taboos of his military caste. He cannot do as he pleases. He too dare not venture to call the military public's attention to his unique array of virtues by running full-page advertisements in the *Army and Navy Journal*. There are both written and unwritten codes governing the behavior of members of police departments and of fire departments. Sometimes these are embodied in imposing " manuals " or booklets of " Official Regulations " and constitute the rules of the game for the members of each of the groups concerned. To violate them is often tantamount to inviting " super-ego " trouble; for they constitute the professional conscience of the persons belonging to such groups.

This " super-ego " aspect is revealed in such familiar phrases as " medical ethics," " military etiquette," " Bar Association's Character Committee," " behaving like an officer and gentleman," and " the honor of the department." Every institutionalized group from a union of dockworkers to the hierarchy of a religious organization develops its own standards of conduct to which its individual affiliates are expected to conform. That is why people would be shocked to see priests, rabbis, college professors, or admirals playing poker in some waterfront dive. Similarly, they would be astonished to hear of the members of a labor union urging·scabs to fight the picket line. Differences in the codes prepare people for contradictions in behavior; hence they are not shocked if their lawyer refuses to undertake a case without some advance payment, euphemistically called a retainer, but would be very much shocked to learn of a physician who refuses to examine a patient without an analogous medical retainer. The ethics of one profession are not necessarily identical with the ethics of another.

To the mental hygienist it is interesting to note how eagerly most young initiates adopt, endorse, and strive to live up to the particular code of their professional groups. As William James once stated, " Already at the age of twenty-five you see the professional mannerism settling down on the young commercial traveller, on the young doctor, on the young minister, on the young counsellor-at-law." These professional mannerisms are often deliberately assumed even before professional training is completed. The future lawyer or engineer or rector is apt to ape the bearing, dress and vocabulary of some veteran leader of his profession. The young man identifies himself with this leader and the problem of right and wrong professional conduct is solved by using the leader as a model. What merits explicit emphasis is that such a problem is not necessarily solved in terms of a reasoned analysis of the logic of the situation. The solution is often altogether remote from the realm of reasoned understanding. Why should the young army officer wear metal ornaments on his shoulders and not on his sleeves? Why should the young nurse wear a little white cap and a pin on her blouse, but no metal shoulder ornaments? Quite manifestly any such departures from official uniforms would destroy the uniformity of the professional garb. But why have uniforms in the first place? Why not let each person dress as he pleases in terms of personal comfort? Professional codes seem to interfere with private initiative and preference. Still, in most instances interference of this kind is not very noticeable. The young candidate *welcomes* the " interference " as a privilege. The young nurse is thrilled the first time she can appear in public as a duly registered and correctly garbed nurse. Almost every West Pointer dreams of the day when he can don the symbols of a second lieutenant's distinction. The rookie in a police school looks forward to the occasion of his initial stroll along the street as a brand new cop in a brand new uniform. It may be a hot day and the uniform may be uncomfortable, the service revolver heavy and the shoes still heavier, but, nevertheless, for him the occasion is a glorious one and the discomfort hardly noticeable.

To be accepted by the group and to identify oneself with the group makes for almost enthusiastic, even uncritical, endorsement of the folkways, codes, and ways of behavior characteristic of the group. The group may be a neighborhood gang, a high school football team, a County Medical Society, an Epworth League, or a union of master electricians. The restraints placed on individual impulse by such codes and folkways are not necessarily experienced as frustrations. Because they serve to enhance the prestige of the ego, these restraining and directive super-ego forces fail to evoke protest and rebellion. They are accepted as self-evidently appropriate and desirable just as the ambitious debutante accepts uncomfortable high heels or chilly evening dresses. In other words, " super-ego " restraints, standards, codes and laws are by no means to be envisaged as yokes ruthlessly imposed on rebellious and protesting egos in the way in which a wild horse is tamed to accept the restraints of saddle and rider.

A vast area of socialization of the individual both in his capacity as private citizen and in his capacity as member of a professional or vocational or religious group is taken care of rather smoothly and often with an almost over-eager readiness to conform. The mores of the group are taken so much for granted that the neophyte rarely questions their utility, wisdom, or necessity. For a judge to wear a white wig seems altogether " natural " to the young British barrister. Similarly, the students in some theological seminaries are altogether prepared to wear clerical collars following their ordination. The youngster with baseball ambitions never questions the eminent correctness of the ways of big league players. Should he obtain a chance to join a professional outfit, he will not have to be coerced into wearing spiked shoes, the team uniform or rubbing the head of the team mascot before going to bat. One does these things because the tradition of the group ordains them as proper and appropriate. They are accepted as spontaneously as the college boy accepts the wearing of a Varsity sweater on the campus, a tuxedo at a formal dance, and swimming trunks at the bathing beach.

One accepts them in the same unquestioning fashion in which one accepts the fact that six games comprise a set of tennis, nine innings a game of baseball, twenty-one points a game of handball, and sixty minutes of play a game of football. There is no period of organized questioning and speculation prior to such acceptance. Even the person who prides himself on his rationality and who demands " proof " on all issues from the existence of God to the need for vitamins seems to overlook these challenges to his rationalistic urges. Otherwise, when introduced to baseball, he would plague his mentor by questioning the wisdom of limiting batters to three strikes instead of some other number, playing the game on a diamond instead of a pentagon, and having six players in the outfield instead of three. In other words, an alert youngster who keeps parents and teachers tense by a never-ending series of " whys " could enjoy a field day of interrogation by training his questions on any standardized game. And yet this fails to occur very often. The youngster's question marks are converted into periods by categorical comments like " that's the rule " or " regulations require that " or " you have to do it that way to play the game." In fact, almost from the start the youngster himself becomes a most dogmatic advocate of adherence to the rules as he learns them. Decidedly arbitrary practices associated with the game as played by his gang are tacitly adopted as the " right " way of doing things. Thus one gets his place in the batting order by yelling " first up " and his position in the field by calling " pitcher " before anybody else does. The folkways of the play group become his folkways without an undue amount of argument concerning the reasonableness of the group's way of doing things. The very fact that *his* group does things in a given way seems to be all the reason he needs.

WHEN CODES AROUSE PERSONAL CONFLICT

Justification by reason fails to obtrude itself until there is a clash between rival group practices, a contradiction in standards, or antagonism between individual impulse and the code of the group. Such clashes, contradictions, and antagonisms furnish the battleground for inner conflict and often pave the way for qualms of conscience. It will facilitate understanding of what this implies for the victim's mental hygiene if some definite illustrations of this kind of conflict are introduced for the purpose of showing how common and how varied such personal difficulties are.

In the realm of religion there is apt to be conflict when, as sometimes happens, personally irreligious parents send a child to a parochial school. At the school the youngster comes to regard a given kind of ritualistic form as necessary for the " good life," while at home he notes indifference to such form on the part of his parents. Another common example from the field of religion is that of the young man of Protestant or Jewish parentage who falls in love with a Catholic girl. As a consequence, he finds himself the victim of protracted inner debate regarding the merits of issues he may have taken for granted during all the preceding years. In the field of personal ethics we find such examples as that of the youth brought up to regard any kind of dancing as immoral going off to college and finding that many of his seemingly fine associates go to dances without losing caste in the college community. To complicate matters for such a youth, he soon finds that boys and girls who refuse to dance are not necessarily applauded for their refusal. They may actually be classified as " queer ducks." The conflict is the conflict between home standards and college standards.

Sometimes there is an acute conflict between personal ambition and devotion to family. A common instance of this is the case of the youth longing for a career which is frowned upon by his parents: the boy who wants to be a professional actor while his parents want him to follow the family tradition of the banking business, the law, or the church. Not infrequently there is a conflict between differing cultures. This is particularly observable in the first generation of children whose parents were reared in some European community. An Italian immigrant mother has ideals of dress and deportment which she quite spontaneously holds up to her American-born daughter as the " right " way to dress and behave. However, the Italian mores may differ from the American ones of the daughter's high school associates. The child has to decide between incurring the disapproval of her mother by, let us say, wearing dresses shockingly abbreviated in terms of Italian fashion, but quite the mode in terms of American style, or else braving glances of contemptuous ridicule which conformity to non-American standards might entail.

It is not at all uncommon for children to be ashamed of the old-world customs and habits of their immigrant parents. The very existence of such feelings of shame is indicative of the existence of a personal conflict. To experience shame is to feel guilty or humiliated. Once again it is to be noted that shame may be a consequence either of a breach of etiquette or a breach of ethics. The occasion for the feeling is awareness of disapproval on the part of others whose approval we crave. An explorer who discovers that a tribe of Brazilian aborigines are poking fun at his goggles, rifle, and helmet will not feel ashamed; because he has no longing for the social approval of savages. However, if upon getting back to civilization he finds members of scientific societies poking fun at some of his claims to priority, he might experience feelings of acute shame. This is especially apt to be the case if there is a public exposure of his ignorance of the work of some predecessor, knowledge of which would have kept him from " making a fool " of himself by claiming credit to which he was not entitled. The ridicule or disparagement by social equals *hurts*, while that of the aborigines may leave him either indifferent or slightly amused. It is to be noted that the hurt in question is occasioned by failure to abide by one of the accepted rules of his scientific group: never claim to be first when you are really second. Whether the explorer recognizes the hurt as the pain of conscience or as damage to his " feelings " will depend on whether he thinks of his blunder as a matter of ethics or as a lapse of good social form. In any event his respect for himself will be disturbed. Loss of self-respect is always of mental hygiene significance. It points to a wounded super-ego and this, in everyday language, means lowered efficiency and lowered morale.

SELF-DECEPTION IS POOR MENTAL HYGIENE

As was just implied, people do not always know how to classify their hurt feelings. They may be uncertain as to whether it is merely wounded vanity, a protesting conscience, or chagrin that is responsible for the persisting hurt. Sometimes their uncertainty is due to inability to make the distinctions such psychological analyses require. More often their uncertainty may be due to an *unwillingness* to face the conflict; for in a vague sort of way they anticipate the consequences of such rigorous self-appraisal. They have a dim apprehension that such appraisal, honestly carried out, would eventuate in a conviction of the self. It is not easy for most people to say; " I was wrong."

This reluctance to probe one's mental processes for fear of discovering evidence damaging to one's self-respect or prestige is what is meant by *resistance*. Because of such resistance many qualms of conscience are not recognized as consequences of immoral urges or unethical conduct. The qualms may be recognized as feelings of inferiority or as a loss of self-confidence or as constant anxiety or even as the beginnings of some bodily disease. The latter possibility may seem far-fetched and lacking in plausibility and yet it is very real and very plausible. To grasp this it is only necessary to recall what was said regarding the diffuse bodily upheaval that characterized the emotional conditioning of the child's " conscience." Mention was made of the loss of appetite, changes in heart action, and other visceral disturbances. Such organic disturbances are part and parcel of the total experience of feeling guilty. What the victim of such feelings sometimes does is to dwell on the bodily symptoms and to ignore the mental conflict responsible for the initiation and perseveration of such symptoms. As a consequence, he often makes the rounds of medical clinics complaining of poor digestion or shortness of breath or palpitation of the heart or chronic diarrhea. Nor is he helped very much by having an overworked, irritated clinician call him a *neurotic* or a *hypochondriac*. To the patient the symptoms are very real sources of distress even though the conscientious medical man can find no evidence of infection or damage to any of the bodily systems. To call the distress *functional* helps the diagnostician more than the patient.

What the patient needs is to have someone give him the insight that will enable him to make the self-discovery of a relationship between his bodily symptoms and his protesting conscience. Another way of putting this is to say that the patient has to be taught to learn to be honest with himself, to cease using his symptoms as a means of ignoring a conflict of conscience, and to make himself whole by effecting a reconciliation between the warring parts of his personality. As long as he persists in his neurotic behavior he is like a house divided against itself. That is why he has trouble standing on his own feet. Once he braces himself and decides to come to grips with the warring parts he is on the road to recovery. Whether he completes the journey will depend on the psychological skill of those guiding him, on his integrity of purpose, on the complexity of the factors involved in his conflict, and, possibly most of all, on his willingness to be altogether honest with himself. But these are technical issues that need not be elaborated here.

For the present it must suffice to stress once again that a personality at war with itself cannot be an integrated personality. Integration of this kind, it will be recalled, calls for teamwork rather than rivalry among the impulses governing behavior. Feelings of guilt suggest poor personality teamwork. Contrariwise, a serene conscience suggests good personality integration, an ordered mental household, and an effective technique of handling conflict situations. And from the viewpoint of sound mental hygiene one of the ways of developing such a technique is to cultivate a basic attitude of rigorous private honesty. To recognize selfishness as selfishness, vanity as vanity, lust as lust, greed as greed, and guilt as guilt as readily in ourselves as we do in others may aid us in warding off the consequences of self-deception. Self-deception is poor mental hygiene. " To thine own self be true " is still a useful mental hygiene slogan.

12... *INTEREST, MOTIVATION, AND MORALE*

I F THE BROADER PURPOSES OF THE NORMAL HOME ARE ENVISAGED in terms of the mental hygienist's perspective, parenthood will be seen as a paradoxical job: doing things for children in order to attach them to the home so that they can eventually detach themselves. The early attachment, it will be remembered, has for its objective the building up of attitudes of security and confidence. It originates with the parent's devotion to the child and eventuates, when all goes well, in a reciprocal devotion of the child to the parent. Because such mutual solicitude may readily become overintensified, detachment from home moorings may be difficult and distressing for all concerned. We have already referred to this kind of overintensified devotion as an instance of *fixation*. There are some further mental hygiene implications of this concept, however, which have not yet been elaborated.

FIXATIONS AND COMPLEXES

Whenever there is excessive or over-emotionalized *identification* of one's interests and values with those of another person or another group of persons, a fixation may be said to have been established. In terms of the emotional factor involved, such a fixation may be described as a *complex*. The young man who finds himself more attracted to middle-aged women than to young girls may be a victim of the psychological consequences of a mother-complex or a mother-fixation. Similarly, the young fascist who identifies himself and his destiny with the welfare of his party leader may be described as having a complex on the leader. In totalitarian countries a deliberate effort is made by party propagandists to create such a complex. Their purpose is to *fixate* the energies, thoughts, and interests of the populace on the personality of the leader. Such narrowing of the range of emotional attachments is what is meant by fixation. In somewhat figurative language it might be said that the central core of the individual's whole scheme of values becomes focused on the object of his fixation. At least this applies to instances of fanatical devotion to a leader, a cause, a wife, a child, a mother, or any other person. Fanatical devotion of this type amounts to obsessive preoccupation with a subject.

To clarify the relationship between the terms *complex* and *fixation* it is well to note their interdependence. Every genuine instance of extreme fixation is also an instance of a complex, but not every complex necessarily involves a fixation. A person may be upset by the sight of blood or by merely hearing the word. The fact of his *emotional* upset would justify classification of this reaction on his part as a complex. He is easily disturbed by any reference to bleeding and may consequently avoid movies described as the " blood and thunder type." He may stay away from prize fights. He would, of course, never consider medicine as a career. In shaving he would exercise more than ordinary care to avoid nicking his skin. In other words, his complex would have some manifest influence on his daily life; but unless he were to find it impossible or difficult to think of other than bloody situations he would not be the victim of a fixation. To cite another example: a woman might be unduly sensitive about her large ears so that she takes pains to arrange her coiffure and to purchase hats all with a view to concealing what she deems to be an esthetic blemish. Any casual reference to the beauty of ears might suffice to arouse her apprehension. Under the circumstances it would be correct to say that she has a complex on the subject of ears. But it would not be correct to call this an ear-fixation. Only the fact of the exaggerated emotional significance would justify the psychologist in classifying the attitude in question as an " ear-complex."

Fixations also manifest exaggerated emotional characteristics. They differ from complexes in being restricted to attitudes of loyal devotion, dominating attachment, and excessive solicitude. A common instance of this kind of fixation is furnished by the bachelor who repudiates the thought of marriage not only because " mother needs him," but also because " modern girls don't measure up to the old-fashioned ones." Such a bachelor has a *mother-complex* in the sense that his emotional life is hypersensitively responsive to the thought of his mother. He has a *mother-fixation* in the sense that he is unable to free himself from the rigid emotional bonds which bind him to his mother. It is this rigidity and narrowness or exclusiveness of his love that makes it a fixation. It is as though his capacity for affection were enslaved by his attachment to his mother. He remains a bachelor because of this enslavement. He needs a psychological emancipation proclamation to break the ties of his fixation.

Of course mother-fixations are not the only kind. There are father-fixations, religious-fixations, business-fixations, research-fixations, and many others. A person, in other words, may become too violently attached and too possessively bound to his father or to his church or to his business career or to his scientific research. A vivid literary example of the latter type of fixation was furnished in Sinclair Lewis's *Arrowsmith*. It will be recalled that Arrowsmith, the young bacteriologist, became so intensively devoted to his research project that he relegated his marriage to a position of secondary importance, and jeopardized his health by curtailed sleep, inadequate diet, and other violations of the hygienist's code. The research problem dominated him to the exclusion of all ordinary interests and duties. It possessed him with a fanatically tense possessiveness; hence the fixation. It is this sort of possessiveness, incidentally, which sometimes handicaps a child unfortunate enough to be the subject of his mother's or his father's fixation. The parent becomes so emotionally bound up with the child that a " complex " on the child might be said to exist.

Before discussing the nature of this complex, a word of caution might well be introduced. Not every case of devotion between child and parent or parent and child is to be classified as a " fixation " or a " complex." These terms are to be reserved for markedly intense attachments or those which interfere with wholesome independence of activity and freedom to develop and expand new interests. A generous dose of such mutual devotion is, of course, not only desirable, but indispensable for healthy mental life. But *overdosing* is necessary in order to produce complexes or harmful fixations.

To appreciate the consequences for the child of such an overdose of parental devotion, it is well to understand that the issue being considered is somewhat different from the spoiling resulting from overindulgence, for unselfish solicitude is often conspicuous by its absence in this sort of fixation. Indeed, a firm disregard of the child's own desires is by no means unusual. In some respects, although the parent may be unaware of this, there is basically more devotion to self than devotion to the child back of the parent's motivation. The biological and social ownership implied in the common phrase " this is my boy " becomes magnified to dominating possessiveness. There is such intimate identification that the parent finds himself living his life over again in the life of the child. He makes plans for the child's future in terms of his own frustrations.

A clear instance of this is furnished by the merchant who brought his son up with the fixed idea of becoming an engineer. All through the years the youngster had been the recipient of suggestions to the effect that a brilliant career in engineering was to be his vocational destiny. Parental pressure was all in this direction. It was taken for granted as a foregone conclusion in the same self-evident manner in which parents ordinarily take it for granted their children will " belong " to the family religion. And yet the boy had very little genuine interest in engineering. He really preferred cattle raising; but this preference had never been taken seriously by his family. As a youth the father had always dreamed of becoming an engineer. Financial reverses had cut this dream short, but the dream was not dead. It continued to lie dormant in the heart of the small-town merchant, who vowed the son would accomplish what fate had withheld from the father.

It requires no profound psychological insight to realize that what such a father might regard as his " self-sacrificing devotion to the boy's eventual happiness " is fundamentally a selfish devotion. He is using the boy as a means of gratifying a balked ambition. In more technical language, the father-son identification has resulted in the projection of this ambition from one generation to the next. When this kind of fixation occurs, it is *as if* the frustrated parent were striving to convert a defeat into victory by having his " own flesh and blood " do the scoring. The very process of identification means that father and son belong to the same psychological team — at least in the father's eyes; hence the possibility of a belated victory. Such a father is really trying to live a double life in successive generations.

The problem mother-in-law

Another and very prevalent manifestation of this kind of possessive identification is revealed by raising a simple question: Why do we have so many mother-in-law jokes and practically no father-in-law jokes? This fact about our folkways suggests a difference in nuisance value; mothers are more likely to interfere in the lives of married children than fathers. It does not mean that the former necessarily have a greater affectionate solicitude for the welfare of the new household than the latter. The solicitude may be equal in intensity; but circumstances render it easier for fathers to pursue a " hands off " policy. In the ordinary family the father is expected to function as a breadwinner by attention to his job or profession. Managing the home and rearing the children are regarded as the chief responsibilities of the mother. This division of labor is not absolute; for the father is also supposed to be mindful of his role as disciplinarian and mentor. His life is actually centered around two foci of activity: home and business. The mother, however, is more frequently restricted to one consuming interest; namely, her family. As a consequence, with the children married and established in homes of their own, she is more likely to experience frustration than the husband. He still has the business to absorb his energy, time, and interest. There is thus no persistent urge to find an outlet for his old paternal role by making a vocation of his status as father-in-law. This is not so true for the mother; hence the frequency with which she yields to the temptation to play the role of maternal manager in the new home. The ubiquity of mother-in-law jokes is an outcome of this state of affairs.

The mental hygienist is interested in the problem mother-in-law just as he is in the problem child. Both are exhibiting adjustment difficulties. Both are upsetting the balance of harmonious family functioning. However, a whole army of specialists is already coming to the rescue of the child; but the poor mother-in-law has never commanded the professional attention her plight merits. It may not be amiss, therefore, to utilize this opportunity to say something about her mental hygiene needs.

In many cases the meddlesomeness of the mother-in-law is a reaction to the fear of being shelved. Another way of expressing this situation is to say that the woman is afraid of being regarded

as having outlived her usefulness. Nobody who has taken pride
and interest in his work can give up that work without some regret.
This is unrelated to the economic aspect of the work. Even independently wealthy college professors are not very happy upon
reaching the age of retirement. Ballplayers dread the day when
they participate in their last game. The pensioned factory worker
likes to dream of some emergency which will induce the boss to
give him another chance to demonstrate his old skill. For many
people, in other words, the prospect of irresponsible idleness is
far from alluring. The thought of having " finished " one's work
with no socially significant projects to take up may be depressing
rather than comforting. It connotes " not being needed," and " being a sort of a parasite." The foregoing phrases all suggest the
despair associated with loss of self-esteem.

Incidentally, to digress from the immediate theme, many cases
of so-called " nervousness " in relatively wealthy but childless
wives may involve inner tensions of a similar sort. These women
have sufficient help to liberate them from kitchen drudgery and
their wealth renders it unnecessary for them to engage in remunerative outside work. Furthermore, they usually lack any special
training for such work. During the first years of marriage the
ritual of country club social life suffices to make their daily routine
not too boring. However, once a member of this younger married
set comes to regard childlessness as her inescapable destiny, symptoms of boredom may put in their appearance to be followed in
time by those of " nervousness."

This is particularly apt to occur in a conscientious woman
brought up to view idleness as sinful. Her mode of life fails to
square with inner ideals of the good wife and " useful citizen."
The signs of nervousness may be signs of a protesting conscience.
Another woman, maybe her sister, who has given birth to a child,
might never manifest such signs despite similar moral indoctrination and similar absence of any time-consuming domestic duties.
It is as if the dim awareness of pain suffered during childbirth induces a more complacent attitude toward what the conscience-
stricken childless woman vaguely regards as a life of almost sinfully idle pleasure-seeking. Such complacency is often the effect
of a notion that putting up with suffering " entitles " one to a
reward. Stated differently, there is a feeling of having " earned "

one's right to loaf luxuriously at the husband's expense because of virtuous submission to the pangs of motherhood.

A condition of this sort is especially bound up with groups whose cultural tradition makes the dual role of wife and mother the expected and normal ethico-biological destiny of woman. To fail to become a mother is consequently to fail in one's destined role. In the drama of married life such failure is akin to that of an actor who, expected to play two parts in a play, fails to make good in one of the two roles. Despite the fact that the childless woman realizes her own lack of personal responsibility for her childlessness, feelings of self-disparagement and frustration may nevertheless supervene. Viewing herself as a failure results in wounded self-esteem.

In the kind of person under discussion there can be no compensatory activity in the way of strenuous housework to make up for the failure in one of her dual roles by exemplary performance in the other. In fact many wealthy husbands would object to such activity as " menial " and as damaging to family prestige. They fear it might be misinterpreted as due to stinginess. For a wealthy woman to do her own housework runs counter to the mores of the group. It just is not done, and to brave the attempt is tantamount to being guilty of a breach of good form.

Because of her wealth, the childless woman is thus denied a means of " earning her keep." Should she chance to come from a home background in which mother had not only to look after the children but also do a good portion of the housework, adjustment to a life of unfettered ease may be harder for her than for a millionaire's daughter married to the son of another millionaire. Unconsciously taking her own mother as a symbol of housewifely virtue — with its emphasis on useful work, the iniquity of idleness, and the blessedness of thrift and efficiency — she finds herself distressed at the thought of being what her mother might have excoriated as " an idle social parasite, little better than a kept woman." Her symptoms of nervousness are a consequence of a chronically goaded conscience. Her life is sterile in more ways than one; hence the difficulties of adjustment.

An excellent way to dissipate such nervousness is to introduce some semblance of " social usefulness " in the daily regime of the victim by persuading her to adopt a baby or two. If circumstances render this unwise or impossible, other projects that *her* mother would have applauded must be made to serve as supports for the fractured conscience. To be effective such projects must demand *active* participation. Merely sending a personal check to the Red Cross, the missionary society, the orphanage, or the Community Chest will not purchase the needed mental therapy. Aiding worthy projects this way is too easy, too impersonal, and too passive. There is no intimate, self-identification with the cause being supported. There is no vital interest aroused, no perseverating sense of responsibility involved, no planning to be done, and no direct sharing in the routine work of the project. Once the check is mailed, the interest and responsibility subside. Only by taking hold of a project so vigorously that one's interest is gripped by the project can the mental hygiene goal be reached. The woman must make it her pet venture as if to say " this is my baby." She must work for it earnestly enough to be genuinely worried when it fails to prosper and elated when it does. It must be momentous enough to evoke sacrifices of time, energy, and effort. Only this kind of sincere interest, as opposed to the toying attitude of the dilettante, will make the self-imposed activity a means of converting an otherwise empty life into a significantly full one. To lose her nervousness she must lose herself in a venture that elicits her self-approval.

What the venture is to be must be determined in the light of the individual's background, talents, and resources as well as the exigencies of the community in which she lives. It need not be related to social service work. The pursuit of a hobby with professional zeal might work just as well for some individuals. Writing, etching, lecturing, painting serve as convenient examples of varying pursuits of this character. Still others have to do with earnest application to music or handicrafts. Some people may succeed in finding a sense of positive accomplishment by making gardening a fine art, some by winning golf tournaments, some by little theatre work, and some others by achieving national or local reputations in such diverse fields as photography, sculpture, stamp-collecting, or animal husbandry. Pedigreed dogs, thoroughbred horses, and clay pigeons may all be drafted by resourceful and ingenious therapists. Any project whatsoever, provided it is calculated to dissipate feelings of ennui and futility, will merit the therapist's approval. His job is to give his client something to live for by developing a zestful schedule to live by. He knows only too well that the leisure of the idle rich is a very dubious mental hygiene goal. He knows that to strive for leisure is commendable only if it does not mean the disappearance of the joy of enthusiastic work, the exhilaration of self-absorption in fascinating tasks, and the thrill of continuing progress toward some alluring objective.

It should be obvious now that the conventional mother-in-law problem is a problem of frustration. With her chief job finished, she lacks a satisfying outlet for her balked energies. Her meddlesomeness is a consequence of these energies spilling over into the domestic affairs of her child's household. To avoid this unwholesome frustration it is desirable to develop vital interests outside of routine maternal responsibilities. Every young mother ought to anticipate the time of her children's independence by fostering skills and interests that will serve to endow her future days of leisure, once she graduates to the mother-in-law class, with plans and projects into which her energies will sluice altogether spontaneously. These plans and projects ought to be as significant to her as her husband's business or profession is to him. By looking ahead in this fashion she can circumvent the mother-in-law hazard just as effortlessly as the average father avoids the stigma of being dubbed a " meddlesome in-law " by his married children.

INTEREST AND CONATION

The development of vivid interests is of such importance for meliorative mental hygiene that analysis of some of the basic psychological factors involved in the concept of interest is of more than academic concern. As mental hygienists we ought to understand what the possession of alert interests means for zestful living. We ought to probe into the meaning of the term *interest*. We ought to ask whether interests can be cultivated and strengthened. What causes people to lose existing interests? How can interests be controlled and fostered? Is the presence of interest in a given project or a given type of work adequate to signify ability to cope with the project or succeed in the work? Does interest in bowling mean that one will become a successful bowler? Does interest in chemistry signify future competence as a chemist? Many questions are thus obviously bound up with the psychology of interest. To answer them, even approximately and provisionally, calls for preliminary consideration of the meaning of this concept of interest.

Motivation and interest are closely related. Interests grow out of motives. One becomes interested in a book as soon as the motive of curiosity regarding the events of the narrative is aroused. The baby shows interest in the bottle once the hunger motive asserts itself. Motives are goads to action. They are tensions which clamor for release and incite the individual to activity calculated to bring about such release. The baby reaches for the bottle and drinks the milk and thus the gastric tension is made to disappear. This disappearance is the purpose of the drinking. Actually, of course, a different kind of tension is experienced as the stomach becomes full of milk. Satiety usurps the place of hunger. In other words, the tension of a full stomach becomes a motive which initiates cessation of drinking. To try to force additional drinking under such circumstances is ordinarily a futile procedure. The baby will resist such efforts most strenuously. It is now motivated not to drink. The nurse will describe this by saying the baby " doesn't want any more." Similarly, if the nurse takes the bottle away before the baby is through, the consequent vocal protests will cause the nurse to say the baby " wants more." She might also say, " the baby is still interested in drinking." This seemingly simple example may be used to develop more adequate comprehension of the psychological issues most closely related to the concept of interest.

To say that the baby is still interested in drinking is to say that getting more milk will make a difference to the child. We are interested in things that make a difference to us. Things that matter are things that make a difference. Reference to the dictionary will show that originally the word *interest* meant " it matters." Whatever matters to us is thus of interest to us. To build up interests for an individual means that we have to find things that will make a difference to him or things that will matter to him.

It should thus be obvious that interest is an outgrowth of motivation. Motives spur us on to seek means of satisfying the motives. This seeking, as was just suggested, is what is meant by the purpose of the activity. Only when the seeking becomes active is one justified in regarding purpose as being present. It is consequently possible to experience motive without purpose, but not purpose without motive. For a district attorney to establish that a defendant had a motive to murder is not tantamount to proving the defendant's guilt. Many people in the occupied countries of Europe have motives to attack their conquerors. However, unless these motives lead to overt action there is no purpose involved. When purpose is present there is striving toward some objective. This factor of striving is of particular importance for due appreciation of the psychology of interest. It will be profitable to consider this factor in some detail, but to achieve clarity of exposition some technical distinctions will have to be introduced.

Just as memory is an abstract term designating those mental events dependent on previous experience, so it is helpful to have a convenient term by means of which to designate that aspect of experience which we recognize as striving toward a goal. The conventional term psychologists employ for this aspect is the word *conation*. A football player struggling through a mass of opposing players in order to bring the ball closer to the goal may be said to be showing what conation means to the psychologist. It has to do with the dynamic set that characterizes every condition of alert endeavor. The very word *conation*, in terms of its Latin origin, suggests the process of trying, of endeavoring, of indulging in active effort.

For a conative impulse to be set in action means that a goal of some sort is in the offing. The goal may be described as the object or purpose of the striving. That which instigates the striving may be called the motive or drive. The football player's motive, for example, may be the desire for athletic prestige; his purpose is to make touchdowns and his conative endeavor is the actual process of striving to get the ball closer and closer to the touchdown marker. As everyone knows, the player is disappointed or experiences unpleasantness when his march toward the goal is blocked. Contrariwise, joy, pleasantness, or exhilaration are his when his progress is facilitated. What this means is that our joys and disappointments are functions of our conative dispositions. Changes in line with the aroused disposition occasion one kind of emotion or feeling, while changes antagonistic to the direction of our striving precipitate opposite feelings. Stated more simply in terms of the football illustration: the touchdown that brings joy to one team brings sadness to the opposing team. To the presumably neutral referee the touchdown is a matter of indifference.

Spectators prefer not to be neutral at athletic contests because they miss the emotional thrills that come with ardent partisanship. Taking sides means to identify oneself with a given contestant. As a result of such identification that contestant's success becomes our success and his failure our failure. This process of feeling oneself into a situation is technically called *empathy*. Because of their empathic responses the muscles of the football spectators strain in the direction of the desired goal as the ball carrier makes his dash for the touchdown. Their self-identification with the ball carrier results in empathic participation. It is *as if* they were carrying the ball and they find themselves playing the game vicariously. This is why active partisans of a team are more exhausted after an exciting game than neutral spectators. Neutral muscles remain more relaxed than partisan muscles. The partisan wants a given side to win; his conative impulses are bound up with the destiny of his team. Conation is the equivalent of active interest in the outcome of the contest. Sometimes spectators experience so intimate a degree of self-identification that they forget the *as if* character of their strivings. This was exemplified some time ago when a young fellow jumped out of the stands and sprinted across the gridiron to block an opposing tackler.

Children and unsophisticated adults witnessing dramatic movie episodes often exhibit similar extremes of empathic absorption. To them the villain of the picture is a very real villain and the hero a very real hero. They become so engrossed in the drama that the make-believe theme is temporarily forgotten. Their emotions become aroused and they experience elation and depression as the hero's fortunes rise and fall. It is not at all unusual for the movie spectator to weep, to yell, to sigh, to bite his lip and to give other overt signs of emotional turmoil. Exciting movies influence the autonomic nervous system of the spectator. His heart may beat more violently, his breathing may become irregular, and his palms may become moist. In fact, the existence of such autonomic changes is what causes him to classify the movie as *thrilling*. To be thrilled is to have one's emotions aroused. Emotional arousal means to experience conation, or to find oneself actively wishing for a given outcome and averse to a contrary outcome.

For most of us the make-believe character of movies or novels is usually in the background of our consciousness. The distinction between truth and fiction or between reality and imagination is still maintained and serves to make the emotional thrills different from genuine emotional experiences. It is because we recognize the "playful" nature of the emotional play that our joys and griefs when witnessing the drama are not confused with genuine joy or genuine grief.

Some psychologists have introduced the term *pseudo-emotion* to describe the emotional consequences of such empathic identification with events vividly portrayed on stage or screen or in a novel. Our joy when the movie child is rescued from the clutches of the kidnapper is not identical with the joy that is ours when our neighbor's child is rescued. The former joy is the outcome of a make-believe situation and the latter is the product of a really earnest situation; hence it may not be amiss to call one a pseudo-emotion and the other a real emotion. However, this does not mean that the autonomic changes taking place as we experience pseudo-emotions are not genuine. The thrills of the exciting movie spectator involve very real changes in blood pressure, in heart action, in breathing, and in the tonus of his muscles. The sham has to do with the external situation responsible for these changes. From the mental hygiene viewpoint it is exceedingly important that the individual learn to recognize and maintain the distinction between sham and genuine situations. It is important for wholesome mental growth that the child learn to prefer the joy of real accomplishment to the joy of imaginary or empathic victories. Pseudo-emotions are shams only in the sense that they are based on imaginary situations.

Imaginary situations may influence human efficiency in other ways as well. In striving toward some goal it is helpful to envisage the goal not only as concretely as possible, but also as coming within the range of *possible* attainment. Striving for fame or success is of little avail to the individual unless his striving is transmuted from the realm of vague generalities to sharply circumscribed, concrete goals. The intention to become a famous athlete will not be more than a dreamy hope until some specific area of athletic endeavor, like high jumping, is selected for intensive cultivation. Furthermore, the future jumper will not make very manifest progress in the realization of his ambition by daily practice sessions during which he leaps into the air as high as he can.

Without a concrete goal in the way of a visible crossbar such practice is apt to prove an abortive endeavor. A crossbar of known elevation gives the jumper a criterion of success or failure by furnishing him with a measure of the efficacy of his practice. His interest in jumping is likely to die out in the absence of any indication of improvement. That is why practice by jumping over a bar is superior to practice by merely jumping without jumping *over* something. For conation to be an efficient factor in the learning process the striving has to be directed toward a definite objective. Not only must the objective be definite, but it must also be attainable with effort. For example, it would be psychologically stupid for a teacher of jumping to place the crossbar at the six-foot level in teaching beginners. The discrepancy between the objective and their first jumps is going to be so large as to prove acutely discouraging. Because of such discouragement the learner will experience a sense of futility calculated to abolish whatever interest he may have had in becoming a proficient high jumper. It would be practically as foolish for the teacher to place the bar so low, say at the six-inch level, that almost no effort is required to clear it. The latter procedure would involve no real striving; hence the practice would be tedious and again interest would disappear.

To maintain interest it is necessary to give the learner a fighting chance to be successful. His goal must be adjusted just at the limit of his competence so that by resolute endeavor it can be attained. As soon as he can attain it with relative ease, it must be advanced a few notches in order to bring the joy of optimal conation into play again. The factors involved in this example are well known to most people who play games. We want contestants to be evenly matched in order to make the game *interesting*. One-sided games are unexciting for the winners, unpleasant for the losers, and boring to the spectators. They are devoid of interest for all concerned. No promoter would think of arranging a series between a university basketball team and one from some junior high school. No novice at tennis would like to take on a champion, and no champion would like to take on a novice. For the champion the match would involve practically no conation and for the novice the utmost limit of his conative resources would still fail to influence the outcome. Interest is a function of successful striving.

Under the circumstances the champion would lack interest because for him there would be no striving and the novice would
lack interest because for him there is not even a remote chance
of being successful.

THE PSYCHOLOGY OF MAKING PROGRESS

The foregoing analysis of the relation of concrete goals to interest as a function of successful or almost successful striving
might impress some people as so self-evident as to require no discussion. They might conceivably regard it as another example of a
pedantic psychologist telling people what they already know in
language many of them cannot understand. And yet the mental
hygiene implications of this " obvious " knowledge are being violated every day. Many school children are confronted with assignments poorly adapted to their talents. A given assignment may be
too difficult for the dull child and too easy for the bright child.
Absence of interest in the work is a consequence for both children.

Many parents and teachers in urging children to strive " to be
perfect " are overlooking the obvious in the psychology of interest.
Perfection is both too abstract and too remote a goal for the young
child. What the youngster needs is a very definite goal within the
scope of his abilities. Admonitions to emulate a big brother or to
" be a little gentleman " are common violations of this principle.
Yelling at a young child not to be awkward as he is striving to
learn to manipulate knife and fork is another common instance
of failure to apply the psychological principle under consideration.
Spattering gravy on the table cloth is almost an inevitable accompaniment of such juvenile learning efforts. The learning is not
facilitated by warnings about awkwardness and preachments
about neatness. It is far more likely to be aided by telling him
to cut his potato into five pieces, let us say. At least this gives him
a definite and understandable and attainable goal. Instead of acting as if a single stain on the cloth were tantamount to utter failure it would be preferable to take stains for granted and to suggest, as if it were a game, that the child try to reduce his score by
having fewer stains today than he had yesterday. Instead of a
counsel of perfection this is a counsel of improvement. Instead of
resentment and despair because there is no chance of ever " pleasing mother " there is more likely to be continued *interest* in being

pleased with himself for approximating goals so patently reasonable in their attainability.

What is true of the acquisition of table manners is also applicable to learning anything else from correct posture to a philosophy of life. We need definite targets at which to shoot and guns
light enough for us to manipulate, otherwise there will be a cessation of learning effort owing to confusion and despair. It takes
skillful teaching and adroit control to adjust target and gun to the
varying requirements of different learners. In the absence of such
teaching and control frustration and loss of interest may readily
supervene. Pious intentions to " improve one's English " or " improve one's health " or " improve one's citizenship " may never go
beyond the stage of evanescent yearning because of the vagueness
of the goals to be sought. The yearning will not eventuate in learning until delimited objectives are formulated. The intention to
enlarge one's vocabulary is less vague than the intentions to improve one's English, hence the first is more likely to initiate action
than the second. Intentions are abortive unless they are followed
by action. A broad intention like improving one's English has to be
broken down into more narrowly specific tasks before action can
take place. Enlargement of vocabulary is such a narrower task.
Deciding to look up every new word and jotting it down so that
it can be mastered and incorporated in speech and writing is a still
narrower delineation of what is to be done. The more definite the
task in terms of objectives to be reached, the greater the likelihood of translating intentions into actions or wishes into deeds.
Final goals are often too remote and too vague and too abstract
to lure the wishful dreamer from relaxed " some-day-I'll-get-
around-to-it " intentions to immediately active pursuit of the distant objective. The wishes may be sincere enough but the absence
of clearly perceived, realizable goals prevents the wishing from
becoming more than an intention. To wish to be educated, to be
charming, to be successful, to be popular, or to be honest may
leave the wisher resolute but baffled.

Abstractions do not readily elicit concrete action no matter how
alluring they may be as abstractions. *The road to hell is paved
with good intentions set in the mortar of abstractions.* The intention to be educated must be reduced to a multiplicity of definite
pursuits like finding out what to read and how to study and ar-

ranging a schedule of daily work that will convert the intention into positive action. The wish for personal charm has to be analyzed into very specific wishes ranging all the way from learning how to care for one's hair to cultivating a pleasing voice. The wish for success has to be translated into a medley of little successes: mastering today's assignment in physics, completing yesterday's unfinished job on the broken fence, and starting some work for tomorrow. The desire for popularity calls for answers to such questions as popular with whom and in what respect. Similarly, the intention to be honest demands consideration of an analytic sort: honesty toward whom, when, and how? Without specificity of analysis there can be no action. Without action there is no shift from the wish to the deed. There is motive, but no purpose. There is yearning without striving; hence the potential self-improvement dies stillborn.

This need for readily attainable goals to keep interest alive is illustrated by many commonplace devices to which people resort when pursuing remote goals. On transcontinental automobile trips, for example, a given city some five hundred miles away becomes the objective for the day's run. Even this goal may prove psychologically too remote for healthy conative functioning and so the ingenious traveler may select distances one hundred miles apart as sub-goals. He keeps striving to push ahead to the next sub-goal as his speedometer shows that the previous one has just been attained. In other words, his total journey from the west coast to the Atlantic is divided into a series of daily objectives and the latter into five subordinate objectives. As he speeds along the highway, his immediate goal is the next hundred-mile marker and he experiences the joy of accomplishment as soon as this distance is traversed. He then initiates a new conative set as he proceeds to work on the next hundred-mile unit. In this fashion there are at least five periods during the day of travel when his resolution is bolstered by tangible evidence of satisfying progress. What would otherwise be discouragingly slow progress toward his final goal becomes relatively rapid and hence joyous achievement of a sub-goal.

It is such a psychological need for sub-goals which induces authors to divide their books into chapters, teachers to divide their field of learning into courses and their courses into circumscribed lessons. Intellectual journeys would be too arduous without such divisions to keep the average student striving toward a goal more manifestly attainable than the vague, general intention of becoming a scientist, a philosopher, a priest, a playwright, or a military strategist. General intentions set the final goal, but sub-goals keep interest functioning and action alive on the long pull from youthful hope to the accomplishment of maturity. The road from the novice's timid blundering to the expert's certainty of touch is marked by a long series of little journeys from one daily job to the next over a long period of years and not by a spectacularly short dash over a royal highway. William James summed this up in the following memorable passage: [1]

Let no youth have any anxiety about the upshot of his education, whatever the line of it may be. *If he keep faithfully busy each hour of the working-day, he may safely leave the final result to itself.* He can with perfect certainty count on waking up some fine morning, to find himself one of the competent ones of his generation, in whatever pursuit he may have singled out. Silently, between all the details of his business, the *power of judging* in all that class of matter will have built itself up within him as a possession that will never pass away. Young people should know this truth in advance. The ignorance of it has probably engendered more discouragement and faint-heartedness in youths embarking on arduous careers than all other causes put together.

Dividing a long-range goal into a series of short-range goals thus fortifies interest and minimizes frustration by converting what would otherwise be almost imperceptible progress into very manifest headway. The student of chemistry, confronted with an eight-hundred-page text when he has to devote two hours of concentrated study to master ten pages, will be more discouraged if he thinks of the eight-hundredth page as his goal than if he selects the end of the chapter on page thirty as his goal. In the former instance two hours of work will mean one-eightieth of a step toward his objective, while in the latter instance the same amount of study will suggest one-third of a step. Interest, it will be recalled, is a function of manifest progress toward a goal in the face

---

[1] James, William, *Principles of Psychology*, New York, Henry Holt and Company, 1890, Volume I, p. 127. (Italics in second sentence of quotation not in the original.)

of optimal resistance. The short-range goal not only renders the progress more manifest, but also keeps the resistance closer to the optimal level by making it appear less formidable and less hopelessly exhausting. Four more hours of intensive study is less likely to dishearten the student than the bleak prospect of one hundred and fifty-eight hours of additional concentration on chemistry.

The introduction of short-range goals enhances efficiency in *measurable* fashion. Approaching a goal has what is technically called a *dynamogenic* effect on the worker or performer. By this is meant that an extra spurt of energy is released as the goal looms up ahead. Even tired runners sometimes seem capable of inducing protesting muscles to indulge in a final sprint as they glimpse the tape down the final stretch of track. Industrial psychologists have reported an analogous, involuntary speed-up on the part of workmen aware of the end of a work period. If the worker's output is measured and plotted on a curve, this terminal speed-up is graphically symbolized by a rise in the curve. The technical name for this phenomenon is *end-spurt*.

This phenomenon is in part, but only in part, responsible for a paradoxical finding of industrial psychologists and efficiency experts: more work, as measured by output, is accomplished by reducing the amount of time devoted to work and increasing the amount devoted to rest. Two British investigators, for example, found that several rest-pauses from seven to ten minutes in duration, interpolated during the morning's work period, stepped up production by more than six percent on the average. In a munitions plant in England it was discovered that lopping almost eight hours off the working week resulted in a twenty-one percent *increase* in weekly output.

Findings of this kind ought to have a salutary effect on the mental hygiene atmosphere of industrial conflicts. Once management realizes that labor's demands for curtailed hours of work will not inevitably mean increased costs because of reduced output, a crucial source of friction will have been minimized or eliminated. What both parties to such conflicts frequently overlook is the psychological fact that reduction in total working time, the introduction of well-spaced rest-pauses, by furnishing the worker with a series of short-range goals, may not only make for more frequent end-spurts, but, what may be of even greater significance, may strengthen the worker's interest in his work. We are more likely to be loyal to what interests us than in what frustrates us because of its exhausting monotony. A healthy industrial society requires *loyal* workers.

ATTENTION AND INTEREST

Arousal of keen interest is indicated by effortless attention. Everybody is familiar with the picture of the small boy completely absorbed in the exciting events of some dramatic adventure story involving the fate of his favorite fictional hero. His postural attitude while reading the story reveals the wholeheartedness of his attention. We may conceive of attention as that postural or mental attitude which predisposes the individual to perceive the object of interest with maximal clarity. A dog attending to a whistle tenses his muscles, cocks his ears, and shifts his body so as to bring the sound into line with his hearing apparatus. Even in the army the command " Attention! " is the signal for a definite postural adjustment. It means to be prepared for the reception and execution of the next command. Another way of putting this is to say that it means to be interested in what the commanding officer is going to say next. The soldier gets *set* to listen. Such a listening-set is exemplified not only by the postural adjustment of the hunting dog or the trained soldier, but also by the sprinter poised in the sprinter's crouch at the starting mark. He is attending to the anticipated pistol shot. For the time being this is his dominating interest. There is thus an obvious relationship between interest and attention. It may deepen our understanding of the mental hygiene factors involved in the cultivation of vivid interests to examine this relationship a little more closely.

Classical psychology has often introduced a threefold division in the category of attention: (a) primary attention; (b) secondary attention; and (c) derived primary attention. In the first division, that of primary attention, there is spontaneous, irresistibly automatic adjustment to the object of attention. A young baby following the gleam of a bright, moving light is a convenient example of this. The startled reaction to a sudden sound like an unexpected clap of thunder is another instance. An aching tooth will also provoke an act of primary attention. So will the sight of an enraged animal rushing toward us. Primary attention, as these instances suggest, is an unlearned act. The adjustment is made to situations possessing immediate appeal in terms of aroused motives. When we are dealing with simple, organic motives like hunger, thirst, and pain we find ourselves attending to or being interested in whatever promises to afford relief. The hungry child looks at the cake in the bakery window; the thirsty traveler searches the horizon for the sign of an oasis; the choking fireman crawls toward the open window. In each case the act involved — the looking, the searching, and the crawling — is part of the adjustment to the object of attention. For the time being, under the circumstances being considered, these objects have supreme interest value. The people concerned do not have *to force* themselves to attend to either food or water or air. This is another way of saying that primary attention is involuntary. The victim of the dentist's drill, trying to avoid " thinking " of the pain by " attending " to pleasant thoughts of tomorrow's picnic, usually fails in these efforts to out-maneuver the mental processes forcing him to intensely morbid preoccupation with the grinding, dental excavation.

Secondary attention involves deliberate effort. It is forced attention. Reading a dull book when one would much rather be out playing golf calls for this kind of inner coercion. Whenever there is a conflict of interests and conditions force one to attend to the less appealing interest, adjustment to the latter is a matter of secondary attention. A good portion of school work, particularly in the traditional school system, leans heavily on the alleged virtue of this kind of attention. It is supposed to be " good discipline " for the child to force itself to attend to what is intrinsically forbidding or " hard." If the youngster complains that he dislikes arithmetic or grammar, he is urged to disregard his aversion and plug away at the despised subjects because such heroic persistence will " strengthen his character." Should the latter appeal fail to move the boy, other appeals are usually available: threats of impending examinations, warning notes to his parents, or the assurance of future regret for present negligence. The significant factor to observe is the need for *extraneous* motivation when secondary attention is to be aroused. This differentiates it from the primary variety. It is the difference between doing what one *wants* to do and what one *has* to do. Reading a book for pleasure as opposed to reading it for the purpose of fulfilling an academic assignment serves to exemplify this difference. In brief, the kind of attention to which so many teachers refer in their stereotyped pleas for " undivided attention " is secondary attention. It does not come easily or eagerly or of its own accord. Grim determination is needed to prevent it from escaping once it does come. The adjustive process is strained and tense because there are counter-impulses to inhibit. For our purposes it is especially desirable to note this absence of keen, vividly spontaneous interest and the pull of antagonistic interests that characterizes secondary attention.

The third variety of attention is of particular importance because of its bearing on many problems of mental hygiene. It points to the fact that absorbing interest may develop out of that which demanded forced attention in the beginning. Such acquired interest suggests that originally extraneous goads to action have been replaced by intrinsic motives. To revert to our earlier example: the youngster who had to force himself to pay attention to arithmetic during his early school years may be *fascinated* by the subject later on. Analogously, a businessman, at the earnest behest of his physician and much against his sedentary inclinations, may start learning to play golf. His motive under the circumstances is not love for the game, but *fear* — fear of possible damage to his health, should there be no change in his daily routine of confining office work unbroken by interludes of outdoor recreation. In this instance the motive is also obviously extraneous. The man's initial attitude toward the game may well be one of grumbling antagonism expressed by muttering, " there's no sense in a grown man spending his time hitting a little white ball with a stick " or " it's foolish to sacrifice valuable business time just because some fool doctor says he's worried about my weight." His antagonism is not likely to be weakened by his first experiences on the golf course: the sense of frustration at missing the ball, the number of balls the caddy is unable to locate, and the humiliation of early scores close to the 200 mark. However, assuming the fear is intense enough or persistent enough to keep the man plugging away at the game, a subtle dissipation of his antagonism will emerge in the course of months. As he becomes more and more competent there will be less frustration, fewer lost balls, and gratifying improvements in score. By this time the man will be taking pride in his golfing prowess. He will talk golf and read golf. In extreme cases he may even think of himself as just as much golfer as businessman. No longer will he have to tear himself away from the office to the links. It will seem " no more than right " to let the younger men get the executive experience they need, while he gets the " exercise so many middle-aged men foolishly neglect." The old fear motive is no longer needed to goad him to play. Forced attention is no longer present as he tees off. The game has a spontaneous fascination for him. He loves it so that he may try to plan his business trips to coincide with scheduled golf tournaments. The golf bag becomes a regular adjunct of his traveling equipment. He is as much interested in his golf as a hungry baby is in its milk bottle: hence, if the baby's attention to the bottle be designated as *primary*, the man's attention to his golf is appropriately called *derived primary*. The adjustive process was derived from the secondary kind of attention, but has come to possess the immediate, intrinsic spontaneity of the primary variety. Extraneous motivations have given way to intrinsic motivation and the drabness of forced interest has been replaced by the glamor of wholeheartedly genuine interest.

The foregoing example of the shift from secondary to derived primary attention was also an example of the way in which interest can be cultivated. It was this latter demonstration which made this excursion into the field of abstract, pure psychology relevant to our discussion of mental hygiene principles. Vivid interests and mental health and a positive attitude toward life are almost synonymous phrases. To keep interests alive and to replace dying ones by new ones is a valuable mental hygiene goal. Attainment of this goal can be achieved provided one is willing to pay the price of forced attention to the fundamentals of new hobbies, new projects, and new skills until the stage of easy familiarity with the rudiments is achieved. This stage marks the early beginning of that competence which becomes the hallmark of the expert.

In general, we like to do what we can do well. As a consequence, it is often unwise to give up a new game or a new subject because it seems " uninteresting " during the first lesson. Learning the elements of a foreign language or of a skill like telegraphy or typing is ordinarily a somewhat monotonous, effortful proceeding. The first lessons are not the " most interesting " lessons. There is too much drill and too much rote memory work associated with most introductions to new subjects and new projects. There are rules to be learned, precautions to be observed, exceptions to be noted, and technical terms to be memorized. The novice feels incompetent and discouraged. His early mistakes and awkward blunders cause him to be dubious of the wisdom of sticking to what appears to be such a hopeless venture. What's the use of going on when you keep making the same error over and over again? Self-distrust and humiliation are apt to be in the ascendant in the initial period of learning a complex game or endeavoring to master an intricate field of knowledge.

One of the chief functions of a competent teacher or an understanding coach is to guide the neophyte through these psychologically hazardous first stages of the learning process. It is his business to keep up the learner's morale: to keep interest alive by adroitly planned short-range goals; to fortify persistence by words of encouragement; to reduce monotony by keeping dull, routine drill down to a minimum and to enhance latent enthusiasm by stressing every chance manifestation of progress.

The transition from voluntary to involuntary attention is ordinarily a somewhat dreary journey; but the passage can be made bearable and sometimes even positively enjoyable by an ingenious pilot in the guise of a psychologically oriented teacher. Such a teacher will act more like a guide and counselor and less like a relentless taskmaster. He will prefer praise to censure, calm reassurance to nagging fault-finding, and understanding friendliness to irritable bickering.

CULTIVATING NEW INTERESTS

The changes in attention which have just been discussed are also accompanied by changes in motivation. Stated differently, the cultivation of new interests is bound up with the cultivation of new motives. Since adequate control of an intelligent regime of mental hygiene is so intimately bound up with control of motives, it may prove profitable to outline the motivational factors involved in the shift from secondary to derived primary attention. An important issue is involved here: are the motives which initiate activity necessarily the same motives which keep that activity going through the years? A youngster may start to study Latin because his father insists on such study. The motive under the circumstances is fear of his father's disapproval. There is no direct, intrinsic interest in the language. The drive which impels the youngster to force himself to memorize conjugations, declensions, and vocabulary is an extraneous drive. The goad to study comes from the outside and the interest is an artificial interest. All this has already been explained. However, what has to be considered in the present context is this question: Will the original motive of fear still be operative in goading the person to work on his Latin years later, after he has become a distinguished professor of classical literature? Actually, as ought to be clear now, very little goading will be required. His love for the language may suffice to keep him studying. Put rather bluntly, we might say that love has replaced fear as a motive.

This replacement of one motive by another has been variously described by psychologists. Of course, to digress slightly, not all psychologists have admitted the existence of this seeming replacement. Both Freud and McDougall have maintained that original or instigating motives continue to be operative all through the years and through all the vicissitudes of the learner's behavior. In terms of our present example, they might have contended that deep within the Latin professor's seemingly wholehearted and joyous devotion to his Latin there may be a latent fear of possible loss of prestige. They would regard this fear as a mental descendant of the old fear of his father's disapproval. The professor keeps studying, they might have said, because he still fears the consequences of not studying. The ghost of his father's voice continues to admonish him in the guise of the " still small voice of his conscience." On the other hand, psychologists like Woodworth and Gordon Allport would reject such an interpretation. They would stress the independence of the new motive — its detachment from any functional linkage to the original motive. Allport has reference to this in writing of what he calls the " functional autonomy of motives." What he means by this phrase is brought out in the following passages: [2]

[2] Allport, Gordon, *Personality*, New York, Henry Holt and Company, 1937, pp. 196–197.

Workmanship is a good example of functional autonomy. A good workman feels compelled to do clean-cut jobs even though his security, or the praise of others, no longer depend upon high standards. . . . A businessman, long since secure economically, works himself into ill-health, and sometimes even back into poverty, for the sake of carrying on his plans. What was once an instrumental technique becomes a master-motive. . . .

The pursuit of literature, the development of good taste in clothes, the use of cosmetics, the acquiring of an automobile, strolls in the public park, or a winter in Miami, may first serve, let us say, the interests of sex. But every one of the instrumental activities may become an interest in itself, held for a lifetime, long after the erotic motive has been laid away in lavender. People often find that they have lost allegiance to their original aims because of their deliberate preference for the many ways of achieving them.

The maternal sentiment offers an excellent final illustration. Many young mothers bear their children unwillingly, dismayed at the thought of the drudgery of the future. At first they may be indifferent to, or even hate, their offspring; the " parental instinct " seems wholly lacking. The only motives that hold such a mother to child-tending may be fear of what her critical neighbors will say, fear of the law, a habit of doing any job well, or perhaps a dim hope that the child will provide security for her in her old age. However gross these motives, they are sufficient to hold her to her work, until through the practice of devotion her burden becomes a joy. As her love for the child develops, her earlier practical motives are forgotten. In later years not one of these original motives may operate. The child may be incompetent, criminal, a disgrace to her, and far from serving as a staff for her declining years, he may continue to drain her resources and vitality. The neighbors may criticize her for indulging the child, the law may exonerate her from allegiance; she certainly feels no pride in such a child; yet she sticks to him. The tenacity of the maternal sentiment under such adversity is proverbial.

This very " tenacity of the maternal sentiment " may sometimes, especially if there is a death in the family, tax the resources of mental hygiene therapy. A dramatic instance of this was furnished some years ago by the acute grief of the wife of a successful scientist whose only daughter died during the influenza epidemic. The mother's devotion to the child had been so intense that in many respects it conformed to what we have already described as a fixation. All of the mother's basic values and dominant hopes had been centered in the daughter. With the sudden death of the latter there was, as might have been anticipated, a catastrophic collapse of the mother's inner psychological household. There was complete frustration — 100 percent complete frustration — of her chief purpose in life. She behaved as if the loss of her daughter had deprived her of every interest in living. Her attending physician had to guard against the possibility of suicide. Even months after the funeral she was still refusing to see her old friends, still refusing to resume personal supervision of domestic duties, still refusing to find distraction in reading and travel. Despite heroic efforts of husband and physician she refused to be comforted. In technical language she was still brooding over the lost object of her fixation. Nothing seemed to matter any more: all interest seemed to have been crushed out of existence. The prognosis seemed to be hopeless until it was suggested that the clothing of the daughter be donated to some underprivileged girl.

By dint of much persuasion she was induced to force herself to visit the squalid home of such a girl. While there the suggestion was made that it might be a fine thing if the community had a settlement home to which such seriously underprivileged youngsters could be sent. This suggestion was followed by the casual proposal that the scientist found such an institution in memory of his daughter. Noting the flicker of interest this proposal aroused in the patient, immediate steps were taken to make it a reality. A house was rented and a sign painter commissioned to make an appropriate sign indicating that the new institution was a memorial to the daughter. By thus naming the institution after the daughter a mental bridge was established by means of which the mother could more readily establish emotional contact with the new venture. In the course of the following days she began to visit the new premises more and more frequently. She began to take an active interest in its management and to interview the orphan children being considered as candidates for adoption. Before long she was more and more absorbed in the lives of the youngsters finally accepted for admission. Her days began to be filled with plans for improving the settlement home. She lost herself in the multiplicity of details of arranging for better meals, getting free music lessons for talented orphans, interviewing school teachers to check on the educational progress of her " adopted daughters," seeing to it that the sick ones were getting proper nursing and the thousand and one other activities involved in being foster mother to twenty-odd girls. Once again she had a purpose in life. More accurately stated, she now had many purposes; for each one of her charges constituted a focus of interest and consequently supplied her with a medley of problems to consider and obligations to discharge. An otherwise empty life had been transformed into a regime full of personally gratifying and significant things to plan and accomplish. The new motives, the new interests, and the new purposes were established on a basis of secure autonomy.

The principle of the " functional autonomy of motives," it should be made clear, thus sums up the genesis of many new interests in life. It points to a frequently overlooked source of salvation for the grief-stricken or despondent individual complaining of the dreariness of the present and the bleakness of the future. When the dominant wish is for death, and life seems to have lost its savor, what can the mental hygienist say or do? One thing he does not do, as has just been indicated, is to indulge in abstract philosophizing on the meaning of life and the iniquity of suicide. Debates on the " is-life-worthwhile " or " is-suicide-ever-justified " themes are not only tedious forensic exercises, but also abortive mental hygiene procedures. What gives life zest is having interesting things to do, personally meaningful projects to complete, and absorbing goals toward which one can strive. Such things, projects, and goals may have to be forced on the grieving or emotionally listless person in the beginning by whatever technique of ingenious coercion the individual conditions warrant; but once the outer push suffices to instigate action, then, in terms of the principle of functional autonomy, that action may still continue long after the push has become a matter of history. The outer push will have been transformed into an inner drive; the forced interest will have become converted into spontaneous and genuine interest, and the general attitude of despair and morbid brooding will have given way to one of wholesome preoccupation with the progress of a venture that will seem almost self-evidently thrilling in its importance. This is the mental hygiene significance of the ancient insight into the paradox of finding one's life by losing it. To lose oneself in the grime and glamor, the setbacks and the forward thrusts of significant work is to find life zestfully meaningful.

13... *COPING WITH REALITY*

As previous chapters have indicated, mental hygiene is concerned with the everyday troubles of everyday people. It was also pointed out that mental hygiene is interested in aiding people to ward off trouble and in meeting it bravely and intelligently when it cannot be warded off. This implies, of course, the existence of craven and stupid ways of handling trouble. Furthermore, one may also note brave and stupid modes of facing difficulties, for bravery and intelligence are not necessarily yoked together. Bright students are sometimes tense with worry prior to examinations, while some dull students may approach examinations with an attitude of debonair confidence. Some financially successful businessmen are mental hygiene failures because, despite their affluence, they are chronically anticipating reverses, anxious about the future, and overtense in the present. Many mothers manufacture troubles for themselves by conjuring up vivid imaginary pictures of traffic accidents to their children. Still other mothers may veer to the opposite extreme of careless indifference by neglecting to take reasonable precautions with respect to traffic hazards. There are people whose attitude toward the future is one of unjustified, indolent optimism just as there are other people whose temperaments seem to predispose them to equally unjustified, frantic pessimism. There are so many ways of reacting to difficulties that it is desirable to survey the varying modes of adjustment, especially those which veer in the direction of maladjustment. Learning to recognize the latter inefficient techniques of adjustment may help us to guard against fostering such techniques.

Some Adjustment Difficulties

A stock slogan of the veteran mental hygienist is " adjustment to reality." He urges teachers and parents to make such adjustment the goal of effective mental hygiene. He warns them to be on the alert for signs of failure to adjust to reality. What are these signs? Well, almost any indication of an extreme exaggeration of a personality trait may constitute such a sign. To be too preoccupied with daydreams may be symptomatic; so may a continuous round of shifting activity with no time out for relaxed and relaxing reverie. Painfully shy meekness as well as glaringly evident boastfulness may also be maladjustment indicators. Another common indicator is a fanatic concern about cleanliness or a morbid fear of germs.

The mental hygienist also makes note of the fact that some people live too cautiously and some too recklessly. The over-cautious ones make too much of every trivial ache, scratch, and fleeting bodily discomfort. They worry about health, accidents, financial failure, old age, school examinations, the morals of the community, the honor of the family, and anything else that may have a direct or an indirect bearing on their need for security. On the other hand, the reckless ones manifest a blind and callous indifference to what the neutral observer would regard as " reasonable precautions." They live so dangerously as to make the mental expert suspect the possible existence of a secret wish to commit suicide. For them a speed limit constitutes a challenge to their driving prowess, a cocktail party an opportunity to drink to excess, and the warnings of the family physician " a lot of boloney." In brief, every instance of a poorly balanced personality, as previously discussed, may be taken as an example of poor adjustment to reality.

As the mental hygienist employs the term, *reality* refers to problems to be solved, difficulties to be overcome, intentions to be executed and goals to be reached. The way in which we tackle problems and difficulties and the manner in which we respond to frustration is revelatory of the adequacy of our adjustment to reality. People who evade their responsibilities by chronic alibis are making inadequate adjustments. People who habitually tend to blame others for their own failures are not facing the reality of their own failures. People who find themselves conveniently threatened with attacks of indigestion whenever a necessary but uncongenial job confronts them may be evading reality. Whatever interferes with honest appraisal of all the factors relevant to handling a conflict situation interferes with adjustment to the reality of that situation. The schoolboy who usually attributes his academic failure to the unfairness of his teachers is deceiving himself by a distorted appraisal of the factors responsible for his poor school work. Grouchy fathers, unaware of their own grouchiness, may attribute the friction within the family to the " ingratitude of the spoiled brats." In doing so they deceive themselves by failing to realize the part played by their own irritability in the production of the family disharmony. Similarly, shrewish wives all too often blind themselves to the reality of their own shrewishness.

The shortcomings of others seem to have a lower threshold of visibility than our own. Many a business and professional man who was not averse to taking two hours for lunch or knocking off for an afternoon on the golf links or at the baseball stadium was righteously indignant over reports of WPA workers loafing on the job. Many a parent has lost his temper while lecturing to an erring child on the virtue of self-control. Probably all of us have indulged in arguments and been irritated by the " pig-headedness " or the " blind obstinacy " of our opponents and rather pleased with our own " courageous firmness " and " honest consistency." All such one-sided, emotionalized appraisals of the pros and cons of controversies constitute examples of difficulty in adjusting to reality. To be psychologically free one must not only know the truth, but be willing to acknowledge it. Considered in the abstract it seems very easy to acknowledge truth or to face reality. However, as soon as we remind ourselves of concrete instances of what this abstraction implies, it will become clear that adjustment to reality is not a slogan to be applied as automatically as the postal clerk applies a rubber stamp to a registered letter.

Most of us are products of a highly competitive type of culture. We Americans lay great stress on the value of success. Our great dread is the dread of failure. Even our schools make poor grades symbols of academic disgrace and society makes academic degrees a mark of distinction. To have a lucrative practice becomes the central goal of the average up-and-coming young lawyer or physician. To rise in the world of business and industry one must keep getting promoted from one job to the next and from one salary level to the next just as one rises in the academic world by successive promotions through the grades and on through high school and university. Hierarchical organizations are not restricted to schools. The army has its hierarchy and so has the church. There is an economic hierarchy as exemplified by no-car families, one-car families, two-car families, and even three-and-four-car families. Automobile manufacturers further cater to this hierarchy by a stratification of their products in terms of price classes from the cheapest product of regimented mass production to the most costly custom-built, individualized model. College professors become enmeshed in a world of competitive intellectual values and they worry about their elevation to membership in learned societies, the number of papers they have published, and the chances of being called to institutions having more prestige than the one with which they happen to be identified. Preachers compete with one another in terms of the size and social importance of their congregations. Debutantes compete in terms of quality and quantity of dates. Shopkeepers compete for customers and radio comedians for listeners. Competition thus runs through the warp and woof of our culture. One of the big realities to which we have to learn to adjust is the reality of this ubiquitous competition and our relationship to it.[1]

We ought to realize that it is hard, not easy, for a businessman to acknowledge that his business failure may largely be due to his gullibility or stupidity. To place the onus on the depression or on the " unfair practices of competition " spares his self-esteem. It is easier for a university instructor to attribute his lack of advancement in the academic hierarchy to the indifference and inefficiency of his superiors in failing to reward excellent work than to face the fact that rival instructors may be more conscientious, more brilliant, and more effective teachers.

In other words, part of the reality to which we often have to adjust is the reality of our own negligence, our own shortcomings, or our own weaknesses. This aspect of reality is particularly hard to face and to acknowledge. We may regard this as the *inner* aspect of reality in contradistinction to *external* reality. By the latter phrase is meant the environmental situation constituting the problem to be solved or the difficulty to be overcome. A worried businessman, for example, may classify his outstanding debts, the clamoring creditors, the dishonesty of his bookkeeper as the external reality of his business distress. His own lack of diligence, foresight, and tact in dealing with creditors and customers may be

---

[1] The mental hygiene implications of this issue are so important that additional aspects of competitiveness will be taken up in the last two chapters.

said to comprise a portion of the internal reality necessary for a complete picture of the factors involved in the total problem. It would be manifestly more of a strain on this man's self-esteem to acknowledge this internal reality than to magnify the significance of the external phases of his problem situation. To urge such a man to " adjust to reality " is to ask him to include his very real psychological liabilities in his total inventory of all the liabilities responsible for the debacle of his business affairs.

The mental hygiene slogan, *adjustment to reality,* is thus somewhat more complex than appears manifest at first inspection. It is not an open sesame to unlock the doors of personal conflicts by a magic verbal formula. Consider, for the sake of illustration, the plight of a sensitive leader of a Peace Society in contemporary Japan. Such a Japanese would be faced with a dire individual conflict: his earnest devotion to the ideal of peace coupled with his conviction of the iniquity of aggressive wars on the one hand, and the reality of the war enthusiasm of his patriotically aroused neighbors on the other. For him to voice his convictions would be tantamount to social ostracism or to vilification by the Japanese equivalents of our epithets like " slacker," " yellow," or " Quisling." This is part of the *external* reality confronting him. In terms of the *internal* reality confronting him, however, there is the realization that silence or outward acquiescence might provoke distressing protests from his super-ego in the guise of an inner voice castigating him as a " moral slacker," a " compromiser with iniquity," a " coward when it comes to fighting for his principles," and similar painful aspersions on his ethical fortitude. His ethical ideals, it should be noted, are just as much part of the reality of his conflict as the existence of the glorifiers of the war. The reality to which the mental hygienist might be imploring him to adjust thus, upon analysis, turns out to be two realities: his inner reality of ethical ideals to which he stands personally committed and the outer reality of war-mongering, professional militarists. Under the circumstances we would not be rendering much aid to the man merely by whispering our " adjust to reality " admonition. He might puncture our mental hygiene complacency rather adroitly by whispering back, " Which reality? " For us to reply, " Both of them! " would be a fatuous answer. It would be as helpful as telling the man to get rid of his conflict by solving his difficulties. No discerning mental hygienist wants his ideal of adjustment to reality to be reduced to an inane shibboleth. It is to be used as a point of departure for the resolution of conflicts and not as a finished, stereotyped verbal panacea.

SOME COMMON WAYS OF EVADING REALITY

The usefulness of the adjustment-to-reality slogan, now that we have warned against its possible abuse, can be brought out by demonstrating some rather common modes of evading realities that ought to be faced in the interests of efficient personal problem-solving. One very familiar technique of evasion is what we might label a *flight into the future*. Instead of resolutely facing present difficulties, we put off the disagreeable job to the definite or indefinite future. The mother who postpones seeking professional advice regarding her child's temper tantrums because she tells herself the child " will outgrow " them is having recourse to a flight into the future. So is the student who dodges this week's assignment by playing golf when he ought to be studying and who quiets the incipient inner protest by planning to make up the neglected work " next week." So is the inveterate smoker who plans to cut down on his smoking as soon as " pressure of work lets up and this confounded nervousness " disappears. So is the father who decides to be " more of a companion to his son when the boy gets older " and, as the father hopes, companionship will be more a matter of stimulating man-to-man talks and less a matter of irritatingly endless childish questions. All of us can supply numerous instances of such evasion of today's reality by easy-going procrastination. The letters we intend to write " when we get the time," the classics we vaguely hope to read during vacation periods, and the regular exercise we plan to initiate once our " affairs get straightened out " all exemplify the functioning of this technique of evasion. Instead of tackling the jobs today by writing at least one short note, reading some solid book for twenty minutes, and exercising strenuously for even ten minutes we put everything off to a dim future whose very dimness makes it hard to recognize as the days and weeks roll by. *Mañana* is invariably another day to one who seeks to solve his problems by a flight into the future.

Another not uncommon mode of running away from the stark

reality of present difficulties involves a *flight into the past*. Wishing for the return of " the good old days " is a stock instance of this technique of evasion. We idealize the past, magnifying its virtues and minimizing its defects, and concomitantly we distort the present trouble by exaggerating its seriousness and overlooking or underestimating our assets. The youngster having trouble at school might find himself longing for the days of pre-school freedom and envying his baby brother who can " play all day long and not worry about teachers and homework." Similarly, the oldster, confronted by financial reverses, sometimes wishes he were back at school again. He dwells on the somewhat imaginary glories of these retrospective school days. In retrospect the big factor seems to be that as a boy he never had to worry about bills and debts and mortgages. Good old dad was always there to look after such matters. He forgets that the same " good old dad " used to discipline him and force him to slave over lessons, help with domestic chores, and attend Sunday School even on mornings when the ice skating was beautifully inviting. The memory of the financial security of his past overshadows or blots out recollection of the long series of daily disappointments, frustrations, and annoyances incident to wrestling with the drudgery of the school curriculum and the strict standards of strict parents and strict teachers. Because of this idealization of the past it is more comforting to think about it than to concentrate on the immediate problem before him.

As a psychologist once pointed out, this kind of retrospective idealization might be designated as the " Old Oaken Bucket delusion." Through the perspective of years the beauty of the scenery and the refreshing water drawn from the coolness of the old-fashioned well seem to be the dominant episodes of a childhood which, from the vantage point of maturity, appears to have been altogether carefree and joyously serene. Somehow the winter mornings when hauling water was a painfully icy proceeding are forgotten. The way in which the handle of the heavy bucket would cut into protesting fingers is not made part of the idealized picture. It is almost as if there had been an imaginative flight from the harshness of the reality of the past and, with the lapse of years, the distorted fantasy of the past gradually comes to be accepted as a correct picture of one's joyous childhood. Nor is this kind of fan-

tasied distortion limited to the past of one's own life. There are
people who glorify the thirteenth as the greatest of centuries. For
them the present century with its skepticism and uncertainty and
war and disease is a bleak one compared with the medieval period
with its romantic pageantry, confidently secure religious orientation, and heroic devotion to high causes. There are people in every
generation who think that the generation of *their* parents was one
of ideal rectitude and that the rising generation is going to the
dogs. The college senior thinks of the present generation of high
school boys as " children " compared with the " big fellows " with
whom he went to high school.

Judicious evaluation of one's own past as well as the past of history is thus fraught with obvious but often overlooked psychological pitfalls. The " Old Oaken Bucket " delusion is at work
when we think of childhood as the " age of innocence," the " age
of carefree laughter," or the " age of utter freedom and abandon."
A variant of the same delusion makes the present toothache seem
much more severe than the one we experienced ten years ago. To
many a college student the final examinations of today are much
more rigorous than those he took at high school. Very often young
mothers find themselves wishing for the return of the " good old
days " when there were no diapers to wash, no sick babies to nurse,
no meals to cook, no socks to mend, and no housework to do. The
nights when they cried themselves to sleep because it looked as
if they were doomed to spinsterhood are forgotten; the days spent
behind department store counters on aching feet trying to placate
complaining dowagers have disappeared from memory; in retrospective fantasy the weary trek from store to store in search of
employment is conveniently converted into an exciting adventure
or else it is not remembered at all.

Not only do people dodge their present responsibilities by taking refuge in the imaginary future or the glorified past, but they
often achieve the same goal by enmeshing themselves in the protective veil of more or less exaggerated symptoms of disease. This
self-protective psychological maneuver is called a *flight into illness*. In its minor manifestations most of us are doubtless personally familiar with this maneuver; for almost everybody has resorted to it rather spontaneously at some time or other. It is a
very, very common technique of evasion. The child who complains

of vague abdominal pains or of a headache on the days of important school examinations, and consequently succeeds in inducing an apprehensive mother to take the precaution of keeping him in bed, may be deluding both mother and himself. His complaint may never have been registered had he experienced identical symptoms during the Christmas holidays. During the latter period such symptoms are dismissed as too trivial to talk about; but when confronted by an unpleasant assignment during the school week, he pounces on such symptoms and utilizes them as a means of running away from the reality of the assignment. Often such a youngster is not to be judged too harshly for such seeming deception. After all, he may merely be applying the same formula he has seen mother use when a " sick headache " is the excuse she offers for breaking the appointment with " that dreadful bore," the wife of the new minister. Possibly he also heard his father explain that the reason a given business venture failed to terminate successfully was that " a sore throat made it hard to talk convincingly to that big-shot executive." Countless alibis, in other words, have been and still are constructed out of the material of casual aches, insignificant pains, and superficial feelings of fatigue. It is very easy to attribute one's failure to accomplish a given task to the intrusion of a handicap in the guise of illness. When illness is genuine there is no question of the legitimacy of such an alibi. However, this mechanism of flight into illness is not concerned with instances of actual tuberculosis or diphtheria or cancer interfering with the prosecution of a person's daily responsibility. It is concerned rather with the magnification of negligible signs of bodily disturbance and the development of almost altogether imaginary symptoms. The housewife, who succumbs to the temptation of an afternoon movie instead of preparing supper and who quiets a mildly protesting conscience by the reflection that the slight ache in her back might become serious if she were to bend over a stove, is circumventing the reality of her domestic responsibilities by deceiving herself by stressing symptoms healthy-minded women would disregard.

Most of us are apt to forget how much first-rate work can be accomplished despite actual pains and despite real physical handicaps. Heinrich Heine wrote some of his best poetry while a helpless invalid. Florence Nightingale, disregarding medical predictions of an early death, lived on for decades working, planning, and writing with an energetic enthusiasm far greater than that of the average healthy person. Both Charles Darwin and Herbert Spencer were victims of chronic invalidism of a degree of severity many alibi-seeking neurotics would doubtless regard as ample justification for withdrawal from vocational effort and a regime of steady work. It is not unlikely, in other words, that many of us are victims of self-deception when we attribute our failures and shortcomings and blunders and long stretches of loafing to anything from weak eyes to palpitation of the heart. We forget how much useful labor is accomplished by people who are blind or deaf or epileptic. We forget the distinguished careers of the blind and deaf Helen Kellers, the deaf Beethovens, and the epileptic Dostoevskis. We forget the army of workers who go about their daily business notwithstanding attacks of asthma or hay fever or occasional headaches or minor colds. Excessive concern about trivial symptoms may consequently be no more than a subterfuge by means of which we elude the rigors of routine tasks or evade the reality of some special personal responsibility.

An additional technique of evasion and self-deception is furnished by man's ability to conceal the harshness of a present reality by covering it with the fabric of his daydreams. Instead of a bluntly honest self-appraisal of his disappointments, defeats, weaknesses and frustrations, he turns away from them and permits his wish-fulfilling imagination to run riot. He permits his inner world of fantasy to carry him away from the struggle with outer reality. This type of mental transportation is technically called a *flight into fantasy*. Almost everybody has indulged in this type of flight at some time, so that it is not hard to recognize as a familiar dodge most of us have employed. However, there are various forms it takes and not everybody is cognizant of these. It will therefore be profitable to call attention to the more common kinds of daydreams people conjure up for themselves when the going gets tough.

Flight into fantasy often takes the route of imaginary heroic conquest. This is the *conquering-hero* type of daydream. The schoolboy, reprimanded by his biology teacher for neglecting his assignments and scolded by his parents for his academic failure, may retire to a corner of the living room and open the biology text for the ostensible purpose of buckling down to the serious business of study. But the reprimand and the scolding still rankle. He has difficulty in concentrating on the printed page. Soon he finds himself wondering whether it pays to go to school. His father just told him that boys had " better get an education if they expect to amount to something." He begins to play with the idea of putting this to the test by running away from home. In his developing daydream he proceeds to journey to distant and romantic places. He finds himself hiding from the possibility of pursuit by living under an assumed name. His grieving parents eventually give him up as lost. In the meantime he gets a job as cabin boy on a ship bound for China. At Shanghai he meets an important British business executive who, delighted to meet a boy who can speak English, offers him a position as office boy. Soon his imaginary progress speeds up in spectacular fashion. Promotion follows promotion until he sees himself as head of a vast international oil company. Now, having won fame and security, he dreams of returning home to his aged and white-haired parents with the glorious tidings that not only is their lost boy still living but so affluent and influential that he can do far more for them than they could ever have hoped to accomplish for themselves. Indulging in this sort of self-gratifying, imaginary and dramatic heroics is far less tedious and far more exciting than wrestling with the unemotional details of a biologist's description of botanical or zoological facts. It is easy to understand how many of us can be tempted to substitute such fantasied exploits for the monotony of persistent effort to cope with the difficulties and setbacks of daily tussles with the routine of school or factory or kitchen or office or assembly line.

This same sulking boy may be used to illustrate another familiar type of daydream: the *suffering-hero daydream*. The imaginary response to the hurt feelings takes the form of dreaming of a situation in which those responsible for the wounded feelings are made to suffer an agony of remorse. The boy may, for example, envisage the possible consequences of unrestrained application to study. He dreams of reading for hours night after night until his eyes begin to trouble him. When his dad finally takes him to the eye specialist the boy experiences his imaginary triumph; for the physician finds that the boy has studied so hard that his vision cannot be saved. The distress of his parents is, of course, incal-

culably acute. Even the biology teacher, who gave such long assignments, is made to share the distress of the parents. Sometimes
this kind of daydream takes the form of permitting the hero to
experience his own death in an accident. He sees his mutilated
body on the street as his father comes up to identify the remains.
He hears him express acute regret for having spoken to him so
sharply. He may even complete the fantasy by having the utterly
broken parent beg to be forgiven for the scolding of the previous
day. This fantasied suffering is thus utilized as a means of dealing
with the reality of disappointment or emotional frustration by
running away from it into the land of make-believe where the
" you'll-be-sorry-for-doing-this-to-me " type of wish is gratified
in altogether complete fashion. Here too the daydream is not only
an obvious substitute for work to be done, but also an imaginary
fulfillment of the spontaneous desire to discomfit or punish those
who punish us. It is a vicarious outlet for the revenge impulse.

The desire for revenge or the impulse to retaliate may give rise
to its own characteristic daydream in which the dreamer finds
himself saying things to parent, teacher, judge, employer, or any
other reprimanding official that he might never dare say in reality.
A convenient label for this familiar reaction is the *debating-hero
daydream*. All of us have probably indulged in it on occasion.
From the mental hygiene viewpoint it merits particular emphasis
not so much because it involves an escape from or a distortion of
reality, but because it is responsible for much avoidable inner distress and inter-personal friction. Sometimes it is brought into
being by anticipation of a situation which is never realized in
actuality. Our young student of biology, for instance, may find
himself reflecting on the possible consequences of not being prepared for his next class assignment. In fantasy he then proceeds
to carry on a verbal exchange with the irritated and irritating instructor. The fantasy often takes the dialogue form of the well
known " if-he-says-then-I'll-say " type of imaginary inner debate.
To render this recognizable and understandable the following
transcription of such a debate might prove illuminating:

If he calls on me to-morrow, I'll tell him to stop picking on me.
Then he'll say, " Who's picking on you? " And I'll tell him you are
and you know it and you needn't think you can get away with it. Then
he'll get mad and tell me to get out of the class. And I'll tell him my

dad paid his school tax and I'm entitled to be in class. I'll even tell him that if he tries to put me out, my dad'll put him out of his job. That'll scare him and he'll say, " Well, I'll give you another chance."

In reality, as was previously suggested, the events of the next class period may have nothing to do with such an acrimonious interchange of angry words. The boy may not even be requested to recite or he may be asked a question that he happens to answer so satisfactorily as to elicit enthusiastic praise from the instructor. Under such circumstances, the inner turmoil and bitterness engendered the night before by the anticipated argument would have been altogether futile.

This debating-hero daydream is by no means restricted to anticipated arguments. It often *follows* arguments between husband and wife, parent and child, forum leader and heckler, and many other competitive verbal clashes. Brooding over the outcome of such a clash the individual regrets not having buttressed his argument by means of some devastating fact that occurs to him later. He suddenly remembers some vital fact that he should have introduced. Thus in the privacy of his room he proceeds to continue the discussion hours after the real antagonist has gone home. The daydream is, to employ a technical phrase, a *perseverative* reaction. This is to say that the dreamer perseveres in continuing the verbal reactions long after the real occasion for them has disappeared. Such reactions are not merely verbal, but also emotional; for they take place in an atmosphere of bristling antagonism. The imaginary debate is characterized by goading challenges and irritating replies. As the daydream proceeds, one's anger may mount as a severely sarcastic remark is attributed to the imaginary opponent. In this way bitterness toward the opponent may increase. Upon meeting him again some days later it is not unlikely that such bitterness may still assert itself even though it is almost entirely a product of a fantasied argument. Many domestic quarrels are not permitted to die a natural death, but are revived as a consequence of being kept alive in intermittent fashion through the medium of perseverating daydreams. Real or imagined personal criticisms and cutting retorts are permitted to fester within the pattern of the daydream and so to infect the emotional attitude toward wife or husband. It is this possible social consequence of the debating-hero daydream which renders it a menace to mental health. Learning to recognize it so as to choke it off before it has a chance to dominate one's inner life would manifestly be a valuable and healthy kind of learning.

PREJUDICE AS A MENACE TO ADJUSTMENT

As was just indicated, daydreams taking the form of imaginary replies to the imaginary arguments of imaginary antagonists are apt to engender attitudes of bitterness, hostility, and suspicion. Such attitudes interfere with clear thinking and friendly cooperation. If these debating-hero daydreams take place only on rare occasions, their mental hygiene consequences are negligible. However, should they be nursed along day after day so as to become a more or less chronic feature of one's inner life, the consequences may be more momentous. They are then apt to warp the person's outer reactions to life. He is likely to develop what are technically called *paranoid* personality characteristics. These are the characteristics which go with the " teacher-has-a-grudge-against-me " type of reaction.

Our little student of biology, having persuaded himself that his difficulties with the subject are due to the grudge which the teacher bears against him, may readily come to exhibit symptoms the mental specialist has in mind when he refers to paranoid traits. The boy will be on his guard in the biology class. He will interpret the most innocent remark or the most irrelevant gesture as having some reference to him. Should the teacher chance to look in the boy's direction the lad may regard this as a subtle " you-better-watch-out-young-man " warning. On the other hand, if the teacher chances not to fix his gaze on the boy during the entire class period, then this chance failure is taken to indicate studied avoidance and to be sure-fire evidence of hostility on the part of the teacher. To the suspicious boy it means: " The teacher hates me so much that he can't even bear the sight of me." If the boy is called on to recite, he feels aggrieved because, as he feels, the teacher is merely trying " to show me up " or looking for a chance " to make some smart crack about my dumbness." Should he fail to be called on, he will also feel aggrieved; for this will suggest obvious indifference on the part of the teacher, as if to say, " I'm through with that brat and don't care whether he learns anything or not."

Attitudes of the kind just mentioned involve what the psychologist calls *ideas of reference*. This phrase refers to the not uncommon human tendency to regard personally neutral happenings as having a significance for the observer. The small child who thinks it started to rain " just to spoil my picnic " is having ideas of reference. People suffering from consciousness of guilt often experience such ideas. They misinterpret innocent whispering of members in their social group as gossip about them or, in more serious instances, they suspect every policeman as being on their trail. In the example just employed ideas of reference are manifested by the very personal way in which the boy regards everything the biology teacher does or neglects to do as having a direct bearing on the situation of the hostility he believes to prevail between himself and the teacher.

To cultivate ideas of reference is tantamount to losing oneself in a morass of uncritical suspiciousness. Straight thinking and ideas of reference do not go together. Casual remarks are twisted into subtle hints of dire consequences to come and innocent gestures are perverted into malicious warnings. It is by no means a psychological accident that the people who have cultivated such ideas to an extreme of paranoid dominance usually impress their acquaintances as overly serious, humorless, and tense individuals. They see danger where there is no danger and hostile intent where nothing but good will prevails. However, their chronic suspiciousness and the resultant groundless accusations of others renders them socially difficult personalities. They are frequently too argumentative to be pleasant companions. Their ideas of reference cause them to be so wrapped up in themselves as to give the impression of inordinate selfishness. Because of such undesirable social attitudes they soon find people rather reluctant to accept them as warm friends. Argumentativeness, emotional sensitivity, and suspiciousness constitute a group of characteristics calculated to stir up social friction. In order to avoid this kind of friction people have to be on guard to avoid remarks well-balanced personalities would accept as casual conversation, but which paranoid personalities misinterpret as goads to aggressive retaliation. Genuine friends can maintain a relaxed attitude as they exchange ideas and impressions, but a guarded attitude interferes with the spontaneity and freedom of friendly discourse. This is one reason why the paranoid individual fails when it comes to winning friends although he is very successful when it comes to influencing people — the wrong way! Most people dislike bickering and consequently prefer to avoid individuals prone to take innocent statements as personal challenges and invitations to vigorous debate. Furthermore, even if a debate with a paranoid acquaintance should chance to be launched, it is not likely to be an impersonal, intellectually stimulating interchange of fact and opinion. Such an acquaintance will be looking for ulterior motives and will often twist remarks intended to be viewed objectively into some grievous personal slur. This will make it impossible to continue the debate on the level of friendly discussion and amiable rivalry. It may even be hazardous to inject a bit of light banter into the discussion; for the banter is also likely to be misinterpreted as unwillingness to accept an opponent's argument as *serious* evidence.

Paranoid personalities like to be taken seriously. Playful humor is hard for them to interpret. Indeed, it is difficult for them to be playful with others or with themselves. A healthy personality keeps healthy by being able to perceive the incongruity of taking itself too seriously. It can " laugh off " many a jibe and many a barbed thrust at its own pretensions. The paranoid personality, on the other hand, has not equipped itself with this exceedingly valuable psychological safety valve by means of which potential resentment is converted into a good-natured chuckle. What this all adds up to is that the paranoid person eventually finds a good deal of factual support to justify his distrust of people. Others often actually do tend to avoid him, just because he is so hard to get along with and because he makes them uncomfortable by being so touchy and suspicious. What he fails to grasp, though, is that in the genesis of this vicious cycle his paranoid characteristics provoked the avoidance. He reverses the causal relationship and attributes his distrust of others to *their initial* hostility and avoidance. Because of this intermingling of fact and fancy, of reality and fantasy, it is almost impossible to persuade him that his is the major responsibility for his troubles with other people. This is particularly true if his paranoid outlook is of long standing and has become a firmly entrenched outlook. It is not so true of the person whose attitudes are still in a state of flux.

An understanding parent or teacher can consequently be of real service to a child by showing him the relationship between the debating-hero daydream and the personal difficulties of the paranoid personality. Furthermore, all of us can profit by knowledge of this relationship whenever we find ourselves brooding over real or imagined slights or insults. The " teacher-has-a-grudge-against-me " attitude has its adult equivalents. Parents often assume deliberate, malicious intent actuated by personal animosity against them on the part of a given child when neutral appraisal of the " disobedience " would call for a diagnosis of " non-malicious, impulsive mischievousness." Such parents distort reality by believing the child has a grudge against them. Occasionally one finds teachers indulging in the same kind of distortion and acting as if some particular pupil has a grudge against the teacher. The chief point to be stressed again is that once such attitudes of suspiciousness are aroused the behavior of parent or teacher is likely to reveal antagonism toward the child. The alert youngster will detect such antagonism and this, in turn, will influence his behavior. By this time the suspicious adult will have a *real* basis for his hostility. This may nourish the incipient paranoid attitude enough to keep it alive and flourishing. What the mental hygienist urges is that all of us keep the possibility of paranoid thinking ever before us so as to nip such paranoid trends in the bud.

This admonition is especially applicable to people belonging to groups against whom social prejudice of some kind exists as an actual, if regrettable, reality. Whether we like it or not we might as well recognize the existence of religious, racial, economic, and other kinds of prejudice even in presumably enlightened and allegedly emancipated democracies. In our own United States there are people who are prejudiced against Chinese or against Negroes or against Catholics or Jews or Baptists or Atheists. There are people who distrust members of labor unions and other people who view the very wealthy with suspicion. There are people who are prejudiced against all foreigners. Some people are prejudiced against bankers, some against preachers, some against professional educators, some against the proletariat, some against fraternity men, some against lawyers, and some against the opposite sex. Prejudice is so ramified in our social structure that hardly anybody can hope to elude its influence altogether. To the extent that we are bound to be members of a group against which *some* people are prejudiced, each one of us is at some time likely to be a victim of the prejudice of such people. If we are religious, atheists are going to view us askance, and if we are atheists, the religionists are going to be wary of us. If we are white, there will be Negroes whose attitudes toward us will be warped and, contrariwise, if we happen to be born Negroes, there will be whites looking down upon us and discriminating against us. In fact, relatively few white people have an adequate understanding of what this involves. They fail to appreciate the magnitude of the problems of adjustment confronting the Negro child and that these are decidedly acute mental hygiene difficulties. It is hard to estimate the extent to which the personality of the Negro is warped by our unconscious national perjury in our general neglect of the full implications of the phrase " with liberty and justice for all " when we "pledge allegiance to the flag." As Sutherland has put it in a recent volume: [2]

White children in the United States take many things for granted. Very early in life they learn, without being told in so many words, that they are as good as or better than any other people in the world and that they live in a land especially blessed.

On the other hand, American children who are born with Negroid features have to learn a different conception of themselves and of their opportunities. They may thrill to patriotic music, respond to stirring historical accounts of the nation's founding, and take pride in the country's rapid growth, in the development of its great cities, and in its preparation for defense, but that pride is often tainted by the realization that these great achievements really belong to the white man's world. The Negro boy or girl is inclined to feel that though a native, he is still a foreigner. Though he helped create these wonders he can-

[2] Sutherland, R. L., *Color, Class, and Personality,* Washington, D. C., American Council on Education, 1942, p. 40.

Readers interested in adjustment problems of Negro young people will find a wealth of relevant material in the *Negro Youth Survey* by the *American Youth Commission of the American Council on Education.* In addition to the volume from which the above quotation was selected, there are six other books containing the fruits of the *Survey.* Information regarding these volumes will be sent upon request by communicating with the *Commission* at 744 Jackson Place, Washington, D. C.

not show them off as " mine." Though he may rise to a high position within his group, he must always be on guard lest his color bring embarrassment or outright insult.

Prejudice is by no means restricted to matters of skin color. Religious differences continue to provoke discriminating attitudes in our democracy. In some sections of the United States it is hard for a Roman Catholic to secure appointment as a teacher or a school superintendent. In still more sections it is even harder for a Jew to obtain such employment. In almost every section the *avowed* atheist will find it practically impossible to get on the public school payroll as teacher or administrator. The ubiquity of prejudice is reflected in the advertising of our large city papers. Perusal of the advertising columns reveals such familiar phrases as " Gentiles only need apply," or " Wanted: intelligent, alert Protestant."

Understandingly enough, the victim of such prejudice rebels against its unfairness and stupidity. This is true even if he harbors prejudices against other groups or other social classes. Frequently he fails to recognize his own prejudices as prejudices; for he classifies them as wise judgments about dangerous and consequently undesirable people. All too often we dispose of the prejudice against us as a product of hostile fantasy while our prejudices against others are blithely accepted as the products of realities so obvious that it would be foolhardy to question them. Thus many people have never questioned the following widespread beliefs:

Frenchmen are sexually more immoral than Americans.

A Catholic cannot be a good American because, when it comes to a showdown, he will obey the Pope rather than the President.

All Negroes are promiscuous.

Jews are notorious international bankers.

Most Jews are capitalists.

Most Jews are communists.

Scotchmen are stingier than Americans.

Relatively more crimes are committed by foreigners than by native-born Americans.

Atheists are not governed by allegiance to any code of ethics.

All Orientals are deceitful, cunning, and unscrupulous.

Men can reason better than women.

Blondes are more fickle than brunettes.

Americans have a better sense of humor than Englishmen.

Members of the white race are born with better brains than members of any other race, particularly the black race.

Not a single one of the foregoing beliefs is in accord with fact. Every one is false. And yet thousands of people act *as if* they were true and treat the members of the groups involved accordingly. Under the circumstances, if the victims of such stereotyped and fallacious beliefs feel discriminated against and resentful and prompted to take a guarded attitude, they are not to be stigmatized as paranoid personalities. As long as prejudice actually exists in the world, its victims would be indulging in wishful thinking or in unrealistic thinking if they completely ignored the prejudice by pretending it was nonexistent.

How PARANOID THINKING WARPS REALITY

Not every boy who complains that his teacher has a grudge against him is necessarily distorting the reality of his classroom world; for occasionally some teachers, being human, do harbor prejudices. The Catholic boy may thus find himself resenting some anti-Catholic comment made by his Protestant teacher just as a Protestant boy may feel aggrieved if a Catholic teacher should chance to cast aspersions on non-Catholics. Similarly, the Jewish lad may rightfully come to wonder whether he can expect a square deal from a teacher whose casual comments about Jews reveals a strong anti-Jewish bias. Every mental hygienist recognizes that realistic thinking calls for frank recognition of the possible existence of bias and prejudice and discrimination and injustice and unfairness. One cannot cope with these attitudes effectively by dreaming of their nonexistence.

Neither can one cope with them effectively by magnifying their importance or by assuming their existence where impartial investigation fails to reveal their presence. It is the latter possibility which merits particular consideration; for it is frequently responsible for the kind of warped mental reactions to which the adjective *paranoid* [3] is legitimately applicable. Examples of this possibility are easy to find. The Negro janitor, dismissed because of drunkenness and inefficiency, may minimize these reasons for his

[3] Cf. Cameron, N., " The Development of Paranoic Thinking," *Psychol. Rev.,* 1943, *50,* pp. 219–233.

dismissal and blame everything on the alleged prejudice of his white employer. A Catholic girl may gloss over the fact that she failed to type as rapidly and as accurately as some non-Catholic competitor, when a prospective employer tested them both for a secretarial position, and consequently may delude herself into believing that the competitor landed the job because " she belongs to the same church as the boss." Analogously, a Jewish student may protest that his " D " in chemistry was due to the fact that the " professor hates Jews," overlooking the relevance of such deficiencies as failure to turn in all laboratory reports, three poor recitations, and shoddy work on the final examination. An army lieutenant may attribute his failure to be promoted to the rank of captain to his possession of a " foreign-sounding Polish name and the big shots prefer good, old American names." Impartial scrutiny of his military record may show such glaring shortcomings that the investigator is more perplexed by the tolerance of the lieutenant's superiors in not demoting him than by their failure to promote him.

It is harder, as was just implied, to face the reality of our own inefficiency or neglect or inferiority than to hide behind the protective wall of presumed prejudice against us. By attributing our failure to the unfairness of others we free ourselves from the onus of self-disapprobation. In technical language we *project* the blame from ourselves to another person. We are behaving like the ballplayer who accounts for his poor batting average by saying, " the umpires in this league don't know their business." Projection is also revealed by the incompetent workman whose chronic excuse for his incompetence is " the bum tools I've got to use." To overlook our own incompetence and our own shortcomings and to dwell exclusively on the bias of the boss or umpire or the inadequacy of our implements is to be dishonest with ourselves.

Sound mental hygiene demands rigorously impartial appraisal of *all* factors responsible for our disappointments, frustrations, and conflicts. This means, of course, that the possible influence of the other man's prejudice or the possible handicap of second-rate tools should be included in the appraisal. But it also means — and this is of especial importance — that our own possible negligence, indolence, and inability should not be left out of consideration. Even if it hurts, it is better to acknowledge our own deficiencies to ourselves than to indulge in the wishful fantasy of a pretended self-perfection.

Honest self-appraisal is particularly hard to achieve in situations where prejudice *may* be operative. It is so much easier and so much less painful to shift the entire burden of responsibility on to the shoulders of a presumably prejudiced official. By making him the scapegoat we exonerate ourselves from any blame. We are also likely to exaggerate the degree of his interference and consequently to brood over his seeming hostility. In this process of brooding we can often be tempted to indulge in both suffering-hero and debating-hero daydreams. We may also be tricked into developing ideas of reference and fostering attitudes of suspiciousness altogether incommensurate with the actual facts. The consequent distortion of our thinking and feeling may render it impossible to recognize the crux of our difficulty in holding a job or in getting along with people, even prejudiced people.

Since prejudice is so ubiquitous, no one of us can hope to avoid all contact with people whose biased attitudes toward politics, religion, race, economic status, or social position are bound to enmesh us to some degree or in some respect. It is therefore desirable to have an understanding of the psychological pitfalls to which dealings with prejudice may expose us. This is the chief justification for this extended discussion of the subject.

Our resentment against the prejudice may so easily lead to the mental warping of the paranoid personality that our own dealings with others may soon be characterized by the vicious onesidedness of bigotry. In fact, many prejudices are born this way. A housewife may refuse to employ a Negro maid because years earlier a Negro girl had insulted her on a New York subway. Instead of regarding the insult as a symptom of poor breeding on the part of a single passenger the housewife mistakenly indicts an entire race, forgetting Edmund Burke's warning about the fallacy involved in the indictment of an entire people. Some years ago, to cite a specific example brought to our attention, an influential member of a school board went on record as saying that he would never approve the appointment as superintendent of schools of a member of the Campbellite Church. His prejudice was the outcome of a single irritating experience with a high school principal who chanced to be a member of this sect. To cite another example, a psychologist of our acquaintance discovered the existence of bitter antagonism toward all things French in one of his young students. The young man would have nothing to do with French people, French literature, or French cooking. Investigation showed that his vehement hatred was the product of a single unfortunate experience with a group of French boys who ganged up against him at boarding school and made him the victim of a hazing episode.

In other words, the inveterate human tendency to *classify* experiences may make for unsound generalization. What this means can be brought out by reverting to the preceding examples. The housewife, to take our first example, in reacting to the insult of the Negro girl is primarily conscious of the racial group to which the offender belongs. The mental act of classifying her as a member of the Negro race occurs as automatically as the very recognition of the Negroid facial characteristics. So far no harm or injustice has taken place. However, the instant the housewife attributes the insulting behavior of this individual girl to *all* members of the race, crooked thinking and injustice is in the offing. The entire race is being endowed with the regrettable attribute of an isolated member. Similarly, in the case of the prejudiced school official, unseemly behavior of a single member of the given church was uncritically regarded as a trustworthy *sample* of the behavior of *all* Campbellites. In like fashion the young man so bitterly prejudiced against all things French had taken his one experience with French bullies as a representative sample of what it means to be French.

The logic in these instances is akin to the logic of the person who samples one orange and judges the entire crate by the result. It is like arguing that if one member of a family is studious, every member of the family must be studious or that if one German is shy, all Germans must be shy. One does not have to be a professional logician to perceive the fallacious nature of this kind of reasoning. And yet in the realm of social prejudice we permit this kind of sloppy thinking to influence our attitudes and our conduct. Once having made our generalization we tend to cling to it irrespective of subsequent contradictory experiences. We cling to it because our emotions are bound up with the objects of our prejudice and it is notorious that straight thinking and strong emotion do not go together. An angry judge is not likely to weigh evidence with judicial impartiality nor is the lovesick youth likely to give due weight to the character defects of the flighty object of his romantic attachment. A premature, prejudiced generalization of the sort we have been discussing is hard to rectify, once it has been adopted, precisely because its emotionalized origins interfere with judicial evaluation of relevant evidence.

As was just suggested, even if this relevant evidence manifestly contradicts the meaning of the prejudiced generalization, it is shunted aside as an annoying, inconsequential exception. The generous Scotchman or the gentlemanly and refined Negro are classified as " freaks " by people convinced of the parsimony of the Scotch or the boorishness of Negroes.

In fact, they like to dispose of such contrary evidence by a confident reference to " exceptions which prove the rule." They thoughtlessly assume that this trite phrase makes a rule having exceptions a better one than a rule devoid of exceptions. Actually, of course, their error is due to a failure to realize the existence of two meanings of the verb *to prove*. Originally it meant to test or try out. Later it came to mean to demonstrate the correctness of a conclusion. To believe that " an exception proves the rule " is a sensible belief only in terms of the former meaning of the word. The soundness of the rule is to be checked by seeming exceptions. In this way the rule is to be tested or proved. Should the seeming exception turn out to be a genuine one, then our confidence in the validity of the rule ought to be weakened. To argue that such an exception proves the rule in the sense of demonstrating its validity is to argue carelessly. The rule in physics to the effect that the volume of a gas varies inversely as the pressure to which it is subjected would not become a more trustworthy rule if some investigator should discover an instance of a gas whose volume increases as the pressure becomes greater. An instance of this sort would actually disconcert the world of physics; for it would signify the disruption of a hitherto dependable law. To consider one additional example: the rule that an ounce of strychnine will kill a fox terrier is a perfectly good rule even though nobody has yet found an exception to it. This is what makes it a perfectly good rule. Should some miracle-worker ever demonstrate that the rule has an exception, he would automatically mar its perfection. Furthermore, every time a fox terrier dies of strychnine poisoning the

rule is *proved* in the sense of being tested and found still functioning in accord with expectations.

It should thus be obvious how glaringly unscientific we are in
our thinking when we regard exceptions to our fond beliefs as supports for those beliefs. However, if we were to follow the scientist's
example and make a note of every experienced exception to our
prejudiced generalizations, we might more frequently find ourselves forced to give up the fantasy of wish-fulfilling interpretations in favor of sober, if unwelcome, reality. To persist in clinging to a prejudice is to cling to what we would *like* to believe
instead of believing in facts as they really are. This is what makes
social prejudice a species of make-believe, of unrealistic thinking
and sometimes of paranoid hostility.

Failure to recognize the elements of fantasy or make-believe
characterizing many of our cherished convictions is to practise
poor personal mental hygiene. In view of this, it might be well for
all of us to take occasional stock of many of our " firm convictions " and " well established rules " about people and races and
religions and social institutions. Stock-taking of this kind, honestly carried out, will often serve to shock us into a realization of
the magnitude and intensity of our prejudices. Without such realization there can be no mental house-cleaning. The accumulation
of prejudice and fantasy has to be recognized for the useless stuff
it is before we can know enough to throw it out.

STRAIGHT THINKING AND EMOTIONAL CONTROL

Training for effective mental hygiene, it can now be seen, calls
for training in effective thinking as much as for training in emotional control. Wishful thinking is not only wishful, but also thinking. The onesidedness, impulsiveness, and undisciplined drift of
wishful fantasies can be partially corrected and curbed by cultivating the habit of realistic appraisal of the products of such
fantasies. What this habit involves is the transfer to daily life of
the scientist's mental operations when he is working as a scientist.
These operations bristle with question marks: Is this really so?
Are there any exceptions? Does this follow? Will the evidence
justify the conclusion? What must I do to verify this? Should this
theory be scrapped? Had I better modify this conclusion? Am I
wrong about this? Questions like these dominate the scientific

mind. The persistent effort to answer them keeps the man of science closer to the realities of his subject than the man of dogma living in a world of prejudiced conviction which he blithely accepts as established truth. Dogmatic thinking tends to be fixed and stereotyped, while scientific thinking is flexible and adjustable. The difference is the difference between a closed mind and an open mind. It is the difference between regulating one's conduct in terms of stereotyped convictions as opposed to conduct regulated in terms of principles modified to fit new evidence as it accumulates. It is the difference between an unwillingness to acknowledge facts conflicting with our pet theories or wounding to our vanity and a readiness to face facts honestly and courageously even though they run counter to our prejudices, hurt our self-esteem, or demolish a cherished hypothesis.

The subtle way in which prejudice may distort our thinking is clearly revealed by Britt [4] in a recent volume. He quotes the following paragraph taken from a book entitled *What Is Communism?* and written by Earl Browder, former presidential candidate of the Communist party:

Whenever any form of government becomes destructive of certain ends, it is the right of the people . . . to institute a new government, laying its foundations on such principles and organizing its powers in such forms, as to them shall seem most likely to effect their safety and happiness. . . . When a long train of abuses and usurpations, pursuing invariably the same object, evinces a design to reduce the masses under absolute despotism, it is their right, it is their duty, to throw off such government and to provide new guards for their future security.

Quite evidently Browder approves of revolution. Can we endorse the doctrines embodied in the passage just quoted? Most of us will find it hard not to classify the teachings as dangerous and subversive. Some of us may even stigmatize them as foreign and un-American. Our bias against communism in general and Browder, its leader, in particular will arouse a wish to oppose whatever has communist approval. Once a person has been persuaded to express his repudiation of the ideas expressed in the paragraph it may prove psychologically interesting to note his reaction when he learns that Browder copied the passage from the Declaration

---

[4] Britt, S. H., *Social Psychology of Modern Life,* New York, Farrar & Rinehart, Inc., 1941, pp. 137–138.

of Independence. As good Americans we venerate the latter document. However, our approval of its teachings may depend not so much on a critical analysis of what these teachings imply as on a diffuse glow of patriotic pride in the document as a national symbol. The same teaching experienced in a context for which we have apprehensive contempt may not even be recognized as the same teaching; hence we view it as an alarmingly radical teaching. Our prejudice against the context has colored our evaluation of the meaning of the passage. A hostile wish has been father to a twisted interpretation: The " real meaning " of the passage has been perverted because of our emotionalized hostility against " communism and all its teachings."

Another example of the insidious influence of prejudice on straight thinking was furnished by Professor Thouless.[5] As he implies, most people, at least in our culture, are taught to disapprove of the quitter. We like to think of ourselves as steadfast, persevering, and courageous fighters to the bitter end. Firmness is consequently an ideal we like to attribute to ourselves and hesitate to attribute to people we dislike. As Thouless puts it, we reveal this bias by the way in which some of us vary the term " firmness " in the give-and-take of everyday life as if the correct conjugation were: " I am *firm,* thou art *obstinate,* he is *pig-headed.*" To the neutral observer the behavior in question may be practically identical, but our personal bias provokes a perversion of reality that induces us to see three kinds of behavior instead of one. It is akin to the bias, as Thouless also reminds us, which induces us to condemn the brutal onslaught of the enemy as an *atrocity,* and to condone the same sort of brutality indulged in by our own troops as *wise severity.*

The distorting effects of wishes and prejudices on the course of straight thinking are by no means restricted to the " ignorant masses," the unlettered and the immature. All of us are subject to such influences. Even college professors, trained to guard against the trickiness of wishful thinking, may sometimes succumb to the lure of private prejudice. What is more, not even professional psychologists are entirely immune. An amusing and instructive instance of this lack of immunity was brought to our

[5] Thouless, R. H., *Straight and Crooked Thinking,* New York, Simon and Schuster, 1932, ch. I.

attention not so very long ago. A scholar had written a paper on a technical aspect of psychology and submitted it to the editor of a professional journal. This editor happened to be the leader of a school of psychology somewhat opposed to the ideas sponsored by the psychologists mentioned in the paper. However, as editor of a scientific, nonpartisan journal, he should have kept his private preferences under control in order to give all parties, including the " opposition," an opportunity to present relevant evidence. Like the ideal judge, the ideal editor of a scientific journal is expected to be impartial and unprejudiced. Nevertheless, this particular editor sent the following letter to the scholar in question:

Dear Professor _____:

I am returning your paper because I feel that the *Journal* has spent. enough time upon learning based upon past experimentation. To my mind both Thorndike and Koffka are both vitalistic and animistic and hence although you have done the paper in a marvellously clear way I would rather not devote the space to the discussion.

For this psychologist to write, " I would rather not devote space to this discussion," was tantamount to saying, " It is my wish to stifle any further publicity of the ideas of the opposing camp." It was not an instance of realistic, critical thinking but of thinking motivated by the fantasy of complete domination over professional rivals. The insidious ways in which such wishes or personal preferences influence our evaluation of evidence can hardly be overestimated. It is notorious that much less proof or evidence is required to convince us of the truth of something we would like to believe than to persuade us of the truth of a personally distasteful conclusion. It is easier to convince a person of his actual possession of desirable character traits than of uncomplimentary ones. It is easier for the parent of a child making a high score on an intelligence test to be won over to an endorsement of the test's validity than it is to win over the parent of a youngster making a low score. Evidence in line with our desires and hopes is enthusiastically welcomed, while contrary evidence is more likely to be subjected to critical scrutiny.

Our beliefs, conclusions, and convictions, to a far greater extent than we ordinarily realize, are fathered by our desires with the reality of evidence playing only a minor role in the process. This may be formulated more convincingly by reference to a statistical description of the relationship between belief and evidence. In terms of the outcome of an experimental investigation of the problem, one psychologist [6] reports a correlation of .42 between belief and evidence, while the correlation between belief and desire was more than twice as great, being .88. The heart seems stronger than the brain in determining the acceptability of beliefs. Wishes may be more potent than logic. Even those of us who are confident of no longer believing in myths and fairy stories may still be doing much of our thinking in terms of beliefs whose psychological roots are embedded in the soil of unrecognized wishful make-believe. In technical language, much of our thinking is *dereistic* or, as it is sometimes called, *autistic.* The latter adjective stresses the part played by the *self* in encouraging the impulsive drift of ideas and beliefs in line with wishful fantasy. The other adjective, *dereistic,* emphasizes the tendency of such thinking to disregard the reality of evidence, especially uncomfortable or unpleasant evidence, in favor of the less real but personally more congenial fictions conjured up by an ingenious and uncritical fantasy.

THE ROLE OF FANTASY IN MENTAL HEALTH

These warnings regarding the mental hygiene dangers of dereistic thinking should not be construed as blanket indictments of any indulgence of the life of fantasy. Such a conclusion would be no more justified than would warnings regarding the dangers of swimming in treacherous waters justify a resolve never to swim in *any* water. Once again we must return to our ideal of the *balanced* personality and realize that exclusive preoccupation with the stern realities of existence may be just as one-sided as complete absorption in wishful daydreams. The slogan of " adjustment to reality " may be taken too literally and too seriously. A grim, humorless, painfully sober attitude toward life may be engendered as a consequence. To develop such an attitude is to deprive oneself of the tonic and relaxing and often rejuvenating effects of playful moods, diverting daydreams, and distracting fiction.

Imagination can be a form of play as well as a means of escape

[6] Lund, F. H., " The Psychology of Belief," *J. of Abnor. and Soc. Psychol.,* 1925, *20,* pp. 174–196.

from an unwelcome reality. It can be a form of creative pleasure and not merely a morbid distortion of events that frighten, annoy, or discourage us. After all, many of our esthetic pleasures are products of fantasy. Poems, novels, symphonies, and paintings do not have to be " realistic " to exercise an esthetic appeal. No competent mental hygienist would condemn our indulgence in such esthetic pleasures. Nor would he object to the occasional self-aggrandizing daydream or the altogether fictitious funny story or the fables and fairy stories with which we regale children. All that he would condemn is the possible failure to maintain the distinction between the real and the unreal, the sober and the sportive, the deed and the wish, or fact and fiction. Provided there is no confusion between reality and make-believe, the life of fantasy, he would say, ought to be strengthened and cultivated in the interests of full and balanced personality development. However, when there is such confusion, — and this is the crux of his warning — then we are likely to substitute wishing for doing, dreaming for action, and prejudice for fair play. When there is such confusion, important facts may be overlooked or distorted and the myths of our fantasy may be erroneously interpreted as established truths. Such erroneous interpretations make for crooked thinking and inefficient problem-solving. They make for the suffering or the conquering or the debating-hero types of daydream. They make for the continuation of wishful and prejudiced attitudes. They drive us away from honest appraisal of our defects and shortcomings into the land of make-believe, where we deceive ourselves by twisting facts to suit our fancy without recognizing the self-deception involved.

Wishful thinking militates against effective adjustment because it is a species of crooked thinking. The emotionality back of it distorts our logic and consequently interferes with honest self-appraisal. After all, when the mental hygienist urges a person to " adjust to reality," he is substituting a professional formula for the colloquial " don't kid yourself." To " kid " oneself, in other words, is to evade unpleasant facts by taking refuge in the land of wishful make-believe. It is by no means easy to learn to face and acknowledge such facts; but it is a necessary kind of learning if we are to develop the kind of moral courage leading to straight thinking and square shooting.

14... *SELF–EMANCIPATION BY REPRESSION*

REPRESSION HAS SUCH OBVIOUS IMPLICATIONS FOR MENTAL HY-giene that it merits careful study and analysis. Before taking up some of its technical aspects it might be desirable to consider some less technical ones.

SOCIAL *versus* INDIVIDUAL CONTROL

In his rebellious moods the solitary individual may nurture his rebelliousness by envisaging himself as hemmed in on all sides by barriers to the free expression of his spontaneous impulsiveness. He feels himself to be a helpless victim caught in the mesh of society's network of demands and prohibitions. He thinks of himself as a *slave* to artificial schedules, arbitrary codes, stultifying social convention, and grimly repressive legislation. Stereotyped social practice prescribes when he is to report for work, how he shall be dressed, with whom he shall associate, into what class he may marry, to whom he must be polite, and how large a tax he must pay.

The Great Society, which he thinks of by the ambiguous pronoun " they," seems to have conspired to cramp his style. " They " object to profanity, lewdness, drunkenness, gambling, and loafing. If a man feels like blaspheming, seducing, and going on a bender, " they " try to inhibit the impulses. One has to do what " they " say is right. " They " make the rules without consulting you: go to church every Sunday, pay your bills promptly, don't consort with harlots, obey the speed laws, don't be a glutton, keep yourself neat and clean, don't loaf on the job; be a good student, a good father, a good wife, a good daughter, a good citizen, and a good patriot.

Such seeming overemphasis on sheer goodness often intensifies the rebel's bitterness. He finds himself sneering and scoffing at what he contemptuously stigmatizes as " goody-goodyness." He thinks of " them " as a " bunch of self-righteous, joyless, prying, gossiping, puritanic busybodies." " They " boss and dominate and thwart freedom and independence. " They " stand for the *status quo,* old-fashioned tradition, stuffy conventions, and stereotyped social ritual. " They " are the ultra-conservatives and the opponents of individualism, personal freedom, and zestful initiative. " They " enchain any would-be modern Prometheus daring to break through the code-encrusted barriers surrounding the lives of men.

At some time or other almost every person experiences something of this protest against the strictures of the Great Society. At such times civilization strikes him as a vast network of repressive forces. He finds himself envying the hypothetical savage free to do as he pleases, what he pleases, when he pleases. Culture comes to be regarded as the enemy of Nature and Society as the enemy of Freedom.

Such rebellious protests are particularly apt to assert themselves with reference to problems of sex adjustment. Rather drastic personality distortions often center around the individual's quest for a wholesome and personally satisfying reconciliation between the unyielding code of society's standards of sex morality and his imperious eroticism. For many people the quest becomes a momentous personal issue of magnified proportions. They find themselves dominated by a never-ending series of lustful urges, qualms of conscience, longings for self-control, feelings of inferiority, and persistent doubts concerning much of what they have been taught to regard as " right and proper " in the realm of sex. In their perplexity they seek guidance from any chance acquaintance who pretends to have solved the problem. If they can, they obtain books and pamphlets purporting to reveal what the perplexed " ought to know " about sex. Dormitory conclaves as well as fraternity " bull sessions " are often devoted to more or less accurate and more or less fantastic analyses of such problems. Both screen and stage reflect the urgency and ubiquity of problems of sex in the lives of people of all ages from youth to full maturity.

There is little need to catalog the precise nature of these problems. Every " advice-to-the-lovelorn " type of column mentions them. They include perplexities concerning petting, premarital relations, clandestine extramarital affairs, the control of jealousy, and the conquest of erotic indifference. As every experienced physician can testify, people are also perplexed about the consequences of masturbation, the physiological effects of celibacy, and kindred problems. They want to know whether masturbation is a cause of mental breakdown, a manifestation of depravity, or a forerunner of feeblemindedness. Often they want to know whether there is some fixed standard of sex indulgence necessary for the maintenance of optimal personal efficiency. This notion of a standard refers not only to what they designate as a " normal " or " natural " technique of such indulgence, but also to the frequency of such indulgence.

The quest for standards runs through the entire gamut of their perplexities regarding the control of the ramifications of the sex impulse. The search involves both hygienic standards and ethical standards. Indeed, within certain limits, their inner doubts and private broodings center in what they take to be a conflict between such standards; the Great Society sternly taboos sex expression outside of the institution of marriage, while the gods of nature keep registering imperious decrees of passionate urgency that demand violation of such taboos. To put this less metaphorically: the sex ideals of official society seem to conflict with the spontaneous, untutored biologic impulsiveness of the individual. It is not at all astonishing that so many people have been bothered by the thought that it is " unnatural " to have to put off sex experience until marriage. Even after marriage some of them continue to wonder whether monogamy is not " unnatural " or artificial; for they find that the marriage ceremony has done very little to lessen their *potential* ardor for biologic thrills with countless other personalities. Nature's demands seem to conflict with society's demands in distressingly persistent fashion.

In recent decades this age-old problem has been further complicated by the circulation of a notion that psychologists have discovered a menace to mental health in repression of sex impulses. Altogether earnest and conscientious people have consequently been bothered by the possibility of dire effects on mental stability as a result of complete allegiance to the conventional code. They are made to feel uneasy by talk of neuroses caused by repression of sex impulses, mysterious complexes attributed to repression, and all sorts of disturbing quirks of personality emerging from the realm of a mysterious unconscious mind said to be a sort of psychic cave in which repressed impulses are hidden.

All this mystery is rendered more disquieting because it is surrounded with the halo of science. People are influenced to believe in the dangerous consequences of repression by such awe-inspiring phrases as " Freud has discovered," " psychoanalysis teaches," " psychiatrists now know," and " psychologists say." Just what has been discovered and what is known and is being taught and said regarding repression by mental specialists may still be vague to them; but they do know that the alleged evils of repression have been debated by such experts. This is enough to undermine confidence in the wisdom of traditional teachings regarding self-control, chastity, continence, and similar topics. What is more, some people have rather hastily assumed that such teachings are *positively* outmoded in view of what they regard as the latest findings of the latest psychology.

A little reflection will show that, as the term is popularly employed, repression is often used as a synonym for self-control. By means of a simple verbal shift a manifest absurdity in the somewhat prevalent notion regarding the dangers of repression in general and sexual repression in particular can now be revealed. It is tantamount to saying that self-control is dangerous to one's health! Quite manifestly neither the mental expert nor the intelligent layman would endorse such a statement. Of course, strictly speaking, repression is not precisely the same as self-control. It is merely one means of attaining self-control. The verbal shift to which we have just resorted was nevertheless justified; for it helped to bring out one of the purposes of repression. This purpose is that of achieving what is ordinarily called self-control. Another way of putting this is to say that without repression there can be no self-control. This is practically the same as saying that without repression there can be no mental health. If this is correct, there must be something wrong with the prevalent attitude of apprehension regarding repressions. At all events it should be clear that the doctrine of repression is in need of further clarification.

To achieve such clarification it might prove helpful to conjure up the picture of a man completely incapable of initiating any repressions whatsoever. Such a man would be altogether a creature of impulse. He could not even exercise control over his sphincter muscles. In his loyalty to what is " natural " he would be as " free " as a newborn baby in his eliminative impulsiveness; since control of bladder and bowel functions cannot be achieved without some degree of inhibition. Similarly, he would be incapable of curbing his desire for food. The acquisition of table manners, a feeding schedule, and a habit of intelligent choice of foods would not be possible. Uncouth gluttony would be the inevitable outcome. Should such a man chance to have a liking for alcohol, he would have to yield to this desire in uninhibited fashion. Moderate drinking would be an unattainable ideal. With respect to his sex impulses no traditional conventions or taboos could be operative. He would be impelled to immediate and overt indulgence of every erotic urge. Neither friend nor relative nor stranger nor animal would be safe from his overtures. As the helplessly passive agent of every transient libidinous impulse he would have to yield with slavish automatism. Almost the entire catalog of possible sexual activity might thus be exhibited in the person of a single man: incest, bestiality, rape, sadism, sodomy, and every other vagary of sex with which psychopathologists are familiar.

Instead of being " free " to act as he pleases, such a man would have to act as his impulses dictate. He would no more be free than a drug addict is free. Lust would dominate his behavior, and order his actions; for where there is no technique of repression there is no self-control and where there is no self-control blind impulsiveness runs rampant. The victim of the morphine habit is not a *free* man: he is a slave to an impulse. Nor is the roué a free man, for he too is enslaved by an impulse. Emancipation of such psychological slaves cannot be secured until they learn how to repress effectively.

KINDS OF REPRESSION

As was just implied, repression can be either effective or ineffective. It may prove illuminating to examine this phase of the problem. In this connection it ought to be pointed out that repression can be partial or complete, temporary or permanent, as well as effective or ineffective. With respect to the incest taboo in our culture, for example, it is probably correct to say that for most people any latent sex impulses directed upon near relatives are completely, permanently, and effectively repressed. To understand the distinction between partial and complete repression, control of the impulse to steal might be cited as a convenient illustration. The person who refuses to steal under any circumstances no matter how acute his need or how opportune the circumstances would exemplify complete or total repression with reference to this kind of temptation. On the other hand, the avid collector of hotel towels, honest in other respects, exhibits incomplete repression because of his failure to curb the impulse to pilfer hotel property. The difference between temporary and permanent repression is almost self-explanatory. To give up smoking for six months constitutes temporary repression, while the intention to give it up for good constitutes permanent repression.

As applied to sex, the distinction ought to be equally easy to grasp. Conscientious members of the Roman Catholic priesthood have to repress all sex impulses permanently. For the man who takes his marriage vow seriously hospitalization of the wife would necessitate temporary repression. This latter instance may be utilized to bring out the nature of the distinction between effective and ineffective repression. If the man succeeds in going about his routine work during the weeks of his wife's hospitalization without any inner struggles with adulterous impulses, repression is functioning effectively. Contrariwise, should he find himself the victim of protracted and repeated struggles with temptation, then his technique of repression might be called ineffective.

It is ineffective repression with which the mental hygienist is primarily concerned. The basic issue is not repression *versus* complete impulsiveness. It is rather a question of intelligent as opposed to stupid repressions. Life being what it is, repression of some sort is not only necessary, but inevitable. Before indicating why this is the case it might be advisable to show how it happens that modern mental specialists have come to recognize repression as an important factor in personality integration.

NEUROTIC INDECISION

In terms of a larger frame of reference, Freud's approach to the problem of mental instability may be regarded as a study of the ways in which people handle what have been traditionally called good and evil impulses. Freud's doctrine of the super-ego, as we have seen, is concerned with standards set by social tradition, by the church, and by the larger community. The super-ego thus refers to what the ordinary man variously calls his conscience, his moral code, his sense of honor, his self-esteem, his self-respect, his duty, and his personal ideals. It is a convenient label for all of our *socialized* impulses. In like manner what Freud calls *id* impulses the ordinary man regards as his instincts, his animal urges, or his untutored body craving. Taken in the abstract, *id* impulses are *unsocialized*, biologically imperious, amoral goads to activity. However, once the super-ego develops, moral concepts begin to emerge. In the light of such concepts many amoral *id* impulses begin to be classified as immoral impulses. It is now that the developing personality begins to experience conflicts. Problems of good and bad, proper and improper, decent and indecent, right and wrong demand adjudication. Whether personality development is to proceed in healthy or neurotic fashion will depend on the honesty and wisdom of this inner adjudication.

By a neurotic personality the psychologist means one whose efficiency is impaired by chronic uncertainty involving marked emotionalism of an ambivalent kind. The neurotic is thus not to be confused with the healthy skeptic. Because of the tremendous area of knowledge nobody can be certain of the answers to all questions. It is thus not ignorance or uncertainty as such that makes for neuroticism. Otherwise everybody would be neurotic. It is only when we are worried or wrought-up or anxious or persistently tense about our ignorance or lack of assurance that neurotic symptoms begin to appear.

Such symptoms are legion. They include not only what the layman has in mind when he speaks of " nervousness," but a host of others. Restless pacing, gnawing of one's knuckles, repeated rubbing of the chin, biting the lip or the nail, and other kinds of motor agitation are neurotic symptoms. So are persistent feelings of inferiority, strident boastfulness, fanatic cleanliness, and either a foolhardy disregard of common dangers or an equally extreme anxious preoccupation with only remotely possible danger. As was indicated in an earlier chapter, even symptoms of apparent bodily disease such as palpitation of the heart, indigestion, or diarrhea may be neurotic manifestations. They are all symptoms of worry. A psychiatrist once defined worry as a " cycle of inefficient thought whirling about a pivot of fear." This is a helpful definition because it brings out both the cognitive and the emotional factors, the intellectual uncertainty in a setting of anxiety, so characteristic of neuroticism.

Worry is occasioned by uncertainty of an impending outcome threatening our welfare or interest. We may be uncertain of the outcome of a war in Africa, but we do not worry about it unless we chance to have large investments at stake or the military prestige of a close friend happens to be involved. We may be uncertain about our knowledge of the history of the labor movement in nineteenth-century France, but we do not worry about our ignorance until the prospect of an examination in French economic history looms up on our academic horizon. Nobody can be sure that he will be in good health ten years from today, but his lack of cognitive assurance does not occasion worry until symptoms of disease make their appearance in the individual. In other words, worry is never impersonal. It always relates to the welfare of the self. Whatever threatens our security or prestige may be a subject for worry; the more acute the threat, the more acute the worry. In fact, this variation in intensity or worry may be conceptualized by a scale ranging from incipient apprehension at one extreme, passing ahrough moderate worry near the middle, and attaining catastrophic anxiety at the opposite extreme of the continuum of change.

There is a close relationship between worry and action. Good students are apt to worry before examinations and good football players are apt to worry before a game starts. Being keyed up and ready for action on a task of importance to the self, they find it hard to wait for the starting signal. Every coach is familiar with the nervous behavior of players the night before an important game. Similar behavior can be observed in students waiting for the distribution of final examination papers. Many lecturers and actors suffer from mild stage fright as time for the public appearance approaches. However, once they are launched on the evening's work, all the fear symptoms vanish. In the same way the nervous football player is transformed into a calm and efficient tackler right after the opening play. The well-prepared but worried student relaxes his worried look as soon as he tackles the first question. In many situations appropriate action is thus the best antidote for worry.

But not all critical situations lend themselves to appropriate action. The young husband waiting outside the delivery room becomes more and more anxious as his hours of waiting become prolonged. He is confronted with a crisis with which he cannot cope because there is nothing for him to *do* despite his acute desire to do *something*. The result is a repetitious series of purposeless actions: walking up and down the hospital corridor, clenching and unclenching his fists, pathetic glances toward the delivery room door, and other visible indications of a distraught mental condition. The agitation can be interpreted as an overflow of energy into the musculature even though the consequent action is irrelevant and futile.

A personal crisis is always the occasion for emotional upheaval and this usually means mobilization and release of the body's energy reserves. If this energy cannot be utilized in helpful action it spills over into the muscles, and the tensions, tremblings, and twitches so characteristic of agonized worry are the outward manifestations of the inner turmoil. The victim of worry is ready for action but unable to decide on what to do. This inability may be due to the fact that the time for action has not yet arrived as in the case of the aforementioned football player or the public speaker. It may also be due to the fact that, even though the time for action has arrived, ignorance or physical obstacles render appropriate action impossible. Being ignorant of obstetrics there is nothing the anxious husband can do to relieve his wife's suffering. If by chance he should be an obstetrician but prevented from reaching his wife's bedside because of professional duties in a distant city, we would have an example of physical barriers to appropriate action.

Every physician is familiar with this intimate relationship between anxiety and action. Worried mothers beg him to *do* something for the child even though there is nothing to be done except to wait for further developments. Sometimes in order to quiet the mothers the doctor will prescribe a *placebo*. This is any harmless preparation devoid of therapeutic influence. However, it may be useful in mitigating the mother's anxiety; for it gives her something to do which she believes to be helpful. Sometimes an understanding physician will even give her minute instructions with respect to feeding the patient, or airing his room, or bathing him, not so much because he deems such care essential for the patient's welfare, but because he finds such a routine of "nursing duty" good for the mother's morale. Without such a routine she is apt to become more intensely worried. By furnishing her with a schedule of seemingly appropriate action, energy can be sluiced off into the schedule rather than permitted to drain over into distressing motor and visceral spasms symptomatic of severely acute worry. Her worry is relieved or her fear partially repressed by having significant work to do. This may be an important clue for us to follow. Everybody knows how futile it is to tell the worried person to "stop worrying" or "worrying never helps." These verbal admonitions never bring about a repression of the fear. But definite action calculated to dispose of the feared object may do so.

In the light of this understanding of "normal" worry the nature of neurotic indecision may be seen more clearly. What is technically called a *conflict situation* is the basis of this indecision. The neurotic is a victim of antagonistic or incompatible desires. He cannot decide on a course of action because a proposed action is balked by a counter-proposal. A few examples of such personal conflicts will serve to clarify this analysis. Whether to stay home and keep house for a widowed father or go off to college and let him shift for himself may constitute such a conflict for a devoted daughter. Whether to accept an invitation to the movies or to carry out an intention to spend the evening studying is a familiar type of student conflict. A more momentous conflict confronts the parent suddenly discovering infidelity in the marriage partner; for divorce might constitute a devastating shock to the emotional security of the children, while the breach of faith has already disrupted the reciprocal trust of the parents.

In every conflict situation, whether it be trivial or momentous, the victim has to make a choice. Learning to choose wisely is thus of vital mental hygiene importance. Choices can be stupid, impulsive, courageous, intelligent, selfish, executed, or deadlocked. How the individual chooses to act in the face of conflict situations is revelatory of his level of integration.

The neurotic or poorly integrated individual tends to be overwhelmed by the impulses back of the conflict. "What shall I do?" is a question he cannot answer as competing impulses push him first in one direction then in another. His mental organization is disrupted by the warring impulses. He is like a house divided against itself; hence he cannot stand and dispose of his conflict in masterful fashion. What we call neuroticism is a consequence of being overmastered by the impasse of an unresolvable choice. That chronic doubts and persistent tensions supervene is altogether to be expected. Intelligent action is blocked by inability to repress. This inability may be due to the strength of the impulses involved, poor training in repression, or failure to understand the nature of the mental factors utilized by those who have acquired the art of self-control.

Not all conflicts or repressions are of mental hygiene significance. People have conflicts of choice in a great many daily situations without in any way endangering their mental health. Trying to decide whether to purchase black shoes or brown shoes, whether to order chicken or roast beef, whether to write an important letter today or to put it off until tomorrow, whether to invite the Joneses or the Smiths to a dinner party are all examples of innocuous conflict situations. They are innocuous because nothing very momentous for the welfare of the self is ordinarily at stake. They cease to be innocuous as soon as one's self-esteem becomes enmeshed in the choice. One can become reconciled to what turns out to be a poor choice in the matter of an investment provided other competent investors assure us they might have made the same mistake. However, should they cast aspersions on our business judgment or even go so far as to intimate that " any fool would have known better," then we might be headed for trouble. Feelings of chagrin or of inferiority might be added to our disappointment. We hate to have our business associates think we were taken in by a glib stock promoter whose slickness was obvious to them. We might even begin to lose confidence in our business acumen. To lose confidence in one's ability to handle matters of routine business, to suffer from distressing feelings of self-disparagement, to be persuaded that one's colleagues are making our stupidity a subject for gossip around the luncheon table, is to experience some of the mental consequences of the more hazardous type of conflict situation. Experiences of this kind reflect jeopardized morale. They have to do with loss of self-assurance, disturbing inner doubts, and attitudes of defeatism or worried self-depreciation. They induce the sufferer to conclude that he is a failure or that nobody loves him or that nobody respects him. Emotional security is gone, life loses its savor, and despair is in the saddle. Once again we can see why the mental hygienist is so interested in problems of choice and repression.

THE INEVITABILITY OF REPRESSION

To achieve more insight into these mental hygiene factors, the problem of masturbation might be examined in the light of the foregoing discussion. The *psychological* effects of masturbation are of much greater moment than any physiological ones. The way in which the individual reacts to his indulgence is what transforms it from an intrinsically harmless, if somewhat childish, bit of behavior into what he magnifies as a danger of the first magnitude. To him his continued masturbation signifies abject lack of self-control, weakness of will, addiction to a secret vice, and a lowered respect for himself in his own eyes. He is also confident that others would not respect him if they knew. These are all symptoms of shame. They indicate the existence of feelings of guilt. Often the masturbator is rendered even more miserable by believing superstitious or ignorant nonsense about horrible immediate or remote pathological consequences of the act. Nonsense of this kind may be exemplified by stories of insanity that followed prolonged masturbation or feeblemindedness being caused in this manner or sterility or disease or early death or weakminded offspring. That such nonsense is taken seriously by thousands of people is known to every specialist in mental adjustments; for so many of their patients are given almost spectacular relief upon being assured that none of these dire consequences ever result as direct effects of masturbatory practices.

These patients are also helped by learning how common such practices are both in the animal kingdom as well as in all strata of human society. It is found in both sexes and at almost all ages. People who have *never* masturbated are in a distinct minority. Facts of this kind help to give the worried patient a measure of immediate relief by furnishing a non-pathological perspective to his problem. Such a perspective takes it out of the category of morbid perversions. He can begin to think of it as a rather universal exploratory maneuver which has chanced to become a somewhat fixed practice for him. In terms of the mechanics involved he learns to view it as not essentially different from what he regards as the " normal " sex act: friction is used to produce the physio-logical climax of the orgasm. Such an unromantic, mechanistic view helps him because it dissipates fear of irreparable damage as a result of " abnormal " sex gratification. He no longer has to be concerned with fears of " lost manhood," " insanity," " prostate trouble," " bladder disease," and all the other symptoms unscrupulous quacks have incorporated into their not overly subtle advertising. Of course, he may still be concerned about his inability to exercise self-control. He feels that he ought to be able to conquer what he deems to be an unworthy habit. In other words, even after the therapist has succeeded in relieving the patient of the fears of physical consequences, the matter of wholesome sex adjustment still remains to be worked out.

As has already been implied, masturbation is a mental hygiene problem because of the feelings of guilt which follow each lapse from the resolve to give up the habit. These guilt feelings are a product of the social condemnation of the practice. The fact that so many people register horror when it is mentioned and refer to it as " self-abuse " or a " perversion " or as a " sin " or a " vice " serves to reenforce the conviction of guilt. It becomes something to be concealed from others and something that would mean disgrace if exposed. In hating himself for indulging in the practice the victim is projecting the disapproval of his cultural group upon himself. To think of himself as a masturbator hurts his pride in himself; it detracts from his ego-ideal. This is the basis for the conflict between the latter ideal and the masturbatory impulse. It should be noticed once again that we have two sets of impulses here: those connected with the ideal and those connected with the sex impulse. And once again it should be noted that, irrespective of the final disposition of the conflict, repression of some sort is inevitable. If the verdict is in favor of the ideal, then the masturbatory impulses will have to be repressed; contrariwise, if the verdict is in favor of masturbation, then the others will have to be repressed.

This is an inevitable characteristic of mutually exclusive acts of choice. It means that repression of some sort is bound to take place. We cannot eat our cake and have it too. We cannot think of ourselves as honest and still cheat in business. We cannot think of ourselves as law-abiding and still resort to bribery to win official favors. We cannot think of ourselves as loyal friends and still seduce the friend's wife or daughter. The ideals of honesty, good citizenship, fine friendship just cannot keep house together with sharp practices, bribery, and seduction. One array of impulses will have to yield to the other. At the risk of tedious repetition, it has to be pointed that mental hygiene does not advocate the elimination of repression; for this would be both foolish and impossible. In the present context, as we have just seen, people have to decide whether they want to abide by our culturally determined taboo of masturbation or whether they can reconcile themselves to the psychological consequences of its violation by continuing to be masturbators. Only one thing is certain here: they cannot observe the taboo and still violate it. It is in this sense that some kind of repression will have to be introduced.

CULTURAL RELATIVITY AND SEX CONFLICTS

What impulses are to be repressed is something each individual has to decide on for himself. There are no absolute standards to be applied universally, but there are relative ones that are helpful in arriving at intelligent decisions. This is another way of saying that standards differ from age to age and culture to culture. Polygamy is tabooed by us, but welcomed by other societies. The accumulation of wealth and the acquisition of private property is accepted as normal by one society, but stigmatized as sinful selfishness by other cultures. We regard killing a man in a duel as a crime, while our ancestors classified the act as necessary for the maintenance of honor. To the present generation of Americans human slavery is indefensible; but to pre-Civil War Southerners it was a God-ordained institution. Is it wrong for laborers to organize into unions, for women to vote and for married women to own property? Most Americans see no problems here; but not so long ago their predecessors engaged in acrimonious and heated debate on these issues.

What is the line of demarcation between modesty and vulgarity? To the generation of the 1890's the swimming costumes of the 1940's would have constituted a flagrant violation of the standards of decency. There is no need to add any more of the almost endless series of examples which might be introduced to demonstrate that standards fluctuate and practices change both in time and space. The morality of the fifteenth century differs from that of the twentieth and the Nazi concept of justice shocks jurists in other countries. All of this has been summed up in the idea of the *relativity* of morals. Tennyson had reference to this when he wrote about changes in the old order as " God fulfills himself in many ways, lest one good custom should corrupt the world."

People brought up to believe in absolute ethical values are often very much disturbed upon being introduced to the concept of the relativity of morals. They interpret this concept to imply the absence of any standards by means of which right and wrong are to be decided. If what *we* condemn, people in some other country or at some other time regarded as right and proper, then it looks as if the whole subject of ethics is altogether arbitrary and one might as well permit full sovereignty to every passing impulse. Reflections of this kind are a source of conflict to many because they regard themselves as deprived of any sure means of disposing of their ethical dilemmas by an appeal to fundamental principles. The consequence is that every experienced mental hygienist, psychiatrist, and consulting psychologist soon finds himself having to deal with the general field of ethics in his efforts to aid those waiting to be rescued from the muddle into which they have been thrown by discovery of this doctrine of ethical relativity. The victim of this discovery, it should be remembered, is the victim of a conflict, and as he translates this it is the equivalent of asking: " What shall I do? " or " How shall I act? " or " How shall I decide this problem? " Many mental hygiene problems are thus problems of personal ethics.

It often helps those troubled by the implications of the doctrine of the relativity of morals to envisage this doctrine in a larger setting. This doctrine does not mean that what is to be deemed good and beautiful is altogether a matter of private caprice. It means rather that the community of which one is a member has an important influence in determining such judgments. It means that individual acts are to be evaluated in terms of their consequences for the group affected by such acts. The doctrine of moral relativity does not abolish the existence of human values. It merely takes values out of the realm of metaphysical abstractions and brings them back to the here and now of daily association with our fellow men. It serves to remind us that our obligation is to people around us, to their living needs and to their hopes and distresses. How our conduct might have been judged by Tasmanians in 1650 has nothing to do with determining intelligent choices today as we find ourselves a part of the American scene in Florida or Oregon or Vermont.

From one viewpoint, abstract human values may be the same at all times and places, but the techniques for realizing them change through the ages. We all hunger for the approval of our fellow men, but to elicit such approval we must adjust our actions to the standards of a given culture. If we want people to credit us with good taste in dress, we must select our wardrobe in terms of modes current in our community and not in terms of what was fashionable in Washington's day or in the days of Pericles. The rugged individualist who insists that to dress like Pericles is to be his absolute standard will only make himself a laughing-stock by such nonconformity. Such an individualist might also be much enamored of the brother-sister marriages prevalent in ancient Egypt. He might argue that this is an ideal way to keep families " pure " and the " race " unsullied by admixture of foreign blood. But in the light of the strength of the incest taboo prevalent in our culture, this appeal to Egyptian custom is irrelevant. His problem is to anticipate the consequences both for himself and his sister of violating this taboo in America today. He must learn to think of the variety of customs as ways of enhancing group welfare and preserving valuable cultural traditions. As a member of a given group and a given culture he has a personal responsibility of contributing to such enhancement and preservation.

To overlook these cultural determinants of conduct and to search for *absolute* standards is like planning to live in a vacuum. It is akin to asking what is the absolutely ideal breakfast or what is the absolutely true religion or the absolutely best language or the absolutely best music, literature, or government. Not one of these questions can be answered in categorical fashion. Even if someone should be rash enough to commit himself and decide, for example, that Greek is the " absolutely best language," what difference would this make if he finds himself a member of an American community in Alabama? He would still have to communicate in English with his neighbors and read English signs and newspapers. It would be Quixotic to ask the state legislature to abolish

English and substitute Greek. It would be equally Quixotic to plan a standardized " best " breakfast for all people the world over or to plan to have all music except that of Bach outlawed by legislative decree. One can have satisfactory and even superb breakfasts, literatures, musical compositions, and religions without regimented uniformity. This is not to say that any breakfast is as good as any other or that there are no criteria for determining whether a given novel is better than another or a given religious practice more inspiring than another. It is merely to say that the issues have to be narrowed down to specific problems as these problems are calculated to influence the lives of people living in specific cultures.

With respect to such issues these are some of the relevant questions to be raised by the victim of an ethical dilemma: Do people in my community approve of this? If they don't, is their disapproval just a sign of unenlightened prejudice or is it an indication of a genuine threat to the welfare of community values? How will my action affect others both directly and indirectly? How is it likely to affect me not only now but in the future? Is it likely to have any influence on my children? Is what I'm about to do the sort of thing I'd like to see everybody doing? Would I approve of others who should make my impending choice their choice? Questions such as these take a conflict out of the world of abstractions and place it in a context of cause and effect. They furnish the individual with intellectual levers by means of which he can lift his moral burdens and examine them from all sides in order to reach wise decisions. Often, as ethical insight deepens, what we regarded as a wise decision last year may strike us as a stupid one this year. We must be ready for change in our moral evaluations as outside events change and as our capacity for honest self-appraisal and self-criticism grows. To recognize last year's unwillingness to make a community chest donation because " the poor squander the money on drink " as a rationalization is to reveal moral growth — especially if we act on such recognition by making a donation this year.

How is this sort of pragmatic approach to be applied to problems of sex? This is a legitimate question that merits an honest answer. A good way to answer it is to consider how an advocate of this approach disposed of a problem posed for him by a neurotic patient. The patient was a woman of thirty much troubled by feelings of social inferiority as well as by persistent sex tensions. She described herself as " highly sexed " and regretted that fate had not enabled her to find a husband. Her immediate problem centered in her infatuation for a married man. This man was escorting her to night clubs and to movies and had already hinted of his readiness to support a mistress. As she put it, " He is a perfect gentleman and is leaving the decision up to me." She also explained that the man was not happy with his wife and would even have tried to divorce her had he not been so intensely devoted to his two children.

Her conflict was thus narrowed down to the problem of continued allegiance to what she had been taught to regard as the ideal of chastity or to find gratification for her erotic tensions by becoming the mistress of another woman's husband. It was quite evident to the clinician that she hoped he would relieve her of the job of making up her own mind by recommending sex experience as indicated therapy for her neurotic symptoms. A recommendation of this sort would obviously have enabled the patient to shift any onus of moral censure from her protesting conscience to the presumed wisdom of her clinician. However, the clinician made no such recommendation. Instead he urged her to face the problem in all its aspects with relentless honesty. He pointed out that a mature person of thirty, a graduate of a first-rate college, and holding a responsible teaching post in a grade school ought to be able to cope with such personal problems without depending on others to do the thinking for her. This noncommittal attitude disappointed her somewhat for she said, " Aren't you willing to help me at all? " The clinician's reply to this question might well be given in full in his own words:

I'll help you only to the extent of showing you the chief issues you ought to consider before reaching a final verdict. I'm not going to do your thinking for you and dictate to you in dogmatic fashion. If I were faced with your problem, I'd ask myself what values are to be gained by becoming this man's mistress. I'd also make an inventory of values that might be lost by accepting his invitation. With reference to the first question you might as well grant that many exciting thrills will be yours; for sex experience can be exciting and thrilling.

It might also be pleasing to your vanity to dwell on the fact that the man has singled you out to be his — well, in the old days they had a word like *concubine* to apply to such second choices. In the third place I'd also consider the possible material gains of such a proposed arrangement: the gifts and the monetary support coming my way as expressions of the man's affectionate solicitude. Another possible advantage of an affirmative verdict would be the freedom from loneliness and the joy of companionship with a devoted and congenial companion. In other words, if I were you, I'd add up everything that might conceivably make this a desirable arrangement.

And then I'd ask myself in what respects such an arrangement might prove to be undesirable. I'd want to know whether I can really count on the enduring loyalty of the man — will he still be devoted to me after my waning youth has waned? I'd ask myself whether his proposed infidelity to his wife might not suggest a kind of moral instability that augurs unfavorably for his unwavering fidelity to me. I'd even feel constrained to wonder about the possibility of pregnancy. The chances of such an occurrence might be remote, but there is always the chance. How am I to face this contingency? Am I the kind of woman who would be unruffled by becoming the mother of an illegitimate child? My community being what it is, would it be fair to the child to keep him with me? If I send him off to a distant foundling home, would this hurt me in the years to come? I'd also look into the matter of abortions, if I wanted to be altogether prepared to deal with every contingency. Is it possible to get reputable and competent surgeons to undertake such surgery? If so, are there any risks to one's health? Is it expensive? I'd try to anticipate whether I'm the kind of woman who could have recourse to abortion without subsequent qualms of conscience. And then I'd ask myself whether sex experience involving clandestine meetings, furtive comings and goings, planned alibis and deceptions can be as ennobling and free from anxiety as a fine love ought to be. As a matter of fact, speaking of love, I'd wonder about the sincerity and whole-hearted devotion of a man who balks at getting a divorce and yet insists his heart belongs to me and not to his wife. Put more bluntly, I'd wonder whether he wasn't using the word *love* as a euphemism for lust. Not that lust is necessarily to be deprecated. It can be either very fine or very base depending on how it is controlled; but taken by itself it is a much more selfish motive than love. The latter is not to be confused with the former. To have someone love us is a greater tribute to our attractiveness than just to be lusted after. The objective of love is the welfare and happiness of the beloved personality. This is the sense in which it is more unselfish than lust the objective of which is the reduction of pelvic tensions. The distinction is rather momentous and one that you ought to dwell upon before coming to a final conclusion.

Nor is this all. You would do well to consider how hard-boiled you are with respect to public opinion. Would you be bothered by the gossip certain to follow once the community suspects the existence of a liaison? If the suspicion should become a certainty, and the wife sues for divorce how would you react to being named as correspondent? Even if you think of these eventualities as stupid conventions, still they're the ones that operate in your community and you'll have to reckon with them. Matters may have been different at the French court in the seventeenth century; but you're living three hundred years later and the French court is gone. You have to adjust to this situation and to the customs, social expectations, and values of the present. Don't let your thinking wander too far afield.

I'm not sure whether you're the kind of person who is much concerned by the refinements of ethical obligations; but if you are, you ought also to mull over the possible effect of such a back-street romance on the man's wife and children. Would you be giving them a square deal, our community gossip being what it is? Would any of the responsibility for the possible distress of at least three other people be yours? Of course you have a right to what you call happiness, but would you be getting it in the long run if it were purchased at the cost of hurting another woman and her children?

You see there is a good deal more to your problem than you may have suspected. I can only suggest the general drift your thinking ought to take and, as I told you at the start, you'll have to do your own thinking. But I do want you to see why I'm by no means sure that an illicit romance will dispose of your neurotic symptoms. In fact, if my present understanding of these symptoms is correct, I might even predict that such a romance might precipitate a new set of symptoms, you being what you are. You'd be adding another conflict to your present one.

THE DISTINCTION BETWEEN FRUSTRATION AND DEPRIVATION

The foregoing excerpts from a mental hygienist's casebook should indicate that, contrary to the opinion prevalent in some circles, the modern psychologist does not regard uninhibited sex expression as the answer to the evils of unenlightened sex repression. In fact, many of the alleged evils can be avoided by introducing a big dose of healthy enlightenment. This calls for more than the customary talks on the anatomy and physiology of reproduction found in the usual books on sex hygiene. It calls for more than informative accounts of the nature of venereal infections. Over and above such conventional enlightenment a more subtle, less easily teachable kind of enlightenment is to be urged, one that will make for the frank acceptance of sex impulses as wholesome and desirable, rather than ignoble and indecent. Fostering an attitude of honest acceptance of a biologically inevitable urge is more likely to pave the way for effective and intelligent control.

On the other hand, those who have been conditioned to view sex as essentially nasty, a kind of regrettable biological vagary whose very existence is to be deprecated, are the ones for whom *wholesome* repression is apt to be a more difficult achievement. It is hard to deal with a problem when we are reluctant to face the facts connected with it, and people who are ashamed of themselves for having sex impulses may consequently resort to unconscious self-deception in their efforts to deal with the impulses in question. Some of the evils of unwholesome repression are a result of this sort of self-deception. The detailed nature of these evils need not be catalogued here. It will suffice to suggest that development of such an attitude toward sex is poor preparation for marriage and intelligent parenthood; for it associates feelings of guilt and sinfulness and vulgarity with *any* manifestation of sex. These ideas continue to prevail within the institution of marriage and interfere with the cultivation of a joyously healthy, esthetically satisfying, and spiritually ennobling eroticism. Outside of marriage such an attitude may make for fanatic prudishness. This may take the form of a morbid fear of members of the opposite sex, or vehement opposition to any kind of dancing, disapproval of co-education, or concern about having undraped statues in public parks.

The victim of unwholesome sex repression projects his latent sex impulse upon others and misinterprets what may be innocent fun as the beginning of guilty lasciviousness. He fails to realize that the misinterpretation is a consequence of the mechanism of projection and that the ideas of guilt and vulgarity are products of his own warped attitude toward the subject of sex. To put this figuratively: it is as if he were striving to keep his psychological ménage " clean " by throwing what he views as " cheap trash " into his neighbor's yard and then complaining about his " dirty " neighbors, being oblivious of the fact that the " dirt " came from him.

Control of sex impulses by means of wholesome repression is free from these evils of self-deception. The control is exercised because the individual understands that absence of such control will jeopardize numerous other values coordinate in importance with the value of erotic pleasure. As a member of a community he is mindful of his responsibility to that community. He realizes that sex gratification is not exclusively a private affair devoid of social consequences. For him the existence of such consequences justifies the public in venturing to regulate sex expression. By identifying himself with that public he has a share in safeguarding the values of socialized living. The repression is thus not regarded as altogether a matter of " public opinion " forcing him to act contrary to his nature. His super-ego as a constituent phase of his own personality reflects this public opinion and the public control is therefore also a matter of personal control.

In well-integrated personalities, in other words, self-control does not engender rebelliousness; for the frustration of the sex impulse is not regarded as ruthlessly imposed by an alien and hostile society. Self-identification with that society and with its welfare makes the frustration as much self-imposed as extraneously imposed. An analogy may make this clearer. To feel that one is a member of a team is akin to the " consciousness of kind " that goes with the feeling of *belonging* to a community. The loyal team member identifies his welfare with the team as a going concern. In the team's interest he *willingly* subordinates immediate and private joys. He may even be *willing* to accept annoyances and frustrations such as giving up smoking or taking his place on the bench in order to make way for a pinch hitter. The socialized personality like the loyal member of a team adjusts to the need for self-control in the interests of group values with a minimum of protest. Repression, frustration, inhibition, self-control — the precise term is immaterial — comes to be regarded as a necessary rule of the game without which *freedom* to play the game would cease to exist. Unless license is curbed there can be no liberty. This is only another way of saying that without repression there can be no freedom. Ruthlessly impulsive individualism is incompatible with civilized living.

Since all sex desire cannot be gratified, we might raise this question: Is it possible for people to have such desire balked for a long period — even for a lifetime in some cases — without serious warping of the personality? Does not ordinary observation of the irritability and domineering censoriousness of many spinsters demonstrate such warping? The warping may be granted, but whether it is exclusively a product of sex repression is to be questioned. Unless it is questioned one would be forced to assume that spinsters can never develop balanced personalities without having recourse to some unconventional mode of erotic indulgence. However, as was just pointed out, unconventionality of this kind is itself apt to throw the personality off balance. Furthermore, the existence of balanced personalities in the ranks of priests and nuns establishes at least a presumption in favor of the *possibility* of complete repression of sex without serious personality distortion. In other words, not *all* unmarried adults, whether churched or unchurched, are to be regarded as necessarily either neurotic or hypocritically unconventional. Nor is sex indulgence a certain prophylactic against neuroticism. There are far too many neuroses among the married and those engaged in pre-marital and extra-marital amours to justify the conclusion that sex expression will automatically ward off neurotic episodes.

Neuroticism is more a function of thwarted self-esteem than of frustrated sex urges. Whether sex repression will be a cause of neurotic symptoms depends on what caused the sex repression. If failure to attract men dooms a woman to remain a spinster, the psychological consequences will be different from those in the case of her attractive sister, who deliberately spurns offers of marriage in order to pursue a chosen career. The former case involves hurt feelings while the latter is free from any such wounded pride. Both cases will call for frustration of sex desire, but in the first there may be an emergence of the sour-faced unloveliness associated with many eccentric spinsters while the second may go through life devoid of any manifest eccentricity or noticeable maladjustment.

How frustration will be tolerated is thus bound up with the conditions responsible for its causation. To cite a simple example: the adolescent son of the household who happens to be very fond of apple pie may be forced by circumstances to deny himself indulgence in his favorite dessert. Two possible kinds of circumstances may be assumed here. He may have to forego the pie because the family physician has so ordained or because father ordains it as a punishment for impudence. The consequent frustration will precipitate more inner turmoil in the latter case than in the former; for deprivation under the one set of circumstances is symbolic of social disapproval and not so under the other set. We are dealing with the frequently overlooked distinction between *deprivation* on the one hand and frustration on the other. Maslow,[1] to whom we are indebted for this distinction, has summarized its implications in the following passage:

> Neglect of this distinction has created a great deal of unnecessary turmoil in psychoanalytic circles. An ever-recurring question is: Does sexual deprivation inevitably give rise to all or any of the many effects of frustration, e.g., aggression, sublimation, etc. It is now well known that many cases are found in which celibacy has no psychopathological effects. In many other cases, however, it has many bad effects. What factor determines which shall be the result? Clinical work with non-neurotic people gives a clear answer that sexual deprivation becomes pathogenic in a severe sense only when it is felt by the individual to represent rejection by the opposite sex, inferiority, lack of worth, lack of respect, or isolation. Sexual deprivation can be borne with relative ease by individuals for whom it has no such implications. . . .

> This leads to our final hypothesis, that perhaps frustration as a single concept is less useful than the two concepts which cross-cut it, (1) deprivation, and (2) threat to the personality. Deprivation implies much less than is ordinarily implied by the concept of frustration; threat implies much more.

DOES REPRESSION CAUSE ANXIETY OR DOES ANXIETY CAUSE REPRESSION?

As was just stated, neurotic disturbance is bound up with a threat to the welfare of the self. When confronted with a personal crisis like illness in the family the individual experiences such a

---

[1] Maslow, A. H., "Deprivation, Threat and Frustration," *Psychol. Rev.*, 1941, *48* pp. 364–366. For further elaboration of some of these concepts, consult also Maslow's "Conflict, Frustration, and the Theory of Threat," *J. of Abnorm. and Soc. Psychol.*, 1943, *38,* pp. 81–86.

threat. He fears death's disruption of the family circle or anticipates the possibility of severe pain for someone very dear to him.
We ordinarily describe this mental state as one of anxiety. Threat
to the personality and anxiety are thus intimately related. Freud
was one of the first to call attention to this relationship. In fact,
his earliest explorations of psychological territory were undertaken for the purpose of discovering the origin of the stream of
anxiety running through the personal reports of his patients.

Anxiety is not always as obviously related to a manifest crisis
as in our simple illustration of family illness. Sometimes there is
pronounced anxiety without clear-cut understanding or appreciation of the factors responsible for it. The victim is just as perplexed as are his friends to whom he confides his fears. He may
even recognize his fear as " foolish," but be powerless to rid himself of its gnawing presence. It is not a reasonable, precautionary
fear like that which causes us to refuse to drink polluted water,
touch a live wire, or drive with an intoxicated chauffeur. It is an
unreasonable, stupid fear like one which results in refusal to touch
a coin because it " may be covered with germs," or to walk in the
country because " innocent insects might be stepped on and
killed," or to take a shower because " that's almost the same as
baptism by sprinkling."

Fears of this kind are rather common among neurotic patients.
Many of us who are proud of our freedom from " neurotic weaknesses " harbor fears not radically different from the unreasonable ones just listed. There are " normal " people for whom a
solitary, nocturnal stroll through a country cemetery would be inwardly disturbing. Handling a harmless garter snake suffices to
throw many " normal " persons into a panic. Having to make
speeches will have the same effect on many of us. The fear will
be there even when we strive to reassure ourselves that " there's
nothing to be scared over with the speech all memorized and all of
our friends in the audience." To explain the occurrence of these
unreasonable anxieties — both normal and morbid — is not always easy. Nor are we immediately concerned with considering
their explanation. We are primarily interested in mentioning the
existence of the difficulty by way of justifying Freud's protracted
concern with the problem. Simple, everyday cases of anxiety may
seem so obvious to the ordinary man that he might otherwise be

tempted to regard the specialist's perplexity as the equivalent of much ado about nothing.

In his early theorizing Freud regarded anxiety as the product of repression. The latter was viewed as the *cause* of the anxiety. Very likely it was this first Freudian teaching which was responsible for the popular opinion that " modern psychology says repression is bad for you." What is more, this notion can be given a superficial plausibility. All one has to do is to *assume* the following to be the sequence of events responsible for the rise of anxiety : (1) illicit desire; (2) repression of the desire; (3) dynamic, but unconscious survival of the desire ; (4) anxiety for fear the balked desire may break through the defensive forces holding it in check. If this is correct, then the repression precedes the anxiety. Stated differently, had there been no antecedent repression there would have been no consequent anxiety or neuroticism. Repression is thus made the villain of this psychological drama. However, what many casual students of Freud seem to have overlooked is that Freud himself rewrote the drama as continued study revealed its shortcomings and inaccuracies.

The early Freudian formulation was just referred to as superficially plausible. This suggests, of course, a lack of plausibility discoverable upon more profound analysis. To find the weakness in the formula we need to ask, " What induces repression of an illicit desire ? " Item two in the preceding formula is made to appear as if it were independent and altogether separable from the other items, particularly item four : repression comes first and is followed by or causes anxiety. But why should a desire be repressed ? What induces us to curb the thousand and one impulses and wishes experienced every week and not translated into action ? All sorts of wishes are denied expression every day. People wish for new cars, for the death of rich uncles, for thrilling amours, and for less noisy neighbors without taking any steps to gratify such wishes. Why the self-denial ? This appears to be the crucial question with which Freud was concerned in his later work.

The answer he worked out necessitated a revision of the earlier formula ; for Freud came to believe that the self-denial, the repression, is a *consequence* of anxiety. In his own words,[2] " it is not the

---

[2] Freud, S.: *New Introductory Lectures on Psychoanalysis,* New York, W. W. Norton and Co., 1933, p. 120.

repression that creates the anxiety, but the anxiety is there first and creates the repression! " What this means is that the wish is not merely father to the thought of its own gratification, but also to the thought of the results of such gratification. Along with the thought of an illicit amour comes the anticipation in imaginary terms of possible unpleasantnesses to follow. Anticipation of such potential disaster arouses incipient or manifest anxiety and it is this arousal which precipitates the curbing or repression. The would-be Casanova anticipates violent disapproval of parents or wife or children and loss of their love and respect in case his wished-for private amour should become a public scandal. It is the thought of this potential threat to his emotional security which he experiences with apprehension. Because of this apprehension the illicit wish is not acted out.

In schematic terms the sequence of events may be compressed into the following formula: (1) illicit desire; (2) anticipation of both pleasant and unpleasant consequences of gratification; (3) anxiety because of possible threat to emotional security; (4) restraint or repression of desire. This new formula, it will be noted, makes anxiety a cause of repression and thus contradicts the old one, which made repression a cause of anxiety. Presumably, if the repression is decisive and complete, the conflict will be over and done with; if, however, as was suggested earlier in this chapter, it should be half-hearted, qualified, and reluctant, the conflict will persist and the cycle of the mental processes symbolized by the four steps of the formula will recur to plague the victim over and over again.

In the interest of successful mental hygiene it is therefore necessary to learn how to achieve successful repression. Unfortunately, the little formula with its four neat steps fails to be of much practical aid. It seems to suggest that the way to accomplish the job is to conjure up states of fear or anxiety. But these are not wholesome mental states; they militate against sound morale and zestful living. It may even be that they will breed after their own kind and intensify the distress and indecision of the conflict-ridden person.

There is a well-known psychological principle, called the *law of emotional congruity*, whose operation cannot be squared with this second Freudian formula without some elaboration and modi-

fication of the formula. The principle in question sums up the familiar fact that our ideas tend to be in harmony or congruous
with our moods. A joyous frame of mind tends to provoke cheer-
ful thoughts, gloom touches off gloomy associations, and a belligerent mood makes for warlike ideas. Moods, to put this technically, function as directive sets to facilitate certain associations
and to inhibit others: the ones facilitated being in line with the
mood, while the ones inhibited are incongruous with the dominant
mood. This psychological fact explains some of our embarrassing
moments, a stock instance being the futility of trying to think of
" sad " ideas when the " giggling impulse " overcomes us during a
religious service or other occasion for solemnity.

According to the Freudian formula, anxiety, represented in consciousness by thoughts of dire consequences, brings about repression of the illicit wish. However, in terms of the law of emotional
congruity, with the thrilling wish buried, the anxious mood ought
to have full sway and thoughts of foreboding and doom ought to
follow thick and fast. The victim of the conflict would thus fail
to secure inner peace by making anxiety the mechanism of repression. He might even reenforce and prolong his anxiety by thinking of more terrifying possibilities. The worried man does not
succeed in repressing the source of his worry as his anxiety becomes more acute. The anxiety functions as an emotional set to remind him of more things to worry over.

The Freudians have introduced another principle to offset these
implications of the law of emotional congruity. This other principle is that of *oblivescence of the unpleasant or the disagreeable*.
In everyday language this principle holds that we have a tendency
to forget the annoying, the humiliating, and the irritating experiences of the past. Because of such forgetting we are apt to glorify
the good old days and the days of our childhood and find it hard
to recall the disappointments and worries that once were ours.
Very likely it is because of this process that mothers are supposed
to forget the pangs of childbirth and to look forward to having
more children as the joys of motherhood blot out memories of the
pain. To what extent this principle is valid and under what circumstances it operates is still a moot question. At all events it is
quite certain that it is by no means a dependable source of relief
to those who are worried about possible disaster. The mother

whose boy is with the fighting forces " simply can't forget what might happen to him," and then proceeds to elaborate a whole chain of morbid associations reminiscent of the entire catalog of misery incident to modern warfare. In situations of this kind the principle of emotional congruity seems to triumph over the doctrine of the oblivescence of the disagreeable. Under the circumstances it is hard to understand how fear or anxiety can function as the repressing agency. The Freudian formula leads to an impasse, as McGranahan has demonstrated. His account of the difficulty is so clarifying that the following quotation merits careful study: [3]

We have already seen that the most common view attributes repression to fear or anxiety. There is a plausibility in this view because fear and anxiety are factors in human motivation that determine avoidance. We avoid external objects because of fear, and so, it is easy to believe, we also avoid certain thought processes because of fear. There seems to be a simple formula in the minds of analysts and others who deal with the relation of motivation to thinking: wishes directly cause the appearance of pleasant, gratifying thoughts in dreams and emotional beliefs (wish-fulfillment); fears directly cause the disappearance of unpleasant and frustrating thoughts (repression).

But this formula is based upon a very patent error. It is true, when hungry we think or dream of food objects and ways of getting food; when thirsty, of water; and when sexually aroused, of sexual objects. But it is also true that when possessed by fear, we tend to think of fearful things. Defoe, in his *Journal of the Plague Year*, reports many an incident where the fear that was spread throughout the populace created terrible visions. And Murray has shown experimentally that when a state of fear and anxiety is aroused in children by telling them a murder story, they tend to judge more unknown individuals (presented in photographs) as being malicious and dangerous than otherwise. Yet psychologists, and particularly psychoanalysts, have in general refused to recognize this direct action of fear upon thought. Freud has been much criticized for his failure to deal adequately with the problem.

[3] McGranahan, D. V., " A Critical and Experimental Study of Repression," *J. of Abnor. and Soc. Psychol.*, 1940, *35*, pp. 212–225.
For a stimulating analysis of the relationship between repression and the forgetting of items painful to one's self-esteem see Rosenzweig, S., " An Experimental Study of ' Repression ' with Special Reference to Need-Persistive and Ego-Defensive Reactions to Frustration," *J. of Experim. Psychol.*, 1943, *32*, pp. 64–74.

AN EXPERIMENTAL STUDY OF REPRESSION

Realizing the inadequacy of Freud's explanation of the mechanism of repression, McGranahan proceeded to supply a more satisfactory one. For this purpose he planned a simple experimental situation calling for ideational control. A list of 100 nouns was drawn up to which 16 experimental subjects were instructed to respond with the first *adjective* that came to mind. Of these 100 nouns about 20 were closely linked up with associations suggesting a color like *grass*-green or *apple*-red. Now these subjects were also warned that they would receive an electric shock on the wrist as intense as they would tolerate each time they responded to a stimulus word with an adjective signifying a color. It was thus to their advantage not to think of color adjectives. Another way of putting this is to say that the experiment called for repression of ideas suggesting color. Of course it was possible for a subject to substitute a non-color adjective for a color response and thus avoid the shock. To check on this possibility McGranahan had all of the subjects report such substitutions after the experiment was over. These substitutions or " hold-backs " were then recorded as failures to inhibit or repress. To ascertain the number of color associations one might expect under ordinary conditions a control group of 15 subjects was asked to respond to the list of nouns with the first associated adjective, no mention of colors being made and no shock being used.

In this kind of experimental situation the maintenance of " security " obviously requires control over the " impulse " to think of colors. The instructions given the subjects are such as to arouse a mental set in line with such an impulse. However, the instructions also make yielding to such an impulse hazardous. A conflict situation is thus created: the impulse to avoid the shock conflicts with the impulse or mental set to think of colors. In terms of the mental processes involved, the task confronting the experimental subjects may be compared to that of the student whose sense of duty impels him to think about his mathematics, but whose aroused sex interest impels him to indulge in an erotic fantasy. Without repression of the latter, there can be no concentration on the mathematics assignment. In other words, McGranahan's experimental situation duplicated the kind of personal conflict which a Freudian would regard as involving the super-ego *versus* the id and which popular psychology would variously describe as will-power *versus* fear, courage *versus* cowardice, control *versus* panic, or self-mastery *versus* instinct.

The results obtained in this experiment merit careful consideration. In the control group the number of color associations ranged from 13 to 26. This squares pretty well with the fact that about 20 of the nouns were such as to suggest ideas of color. As contrasted with the control group, the experimental group revealed a range of from 4 to 50 color associations. The threat of the shock influenced individual subjects differently: some had more " tabooed " ideas come to mind and some had fewer than would normally be expected. The ones with the fewer associations were repressing more effectively or exerting better ideational control than those with more. The latter were dominated by anxiety; hence their thinking was more disorganized. It seemed as if those who could set themselves a specific task, like thinking of adjectives denoting size or shape — anything except color — and who could persevere in subordinating their thinking to this task idea, were the ones who did a better job of repression. They were the ones who kept relatively cool during the " emergency " created by the experiment.

To check on this interpretation McGranahan introduced a second test. In this test the 16 experimental subjects were required to carry out a task demanding coordination of eye and hand (pursuit-meter test) while an electric shock was intermittently applied to the performing hand during every other trial. There were six trials of a minute each, three with the shock and three without. The mode of scoring was a little too complex to be summarized here. For our purposes it will suffice to point out that the measure of success or failure was determined by comparing the records of each subject for the three non-shock trials with the three shock trials. This measure was recorded as the average increment difference, a plus score indicating more loss of control than a minus score. Results on this pursuitmeter test were then correlated with those on the color association test. The rank-order correlation obtained was close to $+70$. This serves to demonstrate the existence of tendency for those less able to handle their thinking effectively in the emergency of the association test to be more disorganized by fear in the pursuitmeter emergency and for those who were masterful in the one to be masterful in the other. The following table summarizes the data in convenient fashion:

TABLE 4

Subject	Total Color Ass'ns	Number Stated	Hold-backs	Average Increment Difference
A	50	40	10	..
B	40	24	16	+2.07
C	34	25	9	+3.76
D	29	21	8	+3.43
E	22	15	7	+7.37
F	20	10	10	+1.92
G	19	13	6	+2.52
H	18	17	1	+1.47
I	17	3	14	.00
J	16	6	10	+1.27
K	15	2	13	+9.17
L	15	15	0	+1.58
M	11	9	2	−2.56
N	9	3	6	−7.88
O	6	1	5	−3.75
P	4	1	3	+ .79

We thus have laboratory evidence to support the claim that what popular psychology labels *self-control* probably involves the same mechanism as the one Freudians have called *repression*. Furthermore, this experiment demonstrates the close relationship between effective repression and personal efficiency. Inspection of the foregoing table shows Subject P as having achieved the best record with only 4 color associations as contrasted with Subject A's 50 color associations. McGranahan reports a revealing remark spontaneously made by Subject P at the close of the experiment to the effect that " he always kept cool under tension." This suggests the kind of poise associated with healthy integration. On the other hand, Subject A manifested the precise contrary of such poise. Reference to the table will show no score in the pursuitmeter test for this subject. It had to be omitted because he could not adjust to the experimental problem. He actually " broke down and cried " and the experimenter had to stop proceedings. These individual cases taken from the extremes of the table thus serve to buttress the thesis that neurotic behavior is associated with a poor technique of repression.

WHAT CONSTITUTES THE TECHNIQUE OF REPRESSION?

What does a person do when he represses? Does he repress impulses directly or does he repress ideas symbolizing impulses? These are important questions of obvious mental hygiene significance. McGranahan has considered them in very stimulating fashion and we shall endeavor to present the relevant issues in the light of his analysis.

The concept of repression to some people connotes a sort of pushing back or thrusting away of an impulse. It implies that one can do something to an impulse by pressing on it just as football players can hold back the forward surge of the opposing line by direct counter-pressure. Just how can this analogy be applied to the mental realm? After all, an impulse is not a tangible object that one can grip in literal fashion. Impulses to strike, to eat, to study, to marry, to pray, to curse, to smoke, or to sleep are not *entities* like football players. They are processes rather than things. Of course such processes involve various bodily organs; but the organs are not the impulses. When angry we may experience an impulse to clench the fist and strike, but the fist is not the impulse. Cursing involves the tongue, but the tongue is not cursing. Still, one may get at the impulse by direct action on the organ involved. The left hand can grip the clenched right and hold back the impending punch. Biting one's tongue is an age-old device for curbing the impulse to curse or blaspheme.

Strictly considered, however, such procedures are not quite the same as repression. They are better classified as instances of *inhibition*. When we inhibit an impulse we prevent it from gaining overt, muscular expression. It is still in consciousness even though it is prevented from gaining its motor outlet. A prisoner in a concentration camp may cherish an imperious impulse to pound the face of a brutal guard, but the sight of the guard's machine gun may cause that impulse to be blocked. Such blocking is due to inhibition rather than repression. This is more than a pedantic distinction; for the inhibited impulse continues to clamor for expression while the repressed impulse, provided the repression is complete and successful, just vanishes. The prisoner can more easily inhibit the impulse to strike his tormentor than he can repress the impulse. Repression thus calls for a different mechanism from inhibition. This does not mean that inhibition has nothing to do with repression. On the contrary, it is altogether likely that every case of successful repression is preceded by an act of inhibition. The latter acts like a brake on the imperiousness of sudden impulse and renders it possible for a repressive adjustment to be made. A man may have a sudden desire for a new car. Without inhibition he might find himself rushing to the car dealer to gratify his desire. By inhibiting the desire he can pause before acting; but unless he also follows this by repressing the desire, he will still be preoccupied with thoughts of his new car problem. An inhibited impulse continues to be a subject for inner debate or persistent brooding while a successfully repressed impulse is no longer an object of immediate concern.

To cite one final example: a chronic smoker may have a struggle to abide by his physician's strict " no more smoking " order. If the termination of every meal becomes the occasion for an inner battle between the impulse to obey the order and the impulse to smoke, we have an example of inhibition, provided the former impulse prevails. The desire for a smoke continues to manifest itself even though the customary response to this desire is curbed. The victim of the conflict is still conscious of the forbidden impulse. A slight increase in the strength of this impulse may suffice to break through the inhibiting forces. Conversely, a weakening of the impulse to obey medical orders may also serve to give the inhibited impulse a chance to dominate. In other words, the status of inhibited impulses is more precarious than that of repressed impulses. Their equilibrium is much more unstable; for the individual concerned is still subject to inner tensions incident to the welter of antagonistic factors fighting for supremacy.

Let us assume that the smoker is also a clarinet player who adjusts to the need for a smoke after meals by turning to his musical instrument. If he merely substitutes the clarinet for the cigar and is still conscious of an ungratified desire as manifested by his inability to concentrate wholeheartedly on the music, we would have but one more instance of inhibition. However, should he succeed in becoming so absorbed in the musical exercises to be mastered that all conflicting ideas are shunted out, then he would be furnishing us with an instance of repression. The fact that both smoking and clarinet playing are respiratory activities may aid the task of inhibition, but not of repression. In fact, some students of Freudian psychology might be tempted to view this as an instance of what they call *sublimation*. By this term they refer to an alleged process of converting the energy of tabooed impulses into socially acceptable outlets. If smoking were primarily a respiratory impulse, then our hypothetical smoker's clarinet blasts might be classified as sublimated smoke rings. Still, there may be something seriously amiss with this entire concept of sublimation and it might therefore be safer to put off a final verdict until additional aspects of the hypothetical case are introduced.

The smoker might be able to repress the forbidden impulse without resorting to another respiratory exercise like playing a wind instrument. He might become so completely fascinated by a detective story that the events of the story leave him altogether oblivious of the impulse to smoke. Similarly, he might become absorbed in playing chess or working on his radio set or developing pictures in the darkroom. Even the veteran smoker under no medical interdict may sometimes fail to light up as he becomes so preoccupied by an altogether absorbing project as to be unaware of the unlit pipe or cigar in his mouth. The fact that he has " forgotten " to light up means that the impulse to smoke is gone — at least for the time being. There is no conflict between warring impulses, as is noted in cases of inhibitions. Nor is there any mysterious sublimation of one impulse into another. What we have here is more akin to the familiar experience of the busy executive who reports, " I was so interested in swinging that deal that I forgot all about being hungry." This means *repression* of the desire for food by vivid attention to a business problem.

Enough background has now been introduced to render the mechanism of repression understandable. The relevant factors can be described in the familiar language of traditional, scientific psychology. Impulses, wishes, or desires are known to the individual by changes in the content of consciousness. A cinder in the eye, a bread crumb in the throat, or a distended bladder — each produces a unique pattern of sensation the meaning of which is learned very early in life. These patterns are accompanied by imperious strivings for instantaneous relief. We are cognizant of the strivings because of the conscious content: the pain in the eye, the distress in the trachea, or the tension in the bladder. In fact, the respective desires involved persist until this conscious content disappears.

Ordinarily there can be no question of repressing desires of this kind. They have to be disposed of by removing the stimulus object. Relief is not experienced until the cinder is lifted off, the crumb dislodged, or the bladder emptied. Incidentally, with respect to the latter it might be pointed out that the previously mentioned distinction between inhibition and repression is clearly illustrated by control of eliminative impulses. Such control is achieved by means of the sphincter muscles governing excretory functions. However, although it is possible to postpone the eliminative act for a time even when the impulse is exceedingly acute, it is not possible to become unaware of the existence of the impulse under such acute conditions of stimulation. We can inhibit the eliminative impulse, but we cannot repress it. There are even limits beyond which inhibition of such impulses is no longer possible. Respiratory control furnishes a clear example of this. As everybody knows, breathing can be voluntarily inhibited for very brief periods, but not indefinitely. In this sense, of course, nobody is free to do as he pleases. Even the most ardent advocate of the old free-will doctrine would have to grant the irresistible determinism of the organic background of mental life. The orbit of such voluntary control is set by the urgency of eliminative and respiratory impulses. Once a critical tension is reached all further inhibitory effort becomes futile. There are impulses, in other words, which cannot be legislated out of existence by a fiat of the will. But this constitutes a digression; for the ones we are more immediately concerned with are those which are amenable to repression. The other kind were mentioned largely because they enabled us to make clear the psychological factors to be considered in an analysis of the mechanism of repression.

We have already mentioned conscious content in terms of which the existence of an impulse becomes known to the individual. Actually two groups of factors are operative here: the content on the one hand and our observation on the other. Following McGranahan, this can be described as the items observed and the observing system. Although observation or perception is a unified act, psychological analysis reveals the validity of the distinction between that which is observed and the process of looking, hearing, touching, or tasting, as the case may be. For the sake of illustration we may select the word " process " in the preceding sentence. This word can be observed in a variety of ways. It can be scrutinized to check on its spelling, to determine the number of letters, to gauge the type size, to note how many other words can be formed by recombining the letters p-r-o-c-e-s-s, to consider its derivation, or to decide on its correct pronunciation. In each of these instances the item, the pattern of visual sensations, remains the same, but the perceptual act, the observing system, varies. Counting the letters of a word is a different perceptual act from noting the accuracy of the spelling. What we do when we change the observing system is to introduce a different *mental set*. The intention to read a passage for meaning requires a different mental set from the intention to read a passage to find out whether the style is simple enough for a little child's comprehension. Whether the numbers 8 and 9 will cause us to think of 72, 17, or 98 will vary with the intention or mental set. To multiply or to add or to transpose numbers calls for three different mental sets. Once again let us point out that even though the items — the numbers 8 and 9 in this instance — remain the same, the observing system as modified by the mental set can be varied.

These familiar facts of the elementary psychology of perception and thinking can now be applied to the phenomenon of repression. The basic question can be reduced to this: Does repression involve a change in the conscious content or impulse to be repressed or does it call for a change in the observing system or mental set? As applied to the conditions of McGranahan's experiment, the ideas to be repressed had to do with colors. Our basic question asks whether those who repressed successfully did something to these ideas or whether they did something to modify the set for color associations. Subject P, the one who achieved the best record and the one who seemed least neurotic, furnished an answer to this question. He explained that what he did was to get set to think of adjectives suggesting shape or size as the list of nouns was called off to him. In other words, he got the same kind of mental content as Subject A, the one with the worst record, but he reacted to this content with a different observing system or mental set. Poor Subject A had to think of words like " red," " yellow," " green," and " blue " because he was set to think of colors. On the other hand Subject P found himself thinking of words like " large," " triangular," " circular," " small," and " medium " because he was set to look for characteristics of size and shape. Repression is thus a mechanism of ideational control. It influences impulses indirectly rather than directly. It calls for regulation of mental sets as opposed to frontal attacks on mental content or tabooed desires.

SELF-EMANCIPATION BY MEANS OF SELF-CONTROL

Many people are likely to regard this reduction of the mechanism of repression to a mere matter of shifts in the observing system as a pallid, undramatic, and possibly useless finding. It might not be as spectacular as the concept of sublimation, but it might well be closer to reality and hence more serviceable to the individual seeking practical guidance from psychology. After all, what we demand of the mental hygienist is that he help us to overcome devastating fears, distracting lusts, and disturbing angers. More specifically: How can the public speaker repress his fear? How can the erotically aroused student repress his lust in order to apply himself to his academic tasks? These are very real and very practical questions. To say " don't be afraid " or " don't be lustful " is to give a rather stupid answer. At best such a negative admonition results in inhibition rather than repression. As has already been indicated, to inhibit an impulse means to continue to dwell on the impulse. When we inhibit the impulse to scratch a mosquito bite, there is no diminution of the itch and no lessening of the concomitant desire to scratch. We are vividly aware of the muscles held rigid in a desperate endeavor to prevent the forbidden act from being consummated. Instead of " forgetting " the itch, we tend to become more acutely aware of its presence.

" Don't " always calls attention to the forbidden act. It is apt to reenforce the very mental set by means of which the unwelcome or forbidden item is perceived. This is illustrated by the old story of the man who promised a boy five dollars if he could avoid thinking of the word " hippopotamus " for an entire week. The poor lad lost the money the very first time he tried to live up to the conditions of the agreement. Analogously, we lose out when we try " not to be scared of the audience " or " not to think of nasty things." Nevertheless, parents and educators repeatedly indulge in such negative admonitions. What the McGranahan experiment renders altogether clear is the futility of such negative appeals unaccompanied by a positive program. Subject A wanted very much not to think of color adjectives and yet, despite his resolute intention, he found himself thinking of more such adjectives than the average person uninfluenced by such a specific negative mental set. A positive program is a function of a positive mental set. Subject P had such a program when he set out to look for adjectives denoting size and shape. The timid speaker has such a program when he decides to concentrate on the *meaning* of his opening sentence instead of his pounding heart and moist palms. The student, obsessed by an erotic phantasy, has such a program when he makes himself turn to the business of solving chemical equations or translating his Latin.

This may sound foolish and paradoxical; but the most effective way of *not* doing something is to do something else. And if that something else can be galvanized into an absorbing project, the prohibited act will have been successfully repressed. Once the scared speaker has lost himself in the theme of his discourse, his fear will have vanished. Similarly, the student who finds his studies an exciting challenge to his intellectual curiosity will cease to be plagued by erotic distractions. He will have substituted the mental set of the vitally interested student for the mental set accompanying libidinous brooding. Without control of mental sets there can be no repression and without repression there can be no self-control. It is in this sense too that there can be no personal freedom without an effective technique of repression; for, as was pointed out earlier, without such a technique man finds himself the helpless victim of unrestrained impulsiveness. Intelligent repression is the instrument of enlightened personal freedom.

15...   *MAMMON* VERSUS *MORALE*

THE MENTAL HYGIENIST EXTOLS REALISTIC THINKING AND DEP-
recates wishful or cowardly evasion of unwelcome truths. He
is of the opinion that one cannot achieve a balanced personality
by concentrating on personality assets and ignoring personality
liabilities. Personal problems, so he tells us, are to be solved by
frank acknowledgment of our shortcomings and mistakes. Unwillingness to admit error, refusal to face the fact of our possible
incompetence, and disinclination to find fault with ourselves are
bound to warp our thinking. Warped thinking blinds us to facts
that ought to be considered if problems are going to be solved.
To run away from facts or to distort them makes for the evils of
autistic fantasies and self-deceiving rationalizations. All of this has
already been described as part of mental hygiene wisdom. There
is no need to elaborate upon this wisdom now. But there is a decided need to bring this very wisdom to bear on the subject of
mental hygiene itself. It is time for the mental hygienist to face
reality and to ask himself some searchingly honest questions.

IS THE MENTAL HYGIENE PROGRAM UTOPIAN?

In a very broad fashion, the scope of the mental hygienist's program has been outlined. What we have to consider now is the
feasibility of this program. Is it a Utopian dream, or can it be put
to work here and now in the lives of the millions and millions of
humble citizens whose welfare it is presumably designed to enhance? This program has much to say about a healthy philosophy
of life, the cultivation of varied and stimulating interests, the
hazards of undisciplined, wishful daydreaming, and the importance of emotional security within the home. It includes references
to efficient techniques of repression and to the healthy exercise of
zestful impulses to play and sing and dance and to go from strength
to strength in body and mind. It mentions the desirability of having friends and the ability to get along with people. It has a good

deal to say about coping with annoyances and frustrations of everyday living. It is not unmindful of the traditional virtues of honesty, courage, neighborliness, temperance, good sportsmanship, and genuine solicitude for the well-being of others. For whom is all this intended? How many of us have a reasonable chance of making such a mental hygiene program operative in our homes? Will it work for the jobless man? Does it apply to a sharecropper's hovel? What about the Jew in Nazi Germany and the outcast in India? What about the millions who are made to feel inferior because of black skins, " mixed " ancestry, or illegitimacy? Does our mental hygiene program apply to them? Or shall we have one kind of program for the dispossessed and underprivileged and another for the affluent? What sort of stimulating philosophy of life shall we hold out to the chronically overworked mother of a family on relief or to the sensitive Negro child whose anguish is expressed in these pathetic lines?[1]

> Once riding in old Baltimore
>   Heart-filled, head-filled with glee,
> I saw a Baltimorean
>   Keep looking straight at me.
>
> Now I was eight and very small,
>   And he was no whit bigger,
> And so I smiled, but he poked out
>   His tongue, and called me " Nigger."
>
> I saw the whole of Baltimore
> From May until December;
> Of all the things that happened there
>   That's all that I remember.

Of the more than 130,000,000 men, women, and children in our country, how many could really initiate the kind of life envisaged by a program of meliorative mental hygiene? In blunter language, does such a program have much chance of adoption by the masses of our fellow citizens? If mental hygiene be epitomized as a sound mind in a sound body in a sound society, can the lone individual

[1] From Countée Cullen's *Color*, published by Harper & Brothers, 1925 and quoted from Bruno Lasker's *Race Attitudes in Children*, New York, Henry Holt & Company, 1929, p. 2.

living in an unsound society safeguard his own mental health or must the community first be won over to its mental hygiene obligations before the individual's safety can be assured?

There is an instructive parallel from the realm of physical hygiene. Unless the community introduces and enforces quarantine regulations the private citizen has difficulty in avoiding exposure to disease. Without official sanitary regulations governing water supply, the purity of food, and the disposition of sewage, he would find himself acutely handicapped in striving to maintain the health of his family. Despite conscientious endeavors on his part to protect the family, there would be constant exposure to contagion from infected neighbors, myriads of flies, tainted food, dust-laden air, swarms of rats, and contaminated water. Private health is obviously a function of public health. Is it also obvious that there may be an analogously significant relationship between private mental health and public mental health? This is a question whose ramifications were anticipated in an early chapter when we stated that mental hygiene involves principles of economics and sociology as well as principles of psychology and medicine. Tracing these ramifications necessitates an excursion into the former fields.

ECONOMIC BARRIERS TO SECURITY

In our discussion of the home and the ideal of a balanced personality the importance of an atmosphere of dependable security was suggested repeatedly. We took it for granted that parents of good will and a modicum of intelligence could engender such an atmosphere by the mere execution of a pious intention. We now have to ask whether the issue is as simple as this. Is security an easily and readily attainable condition for the majority of families? Security, it should be recalled, means to be free from care. In the present context it means, more specifically, to be free from worry about being able to shelter, to feed, to clothe, and to educate one's family. On the positive side it means being able to provide the family with comfortable beds, adequate clothing, an abundance of food, satisfactory medical and dental care, recreational opportunities, and leisure for schooling and study. Security in this sense is more a matter of economics than of mental hygiene. The finest program of mental hygiene will bog down unless certain minimal economic needs are provided. This does not imply that possession of money will guarantee sound family morale and the existence of a home atmosphere in accord with mental hygiene ideals. One does not have to be either a psychiatrist or a consulting psychologist to know that such is not the case. Far too many scions of great wealth have to seek out such specialists for professional advice to justify such an implication. What it does imply is that there is a *minimum* of financial security below which any program of meliorative mental hygiene is doomed to fail. This minimum is to be regarded as a necessary but by no means a sufficient condition for effectively functioning mental hygiene.

As mental hygienists we have to inquire not only into the approximate amount of this minimum, but also into the related question of the number of families possessing such a minimum. The first question is obviously beyond the province of the psychologist. He has to depend on the estimates of experts in other fields, particularly those engaged in working out subsistence budgets for marginal families. To complicate the problem, such budgets fluctuate with the cost of living. However, since our chief purpose is to demonstrate the general nature of the economic barriers to the utilization of mental hygiene principles by the country as a whole, we need not be unduly concerned by this complication of the shifting character of the minimum income under consideration. Although the precise amount may vary from year to year, the ratios in which we are interested can be indicated by taking the figures for almost any year since the first World War. It might be most revealing to consider the decade starting with the year 1920; for this decade was marked by the largest total national income in the history of the country. The acme, as most people might guess, was reached in 1929. This was the peak year when the total income of the nation soared to a record high of over $80,000,000,000. Before we demonstrate how the families of the nation shared in this accumulated wealth, it might be desirable to get an idea of how much was *minimally* necessary for survival during this decade of plenty.

From an analysis of 44 estimates of minimum family budgets during the years under consideration one economist, Abraham Epstein, concluded that a family of five had to have an income of approximately $35 a week or $1,820 a year. Leighton,[2] in discussing this matter, points out that such an estimate represents " the indispensable minimum for decent living without any luxuries." A convenient way to think of this estimate is to convert the $35 per week for five persons into the eqivalent of $1.00 per day per person. And once again the *minimal* nature of this estimate should be stressed. One ought to realize that it assumes a regime of careful economy and that it rules out the purchase of magazines, sheet music, theatre tickets, silk stockings, Roquefort cheese and kindred amenities of civilized living. It calls for a regime of almost Spartan simplicity and implies that the family will be farsighted enough to avoid costly illnesses and other " acts of God," as the lawyers refer to losses incident to lightning, fire, hail, floods, and storms. In other words, this standard of minimum economic security is far from the standard which the mental hygienist would set for the psychological security of the family.

Bearing these qualifications in mind, let us see how many families *failed* to achieve this Spartan minimum during our peak year of 1929. We may even be slightly generous and increase the basic annual minimum from $1,820 to $2,000. According to the report of the Brookings Institution, there were 16,354,000 families earning less than this $2,000 minimum in 1929. More than 16,000,000 *families* lacked the material means of approximating the indispensable minimum of security! And this during the " richest " year in our economic history up to that time! Conditions were much worse during our years of economic depression. Regrettably enough, the cliché about one-third of the nation being ill-housed, ill-fed, and ill-clothed is by no means a rhetorical exaggeration or a statistical distortion. The distortion is to be found in the skewed nature of our distribution of purchasing power. Not even the most ingenious statistician can make the income curve resemble the familiar normal distribution curve.

The foregoing figures are not to be dismissed as exceptions; for later studies reveal similarly skewed distributions. For example, the following table prepared by the *National Resources Committee* [3] reveals the trend for the year 1935–1936:

[2] Leighton, J. A., *Social Philosophies in Conflict*, New York, D. Appleton-Century Co., 1937, p. 156.
[3] *Consumer Incomes in the United States*, National Resources Committee, Washington, D. C., United States Government Printing Office, 1938, p. 18.

TABLE 5

Income Level	Families Number	Per Cent at Each Level
Under $250	1,162,890	3.95
$250–$500	3,015,394	10.26
$500–$750	3,799,215	12.92
$750–$1,000	4,277,048	14.55
$1,000–$1,250	3,882,444	13.20
$1,250–$1,500	2,865,472	9.75
$1,500–$1,750	2,343,358	7.97
$1,750–$2,000	1,897,037	6.45
$2,000–$2,250	1,420,883	4.83
$2,250–$2,500	1,043,977	3.55
$2,500–$3,000	1,314,199	4.47
$3,000–$3,500	743,559	2.53
$3,500–$4,000	438,428	1.49
$4,000–$4,500	249,948	.85
$4,500–$5,000	152,647	.52
$5,000–$7,500	322,950	1.10
$7,500–$10,000	187,060	.64
$10,000–$15,000	131,821	.45
$15,000–$20,000	58,487	.20
$20,000–$25,000	34,208	.12
$25,000–$30,000	22,233	.08
$30,000–$40,000	15,561	.05
$40,000–$50,000	6,603	.02
$50,000–$100,000	10,571	.04
$100,000–$250,000	3,336	.01
$250,000–$500,000	699	Less than 0.005 per cent
$500,000–$1,000,000	197	" " " " "
$1,000,000 and over	75	" " " " "

To facilitate interpretation of the preceding table the families have been grouped into six income levels ranging from a low $1,250 or less to a high of a quarter of a million dollars or more. Reference to the percent column will show almost 55% of the families in America in the lowest group and a relatively insignificant percentage in the highest. In terms of these percentages the skewed nature of income distribution can be brought out in striking fashion as shown in Fig. 4 on the next page.

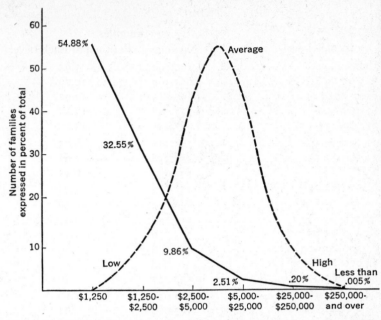

FIG. 4. Solid Line Shows Range of Distribution of Family Income While Dotted Line Indicates Normal Curve Superimposed on Income Curve.

The normal distribution curve, which we have superimposed on the income curve, serves to symbolize the magnitude of the latter's skewness. To appreciate the meaning of this discrepancy between the two curves it must be realized that the normal curve indicates the general nature of the distribution of human ability. It is almost a fixed idea among experimental psychologists to expect approximation to such a curve whenever any specific ability of a large number of people is reduced to quantitative form. This fixed idea is the result of what has been discovered through the years as thousands of mental tests have been administered in schools, colleges, army camps, factories, and so on. Over and over again, when the data have been plotted the familiar lines of the bell-shaped curve have emerged. All sorts of measures of human skill and ability conform to this curve: spelling tests, I.Q.'s, speed of association, memory span tests, strength of grip, general information, size of vocabulary, arithmetic tests, and a host of others. Because of the ubiquity of this curve psychologists are convinced that it furnishes a graphic symbol of the way in which people differ from one another in measurable abilities. In a way this conviction merely reflects the common sense observation in terms of which people are classified as average, above average, and below average with all sorts of in-between scores to make the transition from one class to the next a smooth one.

Now if the normal curve really depicts the distribution of human ability, then factors other than ability are determining the allocation of financial rewards in our business and industrial worlds; otherwise the curve for income distribution would also be a normal one.[4] Quite evidently poverty and business failure are not necessarily indicative of lack of ability and, conversely, possession of great wealth need not be a trustworthy sign of the possession of exceptional ability. To attribute the financial insecurity of close to 85% of American families to " lack of ability to make good " is thus an obvious fallacy in the light of what is known regarding the distribution of human ability. But even if it were not fallacious, the mere existence of the insecurity, irrespective of its causes, would still justify the mental hygienist's grim apprehension as he surveys our economic scene. He cannot help being concerned about the morale of the nation with so many of its families forced to violate basic mental hygiene teachings because of drastically curtailed economic resources. Although happiness is not to be purchased, it is nevertheless true that abject poverty and human misery are hard to separate.

MORALE AND SOCIAL STATUS

It is hard for those few of us whom destiny has placed at the upper end of the income curve to appreciate the adjustment problems of the many congesting the lower end of the curve. Every earnest mental hygienist, reflecting upon the possibility of applying his program to the nation as a whole, finds himself balked by the problem of poverty. He would like to see each American home a haven of security for its members; but he soon comes to recognize this as a Utopian vision. Even the purchasable kind of security talked about by insurance salesmen is beyond the means of

---

[4] We are indebted to the sociologist, Prof. H. J. W. Coutu, for calling our attention to this discrepancy between the financial measure of ability and the psychological.

millions. Poverty and this kind of security are antithetic. For the majority of our people investment in any kind of insurance policy would constitute an extravagant luxury. They are thus exposed to the insecurity of sudden fire, sudden accident, sudden theft as well as sudden death. The security, in other words, which the more affluent can purchase is not for them. Many of them cannot even purchase the security of three solid meals a day for their families; for it takes about $800 a year to provide a non-farm family of five individuals with a satisfactory diet. In 1929 almost three-quarters of our non-farm families were inadequately nourished. The necessary $800 were not available!

All of this means that for millions of American families basic mental hygiene standards are no more within their reach than Rolls Royce cars. When children are complaining of hunger and cold, when parents too are hungry, cold, and overworked or unable to find remunerative work, and when the entire family is thus exposed to the mental and physical bleakness of dire privation, something more than loyalty to abstract principles of mental hygiene is indicated. It might be almost sinfully fatuous to talk to such a family about a wholesome philosophy of life, about morale, and about the dangers of autistic thinking. The latter kind of thinking is inevitable under such circumstances. What parent is not going to dream about getting food for starving children and what starving child is not going to wish for the miracle of three solid meals a day?

Poverty below the subsistence level is simply incompatible with effective mental hygiene. As long as millions of families are below this level it is idle to speak of " mental hygiene for the masses." What we so complacently designate as " the masses " are men and women and children with individual longings and personal aspirations and private worries. What they have in common is their poverty, but the distress is private, unique, and momentous to each individual concerned. To the surgeon an inflamed appendix may be " just another case," but to the suffering patient it looms up as one of the crises of his life. For him it is not to be relegated to the anonymity of a " mass " of similar cases. In this respect mental hygiene has much in common with the teachings of differential psychology. The latter specialty, it will be remembered, deals with the differences which serve to mark off or differentiate one personality from another. The mental hygienist is particularly concerned with the maintenance of those differences which make for the unique worth and self-respect of each personality. As a consequence, he cannot rest content with a cavalier solution of the mental hygiene problems incident to poverty by a contemptuous reference to " the masses," as if the poverty-stricken were an amorphous breed of worthless human beings.

There are numerous mental hygiene issues implicit in the very use of the word *worthless* as applied to the economically underprivileged. Despite an oft-repeated official pronouncement that " poverty is not a disgrace," many of us who are comfortably secure feel superior to those who are uncomfortably insecure. It flatters our vanity to regard our security as a reward for virtuous effort and their insecurity as a penalty for shiftless indolence. Running through the pattern of our competitive culture is the conviction that only the deserving will survive in the long economic run. This conviction is reflected in stereotyped phrases of popular " success " philosophy: " You can't keep a good man down " and " There's always room at the top " and " You can't beat the combination of brains, honesty, and hard work."

A superficially grasped interpretation of Darwinian biology is uncritically applied to our socio-economic struggles. In terms of such an application it is complacently inferred that only the " unfit " gravitate to the lowest economic brackets, the upper brackets being reserved for the " superior " and the " fit," or those " better equipped for survival." We even permit the phrase " being wellborn " to suggest somewhat distinctively superior biological origin to those in the social register as contrasted with those whose families are lost in the shuffle of proletarian obscurity. The aristocracy of wealth thus tends to surround itself with a halo of biological excellence as an almost self-evident justification for its more tangible manifestations of material and social excellence. Stated differently, there is a tendency for the " better families " to attribute their good fortune both to superior germplasm as well as to more assiduous devotion to self-sacrificing duty. The rationalizations implied are not very different from those which have induced white people to feel superior toward non-Caucasians. We quietly endow ourselves with better brains, better morals, and better looks than members of the " lower " races. With debonair conceit we tacitly make the " white race " the measure of all eth-nic superiority. In terms of a crude anthropology, skin pigmenta-tion is taken as an easy criterion of membership in the chosen and choicest group. The more the pigmentation deviates from this cri-terion, the " lower " the race. This furnishes many people with a rough and ready racial hierarchy in which their white associates are elevated to the top rung of the racial ladder, pale Mongolians are pushed a little lower down, brown Malays still lower down, and the black Africans made to occupy the lowest rung. A scheme of this sort caters to our vanity; for it is tantamount to saying that the more a people resembles *us* in physical appearance the greater its degree of superiority. An invidious phrase like " keeping the Negro in his place " is but a reflection of this racial vanity ex-pressed in terms of a hierarchy of social position.

Psychological analysis has revealed three basic attitudes people can take toward their hierarchical niche in a competitive society. These attitudes are related to what some psychologists have de-scribed as sentiments of self-assertion and self-abasement. To these familiar two sentiments a less familiar third may be added: a sentiment of equality. These three sentiments refer to differing ways of responding to others. When in the presence of those whom we regard as our inferiors we feel impelled to give the orders, take charge of the plans, make the final decisions, and, in general, exer-cise those prerogatives we associate with domination or superi-ority. This is what is implied by the self-assertive attitude. It can be observed in the behavior of a chief surgeon directing his oper-ating room subordinates, in the conduct of a top sergeant barking at his recruits, and in some dowagers engaged in shopping expedi-tions. Observation of the nurses, recruits, and shop clerks in the foregoing situations will exemplify what the psychologist means by the submissive or self-abasing attitude. Whenever we yield to the admitted superiority of another, this latter attitude is being brought into play. Instances of the third or equalitarian attitude are furnished by every association of mutually acknowledged social equals: a country club golf foursome, a group of locomotive en-gineers chatting in the roundhouse, members of a musical comedy chorus waiting for a curtain call, or a meeting of jobless men at an employment office.

These attitudes assert themselves subtly or blatantly in countless social situations. There is always an adjustment to others in terms of the implications of attitudes of this kind. Strangers to whom we chance to be introduced are automatically appraised as being " our kind " of people, or superior or inferior to us. Just what will determine the basis for appraisal will vary from person to person and from occasion to occasion. Thus some people are so impressed by academic degrees that they tend to be yielding and submissive when in the company of college graduates. Others regard money as symbolic of social status and consequently are overawed upon being introduced to a genuine millionaire. For some a title of nobility may exercise the same influence; hence the prestige value of knighthood and the social impressiveness of being called *earl* or *lord* or *duke*. Uniforms may serve to elicit these attitudes. In this way resplendent rear admirals influence the attitudes of gobs in their undistinguished dungarees. The brass buttons and trim uniform of a traffic cop are not without their effect in eliciting obedience from an otherwise self-assertive motorist. Sometimes superior knowledge or ability will serve to establish the relationship in question. Even the dominating traffic officer may assume a deferential attitude upon being introduced to an academic specialist in traffic engineering. All of our social relationships are shot through and through with such shifting attitudes indicative of our varying adjustments to the varying situations in which we have hierarchical roles to play.

The magnitude and ubiquity of these hierarchical factors even in officially democratic cultures can hardly be appreciated by the casual observer. And yet their mental hygiene implications are so momentous that they ought not to be dismissed in casual fashion. The vast majority of mental hygiene difficulties are not problems of adjustment to our physical environment. They are rooted in our *social* environment. They center around such issues as achieving business success, academic success, social success, domestic success and the general enhancement of family and individual prestige. To be balked in such strivings after success and prestige is apt to cause damaged self-respect, feelings of inferiority, attitudes of self-deprecation and kindred evidences of poor individual morale. This is what accounts for the mental hygienist's interest in our social levels and group cleavages.

The social hierarchy is so close to most of us and is so intimate a part of our lives that not many ever become sufficiently detached to attain the perspective necessary for appreciation of its size and spread. It characterizes all of our institutions. The army and navy are manifestly hierarchical, with stages of success clearly marked by designated ranks of promotion from the lowly buck privates and gobs to exalted generals and admirals. Business firms have presidents, managers, and office boys. Our judiciary ranges from the obscurity of a justice of the peace to the eminence of a United States Supreme Court justice. Universities have tutors and instructors and assistant professors and professors and deans and presidents. Churches have altar boys, deacons, priests, and bishops. Governments have their high-ranking and low-ranking officials. Even such an institution as baseball is characterized by an hierarchical pattern with its major leagues, Class A leagues, Class B leagues, and sand-lot teams. The whole field of organized amusement and recreation reveals this pattern with its emphasis on headliners, Broadway and Hollywood stars, small-town players, bit players, radio topnotchers, and radio unknowns. Nor is this pattern absent from the family. There is a dignity people associate with being the " head " of a household just as there is a loss of status people attribute to such a potential " head " who permits a domineering and shrewish mother-in-law to usurp his headship. Small children have their appointed roles to play as children within the family organization. So have uncles and grandparents and cousins.

In brief, all of our institutions — military, naval, business, judicial, educational, religious, political, recreational, and familial — have their recognizable hierarchies. Ambition, striving, aspiration and all that is implied by the concept of *competition* is brought into play in a culture so dominated by hierarchical institutions. The individuals enmeshed in these hierarchical webs dream dreams of promotion and " getting on " and rising to still greater hierarchical heights. They scheme schemes to outmaneuver rivals and to impress superiors. They brood over real or imaginary shortcomings presumably responsible for their failure to climb the hierarchical ladder. In a large measure mental health is a function of these manifold strivings after Success with a capital S. To be branded a Failure with a capital F becomes the nadir of individual morale. Its zenith for many people is symbolized by elevation to the top rank of a given hierarchy: owner of a chain store, governor of a state, bishop of a diocese, general of an army, or the head of one of America's " sixty families." Learning to be at home, at ease, and inwardly content in the midst of a strenuously competitive culture is thus a major mental hygiene problem for each one of us.

How POVERTY STACKS THE CARDS

This major mental hygiene problem of adjusting to a competitive society is not an exclusively individual problem even though it touches the lives of so many individuals. In fact, the lone victim of this kind of adjustment difficulty is often almost altogether impotent to work out a promising adjustment. He is a victim of a socio-economic system too rigid, too complex, and too big for him to handle. This is another way of saying that the problem is one for society to tackle. The community of which he is a part and the nation of which he is a member must come to his rescue. He, as an individual, can do very little more toward solving this problem than he can toward solving such problems as flood control, business depressions, or child labor. The Great Society must tackle the job for him. Until it does, such slogans as " mental hygiene for the masses " and " building wholesome personality for *every* American child " must remain mere empty hopes; for the cards are stacked against the " masses " and their children.

Allegiance to the ideal of realistic thinking demands that we take up the unpleasant task of finding out just how the cards are stacked. In this connection it will prove illuminating to consider some of the data which social scientists have mobilized by way of demonstrating that even in a democracy such as ours, working-class babies are not born as " free and equal " as babies born into the families of business and professional men. Incidentally, it has been estimated that in our industrial cities about 70% of the earning population is to be classified as belonging to the working class and about 30% to the business-professional group. We are indebted to the diligence of a trio [5] of sociologists for the following picture of what it means to be a member of the economically vulnerable 70%.

[5] Cooley, C. H., Angell, R. C., and Carr, L. J., *Introductory Sociology*, New York, Charles Scribner's Sons, 1933, pp. 307–310.

According to this group of sociologists, there are a whole series of respects in which youngsters of the one class are handicapped as compared with youngsters of the other. These handicaps have to do not only with matters pertaining to health, housing, and schooling but also with an aspect of the doctrine of equality which most people are likely to take for granted; namely, equality before the law. It may prove revealing and not too much of a digression to consider these instances of inequality in moderate detail.

The health of low-income families is jeopardized from earliest infancy. Babies of the poor seem to have less chance for survival than those whose parents are not so poor. The trend is indicated by the results of one survey of conditions among white families where the death rate for babies born into homes having annual incomes of at least $1,850 was 38.3 per 1,000, while in homes with incomes below $450 the death rate shot up to 164.8 per 1,000. At this level a 75% reduction is associated with a 400% increase in infant mortality. Of course, as the investigators admit, some of the increased infant mortality at the very low economic levels may be a function of depleted biological reserves of the people involved. However, this is very likely not a complete explanation; for public health officials are ready to submit evidence of lessened infant mortality once better sanitation, feeding, housing, and free medical care are provided even though the biological stock remains the same.

The menace to health persists through the years following the period of infancy. It shows up when relative rates of physical development for the two classes are compared by asking: does being born poor influence a baby's chances of growing as tall as a rich baby? One British study showed an average difference of more than six inches at age 14 in favor of the sons of wealthy families. To be born poor may doom a child to grow up with the handicap of a poor physique.

Poverty menaces health and development in still other respects. For example, the incidence of disease among working class people is greater and their life span is shorter. Furthermore, there are relatively more accidents occurring among them. In other words, children living on opposite sides of the railroad track have unequal chances of avoiding disease, accident, and death. Public health officials can cite statistical evidence to support such a statement.

They can produce maps of our large cities showing higher rates of disease in the congested regions than in the restricted residential areas. Insurance companies have to keep in close touch with such statistical data. It is very significant in the present context to dwell on the fact that accident insurance rates for business and professional men are lower than for men in overalls. In human terms this means more accident hazards for babies destined to join the ranks of factory workers, machine tenders, and construction gangs than for those whose vocational destiny calls for a white-collar job. What is more, the white-collar destiny presages a longer life. One actuarial expert has estimated the life expectancy of the wealthier group to average 8 years more than for the non-white-collar group.

Another aspect of inequality is to be found in the question of housing: are American babies " born equal " with respect to physical shelter placed at their disposal? This question should not be interpreted as implying that ideally all babies ought to be brought up in dwellings of uniform excellence and regimented comfort. Equality does not necessarily imply identity. What it does imply is the provision of a *minimum* level of adequacy with reference to ventilation, heating facilities, plumbing, and freedom from crowding. A moment of reflection will suffice to indicate how family morale is likely to be jeopardized by an economic fate which compels its members to seek shelter in damp, dark, cold, overcrowded quarters. To have one-third of the nation ill-housed is obviously a threat to national morale. Furthermore, with respect to this matter of housing the cards are again stacked against the working-class children. In one large city it was found that the number of persons per room was from 10 to 26% higher in working-class homes than the number for the city as a whole. On the other hand, in the case of white-collar homes the rooms showed less crowding than the average for the city. As might be expected, overcrowded homes and undercrowded pay envelopes go together.

The specter of inequality also characterizes the educational scene. This merits particular emphasis not only because it is so commonly overlooked, but primarily because of its bearing on national efficiency, national welfare, and individual happiness. Most of us doubtless take it for granted that our system of free, public education ensures every child equality of educational opportunity.

Should a given youngster fail to finish high school and enter college, many people would be inclined to attribute his failure to lack of ability, zeal, or interest rather than to lack of opportunity. Stories of poor boys working their way through school or winning scholarships lull many of us into complacent drowsiness concerning our national impartiality in catering to the educational needs of our youth irrespective of the economic stumbling blocks the less impartial god of dollar distribution may place on the long highway of educational progress. We consequently believe, if we think about the problem at all, that poor boys with brains are given the same chances for educational achievement as the rich boys with brains. In line with this belief we tend to think of our universities as unbiased selective agencies drawing the most intelligent survivors of academic competition on the high school level. Unfortunately, available evidence does not square with such complacent beliefs. Dollars as well as I.Q.'s determine the selection of our college students. The following passage furnishes some thought-provoking evidence: [6]

Most of the A and B brains in this country are in the non-white-collar occupations, yet most of the college and normal students come from the white-collar homes. Lehman and Stoke have shown that farmers, artisans, semi-skilled and unskilled on the basis of Army test percentages produced 2,010,000 A and B men in 1920, while the professional and clerical groups together produced only 1,372,000. In 1929–30 Woody and Keeler found that out of 5715 Michigan students attending the University of Michigan, Michigan State College, and all the other institutions of higher education in the state, including normal colleges, farmers, artisans, and semi-skilled classes contributed just 33.3 per cent, while the clerical, business, and professional classes contributed over 53 per cent. In Middletown the Lynds found economic factors playing a powerful role in determining who should go to college.

Findings of this sort suggest a grievous waste of potential ability and talent. It is impossible to estimate the full consequences of this waste for public welfare. If all those with capacity for outstanding service could receive the requisite professional training to render such service a reality, what significant headway might the near future reveal in municipal administration, in scientific

[6] Cooley, *et al., op. cit.,* pp. 308–309.

agriculture, in medical research, in public health work, in crime prevention, in organized religious work, in recreational planning, in literature, and art, and music, and journalism, and all the multiple functions operative in civilized living?

To what extent is society being deprived of the services of men and women whose poverty bars them from careers of eminent usefulness in the learned professions? Not every boy with first-rate brains and keen devotion to learning and dreaming of a career in medicine can nurse this dream to a reality. To make such a dream come true involves an outlay of thousands of dollars. Taken by and large, only the sons of families in the upper five to eight percent of the curve of income distribution are in a position to choose medicine as a career. The other ninety-odd percent, despite brilliant intellects and genuine interest in the field, must turn to vocational pursuits with more immediate cash returns and less expensive preparatory training. And what is true of medicine is also true in varying degree of training in our *outstanding* schools of law, engineering, theology, and education. Almost all of these schools are on the graduate level. This means from six to ten years of study beyond high school graduation. Even when generous philanthropists provide scholarship funds it calls for heroic self-sacrifice on the part of low-income families to dispense with the possible earnings of an alert youngster over so long a period. What is more, if the alert youngster is also conscientious and sensitive, he is apt to feel that he " has no right " to permit his family to slave and scrimp through the long years when, instead of contributing his share to the strained family budget, he is devoting his time and effort to the prosecution of university studies. As every vocational guidance specialist knows, all too often young people have to reconcile themselves to the misery of balked ambition because the relatively high cost of study bars them from fields of professional endeavor to which they are attracted and for which they seem to possess the requisite aptitudes. What this means in terms of subsequent vocational discontent and chronic vocational regret can be readily envisaged even though its extent and magnitude is not directly accessible to the statistician's quantitative probes. It should nevertheless be obvious that an enormous amount of individual frustration must be occasioned by these economic barriers to the gratification of vocational longings.

The last handicap of the economically underprivileged to be discussed pertains to their civic insecurity. On previous pages the importance of security as a mental hygiene foundation has been mentioned repeatedly. However, our earlier preoccupation with the significance of security in the life of the individual and the family prevented due consideration of its communal aspects. It would lead us too far afield to consider the latter completely. For our purposes it will suffice to raise what many may at first regard as foolish questions: Do all of our citizens, irrespective of their social standing, skin color, and financial status, enjoy equal security when personal crises impel them to seek cover under the protective mantle of our courts of justice? Is the putative impartiality of the law reality or fiction? Is there one law for the rich and another for the poor? Does the majesty of the law render it insensitive to the prestige of financial power as contrasted with the obscurity of the financially destitute?

A categorical affirmative or negative answer to questions like these would probably be misleading. Either answer would call for qualification. Nor should the fact that questions like these are raised be taken to imply that the competence and integrity of the rank and file of our judiciary is suspect. In many instances the inequality is both recognized and deplored by our judges, but they as individuals are altogether impotent to eliminate its causes.

People seeking legal redress for personal injuries, usurpation of their rights, and interference with their privileges have to reckon with the ineluctable fact that court action costs money. The rich and the poor are certainly not equal before the law in the sense of being equally able to avail themselves of what protection the law affords. In one year, according to the Boston Legal Aid Society, 129 cases out of a total of 551 requiring adjudication could not be introduced because the clients were unable to finance the routine court costs. This means that in almost 25 percent of the cases the victims were unable to secure justice because their poverty prevented them from getting to the courts. Here is a sad paradox: *although justice is not to be bought, it takes money to get it.*

For millions of people on the subsistence level justice is thus seen to be a costly and often unattainable luxury. The protection of our courts is not for them. They consequently lack a sense of security to which they are theoretically entitled in terms of the

American ideal of a square deal for all. It is this lack which the mental hygienist deplores; for it means the persistence of unresolved tensions, the bitterness of resentment, and all that is implied by the concept of rankling injustice. When a worker's daughter is victimized by a designing Lothario, the family's distress cannot be alleviated by a breach of promise suit. When the landlord refuses to make needed repairs promised at the time the lease was signed, the resulting quarrel cannot be adjudicated by urging the thirty-dollar-a-week family-head to hire a lawyer. The whole fabric of institutionalized legal protection thrown over a community by our civil courts is evidently not extensive enough to protect those who live on the economic margin of the community.

Economic competition and individual responsibility

All of this means that for about seventy % of American families the security in which wholesome family life should live and move and have its being is either nonexistent or, at best, uncertain. All along the line — in matters of health, of longevity, of housing, of education, and of judicial protection — this security is menaced. In the light of what has already been said concerning the importance of emotional and other kinds of domestic security for the achievement of balance and self-assurance and personality integration for growing children, it ought to be obvious that grave mental hygiene issues are bound up with the relative poverty of more than two-thirds of American families. These are issues with which professional mental hygienists cannot cope. The problems involved are fundamentally those of the Great Society. They are problems concerning which the economist can speak more authoritatively than the mental hygienist; for they are outgrowths of an economic system that seems ill-adapted to a highly industrialized civilization. This maladaptation is revealed by the fact that twenty percent of our national income can go to one percent of the people. It is further revealed, as modern economists [7] have pointed out, by conditions which permit the deliberate destruction of vast quantities of food even though large numbers of people are starving. In 1931, one of our acute depression years, 600,000 peach trees were uprooted in California. During the same year the same

[7] Goslin, R. A. & Goslin, O. P., *Rich Man, Poor Man,* New York, Harper and Brothers, 1935.

state left 431,000 tons of grapes to rot on the vines. The factors responsible for such flagrantly stupid waste are the same as those prompting farmers to plow under the crops and manufacturers to close their factories. With prices falling and profits threatened, both farmers and manufacturers regard it as " poor business " to proceed with their customary economic functions. By a drastic reduction in the quantity of goods put on the market they hope to jack up the prices in accord with the teaching that abundance of supply reduces prices and scarcity elevates them. But with increasing concentration of income in the hands of a small segment of the population fewer people possess the means of buying at the higher prices. This is the vicious economic cycle which makes it possible for people to be in want in a land of plenty. It is a consequence of engaging in economic activity for the sake of profits for the few as opposed to economic activity for the sake of catering to the common needs of *all*. Financial profit — money, dividends, savings, accumulating reserves — is made the objective of farmer, businessman, and industrialist. This is tantamount to confusing means with ends. Money, which ought to be a *means* of rendering life more secure, more satisfying, and more complete, is taken to be an end in itself.

To get rich, even at the expense of the next man, becomes the dream of thousands of young people looking forward to careers on the stage of economic competition. As the play develops, in our modern setting of mechanical power and technological progress, many of them are doomed to play roles of economic failure and to experience the frustrations incident to dire poverty. The heroes of the play like to attribute their successful roles to assiduous work, superior ability, and other virtues of young men on the make. The failures, on the other hand, are apt to be lumped together as shiftless, improvident ne'er-do-wells. It is assumed that they fail because they were born stupid or because they were too lazy to work hard or because they were dishonest, careless, and generally inefficient. In a competitive culture dominated by hierarchical institutions, success and failure is thus accounted for in terms that are applicable to a competitive sport like sprinting. The winner is the man who trained long and hard or who was a " natural born runner," while the loser either neglected to train wisely or was handicapped from the very beginning by inferior bodily equipment.

Is this analogy from the world of competitive athletics adequate to explain our economic failures? Do the Joads fail as farmers because they come from " poor stock " and loafed on the job? Are our jobless men without work because they are either too lazy or too incompetent to find employment? Most of us were taught to believe that the economic race is to the swift and the business battle to the strong. We were taught to believe that anybody who wanted work — *really* wanted work — could find it by diligent searching and heroic willingness to start with menial tasks at the bottom of the vocational ladder. We were led to believe that ours was a land of golden opportunity with plenty of work for all. As a consequence we learned to regard joblessness as a sign of a weak character. We also learned to view poverty as a disgrace — a symptom of moral flabbiness, laziness, and incompetence.

Nobody warned us that this might be a fiction in a profit-seeking, machine-dominated economic set-up. It took the cataclysm of a major depression to shock many of us out of our confident acceptance of these established teachings. We saw loyal, hard-working clerks fired from their posts and thousands of other devotees of our traditional economic virtues lose their jobs as factories closed, banks failed, and shopkeepers went bankrupt. This increasing army of unemployed kept seeking other work, but there were not enough jobs to satisfy the demand. Thousands of well-trained and highly recommended men, laid off for no fault of their own, immediately joined the ever-growing army of job hunters. But the outlook kept getting bleaker: in the summer of 1929 there were 264 applicants for every 100 vacancies. In the summer of 1930 almost 2,000 men, according to employment agencies, were applying for every 100 jobs. By 1931 there were close to 5,000 striving to get the same 100 jobs.[8] A corps of mental hygienists trying to bolster up the morale of the 4,900 disappointed and frustrated " failures " would have faced a futile task. Under the circumstances the mental hygienists themselves might well have been dubbed " failures." If there are not enough jobs to go around, there is not much mental hygienists can do about the shortage.

It should now be manifest that the bulk of welfare legislation has significant mental hygiene implications. Low-cost housing plans, unemployment insurance, workman's compensation acts and

[8] Goslin and Goslin, *op. cit.*, p. 18.

public works projects are not mere vote-getting or mere charitable enterprises. They are ways of giving masses of men, women, and children a measure of security they might otherwise not be able to achieve.

Nor is this inability necessarily to be attributed to some innate qualitative difference between the mass and the class of society. One cannot even be confident that it is due to inferior character traits among the underprivileged. As has already been suggested, those of us who belong to the socially successful and the economically secure upper segments of our hierarchical set-up are often tempted to account for our elevated status in terms of ancestral excellence, individual worth, and exemplary devotion to duty. But there is grave danger of rationalization being operative in this kind of thinking.

It is a serious kind of autistic explanation because it is so apt to make so many of us complacent about the economic *status quo,* just as Plato seems to have been complacent about the institution of slavery and just as the clergy and the nobility of the Middle Ages seem to have been complacent about the institution of feudalism. But to be complacent about millions of modern economic serfs living at or below the subsistence level is to make a mockery of all of our protestations of allegiance to the American ideal of a square deal for all, to the religious ideal of regarding all men as brothers, and to the mental hygiene ideal of a modicum of inner and outer security for every baby born into our society.

This ought not to be dismissed as soft-hearted, unrealistic sentimentalism. It is as real as poverty, as real as unemployment, as real as worry, and as real as the courage with which millions of Americans are facing their poverty, unemployment, and worry. What bothers the mental hygienist, however, is that unless there is a drastic modification of our profit economy there is relatively little he can do for these millions. That is why he welcomes social security measures and other proposals calculated to eliminate the economic barriers to the utilization of his principles by *all* the people and not merely those in the favored end of our skewed income curve.

POVERTY AND MENTAL BREAKDOWN

For years there has been a steady accumulation of evidence, gathered by the ingenuity and persistence of sociologists,[9] all of which suggests an association between environmental bleakness and social incompetence. To understand this evidence it is necessary to call attention to the pattern of development seemingly characteristic of urban growth and expansion.

This pattern can be described in terms of a series of concentric areas. In the center of the city one finds the hub of business and institutions like large hotels, theatres, and banks. In this area of stores and commercial establishments there are few residents except the transients occupying the hotels and the hobos " camping " on the outskirts of the district. The second area surrounding the central hub is a slum area. It is sometimes referred to as a zone in transition because its inner part is gradually being converted into business territory as the central zone keeps expanding. The houses in this second zone are old and neglected; for the owners are waiting for a chance to sell the land to businessmen for business purposes. This means that rents are cheap, but land values high. It also means that the houses are occupied by families of unskilled workers, by lonely occupants of furnished rooms, by denizens of the underworld, and by aliens from other lands. It is in this transitional zone that one finds the ghetto, little Italy, Chinatown, as well as the redlight district.

As the economic status of the people in the second zone improves, they tend to move away from the area to the better homes located still farther away from the central business district. In this third zone one finds many members of second generation immigrant families. One also finds more of the skilled workingmen's homes here. The houses are neater and better cared for than those in zone two, many of them being of the familiar " duplex " type. A convenient characterization for this zone is to describe it as a compromise between the squalor of the slums and the quasi-luxury of the better residential streets. These superior residential areas are found in the apartment-house areas of our larger cities, in the regions where a single family occupies a whole house to

[9] Park, R. E., and Burgess, E. W., *The City,* Chicago, The University of Chicago Press, 1925.

itself, and on the periphery of the city itself from which an army of commuters converges to the center of the city each business day. Upper-middle-class families constitute the bulk of the population in these restricted residential areas. They are more likely to own their homes than the inhabitants of the other zones of the city. A settled way of life and a firmer organization of society is found among them.

There are individual exceptions to this picture in individual cities; but, in general, this somewhat idealized pattern of urban organization seems to apply to most of our larger cities. Starting from a non-residential business center, as we move outward to the periphery of the city to see how the people live, we come across better houses the farther away we get from the center. There is, of course, a steady shift of population as individual families improve their economic lot. The shift is toward the periphery and away from the business and slum areas.

It also appears that the character of the life prevailing in any one area is more a function of the area than of any " racial " or biological characteristics of the occupants of that area. Evidence for this is supplied by studies of some of our older American cities. These investigations show that given areas have been inhabited by successive groups of diverse cultural origin. The Irish may have been displaced by the Germans and the latter then move out as Russian Jews move in. With the passing years the Jewish group may be displaced by a Polish group or a Negro group. However, as these groups move from one zone to the next peripheral zone, the old district retains its old character; but the life of the people moving into the better zone becomes different from the life of their immigrant parents.

Various studies have shown the existence of a significant socio-economic pattern superimposed on this general pattern of urban development. For example, poverty decreases as one goes from the more central slum regions to the more peripheral residential districts. As might be expected in terms of what has already been said regarding the concomitants of poverty, there is also a decrease in unemployment, in the frequency of family desertion, in the rate of infant mortality, in the frequency of suicides, in the amount of juvenile delinquency, in the incidence of contagious diseases, and in the general mortality rate as one shifts from urban center to urban periphery.

But what is of particular significance to the mental hygienist is the outcome of a more recent survey of this general character with respect to the incidence of mental disease. The investigators, Faris and Dunham,[10] ascertained the former places of residence of the mental patients in private and public hospitals. By indicating these places on a map of the city it was obvious that once again the familiar pattern was duplicated: the greatest density in the slum regions and a gradual reduction as the suburban areas were approached. To put this differently, the poorer sections of the city gave rise to relatively more cases of mental disease than the more affluent sections.

When the city was mapped so as to show the possible relationship between given zones and specific types of mental disease, some very interesting findings came to light. The greatest incidence of general paralysis of the insane or dementia paralytica, a condition described in Chapter 3 as resulting from syphilitic infection of the brain, was from the area occupied by lodging houses and in the Negro slum districts. Congestion, vice, poverty, and syphilis thus seem to constitute an interrelated complex. It was also discovered that, as the number of hotel residents and rooming-house occupants increased, the percentage of *paranoid schizophrenia* also increased. It will be recalled that this condition is characterized by attitudes of suspiciousness, delusions of persecution, apathy or emotional blunting, distortion of reality, and compensatory delusions of grandeur. It will also be recalled that, in general, schizophrenic patients seem to manifest a preference for the pleasures of wishful daydreaming in place of actual struggle with the grim realities of the workaday world. The consequent seclusiveness or shut-in nature of the schizophrenic personality make-up has already been pointed out.

In view of this reminder of the psychology of schizophrenia in general and of the paranoid type in particular it is stimulating to consider the possible psychological import of what Faris and Dunham report. The lonely, socially isolated existence of life in

[10] Faris, R. E. L., and Dunham, H. W., *Mental Disorders in Urban Areas,* Chicago, The University of Chicago Press, 1939.

a rooming house or a hotel room may serve to drive lonely people more and more into themselves and thus reenforce underlying schizophrenic trends. Another mental disease which the investigators found to be associated with the solitude of lodging-house existence is the kind of insanity resulting from alcoholic overindulgence. These *alcoholic psychoses* also had a high rate of incidence in some of the immigrant districts. The immigrant's difficulties in carving out a new life for himself in a new country plus his possible nostalgia for the life of his native land may have induced him to seek relief from his distress in the torpor of intoxication. There are several other findings that suggest interesting mental hygiene possibilities, but it would lead us too far afield to mention them here. For our purposes it is enough to give these bare hints of the sort of relationships worked out by these two sociologists. In the present context it is especially relevant to note this additional evidence of an intimate connection between socio-economic factors and mental health.

Our general survey of these socio-economic factors, it must be realized, fails to justify great optimism with respect to speedy adoption by the nation as a whole of something approximating a program of meliorative mental hygiene. Before a modicum of optimism is justified, welfare measures calculated to buttress the basic security of the Great Society must be introduced and made to work. Under existing conditions the Great Society is a sick society. War has even made it sicker. The mental hygiene ideal of a " sound mind in a sound body in a sound society " was never more needed than it is today; but it is still discouragingly remote from realization. Economic ills cannot be cured by professional psychologists or psychiatrists. As long as such ills persist, mental ills will continue to be the lot of millions. As was just pointed out, poverty and mental disease are interdependent. This was known long before the Faris-Dunham investigation. To cite one fragment of statistical evidence: after the first World War, according to data supplied by army psychiatrists, of 57,000 mentally ill white soldiers " only 13 percent were found to be financially well off, while 84 percent were in marginal economic circumstances." [11]

Of course one ought not to oversimplify the interpretation of

[11] Landis, D., and Page, J. D., *Modern Society and Mental Disease,* New York, Farrar & Rinehart, Inc., 1938, p. 59.

such a statistical finding by arguing that poverty causes mental breakdown in direct fashion. The causal interrelationships are far too complex to justify this kind of oversimplification. Furthermore, the very fact that not all financially destitute families become psychopathic plus the additional fact that large numbers of wealthy people do, should indicate that poverty *per se* is neither a necessary nor a sufficient cause. But the figures do suggest that poverty should not be overlooked in a complete survey of factors responsible for mental breakdown. Even those who are inclined to attribute such breakdown to poor " inheritance " are evidently forced to regard poverty as a contributing factor. For example, the two psychologists from whose book the foregoing figures were quoted deliver themselves of the following dictum as their interpretation of these figures: [12]

When mental diseases occur they incapacitate the individual so that he cannot make his way either financially or educationally. To the extent to which mental diseases may be " hereditary " this inability and handicap for economic advancement is passed on to the children so that during succeeding generations the family gradually sinks to lower economic levels.

This interpretation is obviously speculative and debatable. However, to argue its pros and cons would carry us too far afield. It is more germane to our present interest to note what these authors have to suggest by way of recommendations for reducing the incidence of mental disease. The very last paragraph of the book reads as follows: [13]

From the social viewpoint we must always bear in mind the fact that disease affects an *individual*. It is not a social group that becomes ill but certain members of a group who may become ill. The social surroundings of an individual only ameliorate or accentuate the patient's condition. We have shown that social amelioration, old-age care, social security and nonurbanization are socially operative factors which can be brought to bear in the field of psychopathology. Practical hygiene demands that society and government recognize and deal realistically with these four conditions of amelioration or else pay an exorbitant price in human waste.

[12] *Op. cit.*, p. 59.
[13] *Ibid.*, p. 160.

This final paragraph is particularly striking in view of the pronounced hereditarian or constitutional bias that runs through the previous chapters of the book. Despite the seeming conviction of the authors that mental disease is basically a biological problem, their concluding survey of the issues induces them to drift from their biological moorings into the harbor of the environmentalists. Their final sentence in fact is but a reiteration of the thesis of this chapter: realistic thinking " demands that society and government " come to the aid of the mental hygienists. Without such aid the prospect for wholesome national morale will continue to be bleak.

WHAT OF THE FUTURE?

Finding ways to dissipate the bleakness just mentioned is an imperative need. The socio-economic and ethical and administrative factors involved are too complex for any single person's complete mastery. The problems to be considered go beyond the sphere of professional competence of the average psychologist or psychiatrist. Only in broad outline can the mental hygienist venture to suggest what goals must be attained if his dream of a functioning program of meliorative mental hygiene for *all* is to become a social reality. Specific proposals for attaining these goals must come from experts in other fields: in economics, in sociology, in municipal administration, in political science, etc. However, there is reason for belief that progress in the direction of these goals is being made or about to be made. At all events there is increasing recognition of the urgency of the gigantic social task. Men and women in high places are becoming increasingly conscious of its existence. Nor is the ordinary citizen uninformed of the imminence of this incipient progress. The talk about the four freedoms, of the nature of the post-war world, of the liberation of enslaved nations, of lend-lease obligations and kindred themes is not without its influence on the thinking of the common man. There is evidence of change and ferment on all sides.

Even institutions which tradition associates with conservative hostility to change are deviating from that tradition. It is significant in the present connection that so eminent a representative of the Church of England as the Archbishop of Canterbury as a result of the generosity of an American business corporation is enabled to publicize a challenging appeal for " The FULL development of Individual Personality " of *every* child. It may be recalled that in the closing months of 1942 the latter phrase was used as the main caption of an announcement sponsored by the *Pan American World Airways System* and appearing in widely circulated magazines. The announcement consisted of a series of six suggestions made by the Archbishop as his contribution to plans for a better post-war world. He prefaced his concrete suggestions with the following thought-provoking statement: [14]

There is nothing wrong about profits as such. It has always been recognized that both the producer and the trader are entitled to a profit which they have earned by their service to the community. But it is possible, nonetheless, for these two to get in the wrong order. Then the consumer is treated only as a *means* to success . . . *whereas* he ought to be considered the whole end of the process.

In line with this basic assumption the following six ideals were formulated as goals to be aimed at immediately:

(1) Every child should find itself a member of a family housed with decency and dignity, so that it may grow up in a happy fellowship unspoiled by underfeeding — or over-crowding, by dirty and drab surroundings or by mechanical monotony of environment.

(2) Every child should have the opportunity of an education till years of maturity. This education should be inspired by faith in God and find its focus in worship.

(3) Every citizen should be secure in possession of such income as will enable him to maintain a home and bring up children in such conditions as are described in paragraph 1 above.

(4) Every citizen should have a voice in the conduct of the business or industry which is carried on by means of his labour, and the satisfaction of knowing that his labour is directed to the well-being of the community.

(5) After the war, every citizen should have sufficient daily leisure, with two days of rest in seven, and an annual holiday with pay, to enable him to enjoy a full personal life.

(6) Every citizen should have assured liberty in the forms of freedom of worship, of speech, of assembly, and of association for special purposes.

[14] Taken from a *Pan American World Airways System* advertisement appearing in *Time,* November 9, 1942.

Quite manifestly such an interpretation of the meaning of the religious way of life indicates the essential unity of meliorative mental hygiene, of a democratic political philosophy, and this type of religious idealism. Religion, democracy, and mental hygiene can thus make common cause. To the extent that this cause is neglected the outlook for the future will not be bright, but to the extent that its objectives are realized the less justifiable will be a prophecy of gloom. That progress in the realization of many of these objectives may constitute a reasonable hope is not altogether a matter of wishful thinking. At all events it is encouraging to note how many recent books, articles, reports, and programs are concerned with schemes for implementing such progress.[15] Appraisal of the practicability and adequacy of such schemes, as we have already suggested, does not come within the scope of the mental hygienist's professional competence. But their very existence serves to bolster his professional morale by giving him reason to trust that in the decades to come the Great Society will no longer be callous about and unmindful of the morale of the common man and the common man's children.

[15] Those interested in becoming familiar with this literature may find the following list of references helpful by way of general orientation:

Gilbert, R. V., Hildebrand, G. H., Stuart, A. W., et al., *An Economic Program for American Democracy,* New York, The Vanguard Press, 1938.

Hansen, A. H., and Greer, G., " Toward Full Use of our Resources," *Fortune, 26,* 1942, pp. 130–133 and 158–178.

Beveridge, Sir Wm., *Social Insurance and Allied Services,* American Edition, New York, The Macmillan Company, 1942.

Grattan, C. H., Beveridge Plans are not Enough, *Harper's Magazine, 186,* 1943, pp. 369–376.

Condliffe, J. B., *Agenda for a Postwar World,* New York, W. W. Norton & Co., Inc., 1943.

16...
EDUCATING FOR MENTAL HEALTH

EACH YEAR AN ARMY OF YOUNGSTERS, BORN ABOUT SIX YEARS before, is made to toddle up to the shrine of the great god Curriculum. What we call formal education is largely the ritual of propitiating this god. The ritual is as complex as it is familiar; mastering first tool subjects, then content subjects, then more difficult tools to be followed by more abstract content all through the elaborate labyrinth of mental genuflections demanded by the great god as his devotees make their slow pilgrimage from the lowly first grade to the exalted level of the post-doctorate fellowship. It is a long, arduous journey and, considering the vast numbers who begin it, relatively few finish it. The self-sacrifice and grim persistence of these few is eventually rewarded by the acquisition of one or more academic degrees. To possess such a degree is ordinarily regarded as a sign of distinction. The ceremony at commencement time when these degrees are conferred by robed and hooded high priests of the Curriculum is the official rite of initiation into the brotherhood of the academically elect.

Many mental hygienists have examined this cult of the Curriculum in recent decades. They have wondered whether formal education is doing a good job of developing wholesome personalities. They have wondered whether the average teacher can recognize the beginnings of serious personality disturbance. They have wondered what the competitive atmosphere of our classroom procedure with its emphasis on marks and promotions might be doing to the pupils. More particularly, they have wondered about the effect of such an atmosphere on the youngsters who fail. They have wondered about using the entire school system as a means of training the public in the principles of mental hygiene just as this system has been used for years to promote knowledge of ordinary hygiene. Some of them have even wondered about renovating the traditional educational system in order to make room for more assiduous cultivation of mental hygiene values. These thinkers would make the attainment of such values the chief goal of education.

As might be expected, there has been considerable criticism of the schools for their alleged failure to introduce and abide by mental hygiene teachings. They have been criticised for employing teachers ignorant of such teachings. Students of education have been urged to secure the requisite knowledge by enrolling for courses in mental hygiene. There can be no question of the vigor with which official mental hygiene has tackled official education. The result has been an avalanche of books, articles, and lectures on the general theme of mental hygiene in education. It may prove instructive for us to devote a little attention to this general phase of the mental hygiene movement.[1]

As a matter of fact we have already alluded to a portion of this work in our previous discussions of the possible ways in which teachers might be of help in warding off psychotic breakdown. It will be recalled that Chapter 8 contained a rather extended critique of the oft-quoted results of the investigations of Wickman and Stogdill. The soundness and justice of their indictment of teachers and parents was seriously questioned. In addition the investigation by Leigh Peck was cited to indicate that teachers as a class are not nearly as ignorant of basic mental hygiene principles as many writers had led us to suspect. The same chapter also brought out the fact that children are practically immune to psychotic disturbance of the functional sort despite their almost daily exposure to a medley of frustrating experiences. In other words, our analysis of the prophylactic side of the mental hygiene program has already anticipated some of the issues pertaining to the general theme of educating for mental health. It will also be remembered that the upshot of this analysis was to the effect that teachers very likely have a more significant contribution to make to the meliorative than to the prophylactic side of this program. The present chapter will be concerned with an exposition of some of the ways in which this more positive kind of contribution can be furthered.

---

[1] For an excellent introduction to this phase of the work as envisaged by the educator, see Rivlin, H. N., *Educating for Adjustment*, D. Appleton-Century Co., New York, 1936.

THE RESILIENCY OF THE HUMAN ORGANISM

As has been suggested from time to time in the previous pages, too much preoccupation with the subject of mental and physical disease is likely to distort one's perspective regarding problems of health. The hypochondriac represents one possible result of such distortion. He is neurotically apprehensive about the dangers of germs, poor diet, repression, daydreaming, and anything else he has ever learned to view as a menace to health. He magnifies the vulnerability of the human organism. To offset such magnification it might be well for teachers, parents and others responsible for shaping the attitudes of young people to dwell upon the resiliency of the human organism. A healthy antidote to such morbid apprehensiveness is furnished by reports reaching us of the influence of the war on the mental integrity of much-bombed regions of England. A few of these reports were mentioned many pages back at the end of Chapter 9. In the present context it might be well to recall what was said then concerning the great adaptability of children and adults to the effects of air raids. Such recall will be facilitated by considering the following conclusions of a report submitted to the *Medical Research Council* by Sir Wilson Jameson,[2] Dean and Professor of Public Health at the London School of Hygiene and Tropical Medicine:

Air raids have not been responsible for any striking increase in neurotic illness. Crude figures from hospitals and outpatient clinics even suggest a considerable drop.

Reliable data from London and Bristol, and the impressions of good medical observers, indicate that after intensive raids there is a slight rise in the total amount of neurotic illness in the affected area, occurring chiefly in those who have been neurotically ill before. Neurotic reactions may not show themselves for a week or ten days after the bombing; they usually clear up readily with rest and mild sedatives. Hysteria is uncommon, anxiety and depression are the commonest forms of upset.

The incidence of neurotic illness has been low in fire-fighters and other workers in Civil Defense.

Insanity has not increased, so far as figures are to hand, though more persons with senile deterioration have been admitted to mental

[2] Jameson, W., "War and Health in Britain," *Amer. Jour. of Public Health,* 1941, *31*, pp. 1258–1259.

institutions than before, because their relatives could not any longer look after them or the raids had in other ways disturbed their routine and their precarious adaptation. . . . Suicide has diminished both in England and in Scotland.

At the risk of being tediously repetitious it is advisable to dwell upon the implications of findings such as these for those charged with the task of conserving mental health. It is particularly relevant to note the enormous amount of strain the human personality can tolerate without loss of sanity. Both parents and teachers whose self-confidence has been upset by the Wickman-Stogdill type of lecture, as well as students taking formal courses in mental hygiene, psychiatry, psychoanalysis, or abnormal psychology and whose inner equilibrium may have been upset by such courses, may profit by a little counter-propaganda of the kind being introduced in this section.

We believe that mental health can be promoted by stressing not merely the hazards of wishful thinking, personal conflict, and kindred psychiatric concepts, but also our tolerance for disciplined courage in the face of many of these hazards. It will make for a more balanced evaluation to appreciate the ruggedness of most people in all strata of society when faced with trouble: to note how national crises like wars and depressions find us with enough adjustive capacity as a people to come through without any noticeable increase in mental illness. It is reassuring to think of the thousands of families in America whose members succeed in adjusting themselves to the drastic shock of the death of a beloved parent or child. This happens every day in all sections of the country. Each individual bereavement constitutes a grievous blow, but people can take it without necessarily cracking. The resiliency of the human organism is even more amazing than its vulnerability. It is sound mental hygiene to stress this fact along with what little is known regarding the causes of mental disease. It is a healthy antidote to the morbid apprehension of those whose perspective is distorted by excessive preoccupation with the literature of the abnormal in mental life.

The resiliency of the human organism to which we have just referred may be another factor partially responsible for the child's seeming immunity to mental disease. We are thinking of those cases of positive abuse to which so many underprivileged children are exposed, where conditions of life constitute a violation of almost every canon of decency and where even the most elementary rules of physical and mental hygiene are conspicuously honored in the breach. Cases of this sort are known to every welfare agency and to every veteran policeman on duty in a slum district. The child is left to shift for himself from an early age. He is the victim of merciless flogging at home and of the sticks and fists of the older boys on the streets. His meals are meager, irregular, and poorly balanced. His home is overcrowded, dark, and unsanitary. The psychological outcome of exposure to such unmitigated bleakness and abuse is usually anything but a lovable personality; but it is not necessarily a *broken* mind. Just how much pain, frustration, disappointment, and distress the human organism can tolerate without serious or permanent damage to the integrity of the personality has never been estimated. In fact, there are no means of putting this into quantitative units; but, if there were, the figure would certainly be a large one. People can adjust to loss of vision without going insane. Many of the blind are actually better poised and better integrated than many of the seeing. People can also stand up under repeated surgical operations or the torture of the dentist's chair. Limbs can be amputated and teeth extracted without causing mental breakdown. One can be very much crippled in body and yet brilliantly sound in mind. This is not to say that the prospect of bodily mutilation is devoid of mental hygiene hazards. The blind, the halt, the deaf, and the disfigured all have acute problems of adjustment; but the important consideration for us to dwell upon is that splendid adjustments have been worked out by thousands of them. This is what we mean by the resiliency of people. They can cope with enormous adversity and not crack mentally. Some of them even weather the storms of adverse fortune so heroically that the wrestling with adversity seems to magnify their spiritual strength and endow them with a mellowed toughness that keeps them going more steadily and patiently and understandingly than ever. Adversity need not break a man; it may make him.

How schools can promote mental health

From our viewpoint the chief mental hygiene task of the schools is not so much to prevent actual mental breakdown as to reenforce and amplify the functions of the ideal home in building up wholesome and socially constructive attitudes. In other words, what we have called the program of meliorative mental hygiene should be the school's main concern with mental hygiene. This does not mean that an already crowded curriculum should be burdened with one more subject. We are not advocating the addition of a course in mental hygiene at either the elementary or high school level. The scope of meliorative mental hygiene is such that it cannot very well be compressed within the confines of a series of lesson plans or formal school projects.

As has already been suggested, mental hygiene is more like a philosophy of life than a fixed body of knowledge. A philosophy of life is not acquired by taking a course in philosophy. Nor is a philosophy of life ever finished. It is changed and developed as new experiences make for deepened insight and superficial values are discarded in favor of more profound values. Similarly, the mental hygiene perspective calls for adaptation all through the years as insight deepens and new problems loom up. But the basic setting for this perspective is rooted in the experiences of the developmental years in home and school. This setting is so pervasive that no array of pious mental hygiene maxims can furnish the child with the requisite knowledge. Schools can introduce fire drills and tooth brush drills and spelling drills, but not mental hygiene drills. Every class has mental hygiene implications. So does every good book, every friendship, every contest, every examination, every promotion, and every demotion.

The mental hygienist is more concerned about the attitudes built up in the child by school experiences — both curricular as well as extra-curricular — than he is with formal academic success. Every teacher has a responsibility for shaping and influencing the child's attitudes. Wholesome personality development of every child should be the fundamental educational objective. In terms of such a mental hygiene ideal it is just as important to adjust the school to the child as it is to have the child adjust to the school. Mastery of the curriculum should be regarded as a means for enhancing personality development rather than as an end in itself. Existing curricula should be evaluated on the basis of their efficacy in furthering this goal. It is particularly important to consider their range and flexibility; for an extremely rigid curriculum of narrow content cannot be adapted to the individual needs of individual students. Many of our so-called educational misfits are casualties of an unyielding curriculum. Very often it is the school rather than the child which is the misfit in question. Enlightened school officials have long been aware of this and have already made considerable progress in the difficult and expensive task of fitting the school to the vagaries of the individual child.

Even where lack of funds prevents an elaborate curricular change much can be done to promote child welfare as the mental hygienist views such welfare. The psychological atmosphere of the school can be made more like that of a congenial home atmosphere. The child ought to be made to feel safe and secure and at home at school. In a way the school is to be considered a projection and enlargement of the psychological values of the well-administered family. It is the child's training ground for communal living. To achieve the utmost from his activities on this training ground he must be given a sense of belonging to the school community. He must be made to feel a part of it just as he is made to feel his identification with the family group.

SCHOOL FAILURE AND MORALE

We have already called attention to two possible evils of the child's handling by the family: one the consequence of pampering and the other the consequence of neglect. These are the evils of overindulgence of the child and of hostile antagonism. The latter causes the child to feel rejected by the family group. He lacks the anchor of emotional security. These psychological considerations apply to the school community as well. Too much solicitude for his welfare by the teacher may make a child too dependent on others for solving his problems. However, the more common evil is that of the other extreme of not getting enough individual attention to feel that he is understood and welcomed by the teacher. Failure in school work with its attendant expression of disapproval and disappointment by the teacher often induces the youngster to feel that " teacher doesn't like me." It is but a short step from the conviction of being disliked to the feeling of being rejected. One of the crucial mental hygiene opportunities for the teacher is to guide the youngster in wise ways of facing the fact of failure. Individual morale is largely contingent on the possession of healthy techniques of adjusting to failure and a good teacher is one who can help the child develop such techniques.

The mental hygienist is concerned about the problem of academic failure because of its possible damage to the victim's personality. It frequently provokes frustration of the serious kind — the kind which means loss of self-confidence and threat to one's self-esteem. In the language of the psychoanalyst, it means superego trouble, or possibly a disguised Oedipus complex, considering how fathers react to poor report cards. The disciple of Alfred Adler will view it as the basis for what he labels an " inferiority complex." Precisely what descriptive label is employed is not important. What is important is to understand what school failure may mean to a sensitive child — and to some not so sensitive.

For the child, failure in school can be as momentous as bankruptcy or business failure to the business man. A good portion of the healthy sense of emotional security making for zestful daily living is a function of being able to handle one's routine assignments successfully. School assignments are the child's business obligations. They can loom as large in his life as bills do in the life of his father. Prestige, security, and credit are bound up with the way in which such obligations are met. We must also remember how much emphasis a child's family usually places on his school advancement. As a consequence, he fears the loss of the good will of the folks at home as the confusing intricacy of decimal fractions threatens to engulf him. In other words, those whose affectionate approval he craves expect him to handle this school job. Not to be able to live up to the expectation of those who have been good to us and for whose admiration we yearn is hard on the best of us. Even young children soon learn that school failure is regarded as some kind of disgrace by grown-ups. They may even regard it as a stigma on the family reputation. In brief, the youngster is often made to feel *guilty* because he failed at school. He may even be told that he ought to be " ashamed " of himself. Shame and self-respect cannot dwell in the same psychological household and morale goes to smash when self-respect crumbles. This is what makes school failure a mental hygiene problem.[3]

[3] Whether school failure accomplishes any useful purpose either in terms of the child's educational development or in terms of the school's administrative efficiency may be seriously questioned. For an able summary of this issue as well as for a discussion of a plan by means of which the needs of both pupil and school

IS SCHOOL SUCCESS BIOLOGICALLY DETERMINED?

In many respects our schools reflect the bitterly competitive spirit of the world of commerce. To advance, to get high marks, to win honors, to pile up academic credit, to outshine the other students is analogous to rising in the business hierarchy, getting corporation directorships, accumulating reserves, and outmaneuvering competitors. Some even profess to see a relentless law of biology operative both in the world of education and the world of business. Only the fit, so they believe, can weather the academic and economic storms. They project what they take to be Darwinian philosophy into the mad scramble for educational prestige and financial success. Those endowed with the requisite brain, brawn, bravery and whatever else it takes will fight through and come out on top. The weak and flabby and cowardly will just have to take the consequences of having been born into a world where the race is to the swift, the battle to the strong, and the examination to the brainy.

We find some educators thinking of the schools as vast selective agencies impersonally weeding out the " inferior " so that only the " academically fit " will have survived. The implication is the same as if the process of securing a formal education were some sort of colossal curricular struggle. But this whole endeavor to think of human affairs in terms of jungle biology may be more misleading than revealing. One cannot be confident in individual cases of the meaning or the relevance of the survival test. A baby in rural Mexico may die of diphtheria because its touring parents were not far-sighted enough to have it immunized. On the other hand, a Mexican baby in the slums of Chicago may not succumb to diphtheria because a public health nurse acted *in loco parentis*. Which of these two babies was more " fit " to survive? As we are writing these lines there are reports of the death of physically superb Americans fighting for America on various battlefronts. Many of their friends with constitutions too weak for military service will thus survive them by many, many years. Shall we say these friends were consequently more " fit " to survive?

will be catered to without requiring the retention of the traditional practice of failing children at the end of each grade, see Otto, H. J., *Elementary School Organization and Administration,* D. Appleton-Century Co., New York, 1934, pp. 247–257.

A contemporary psychologist [4] has supplied us with a still more perplexing example. He calls it *The Strange Case of Auguste Ciparis*. The case is that of a young Negro who happened to be a prisoner in the city of St. Pierre, Martinique, on the eighth of May, 1902. There were some 40,000 people in the city on this day. They were there at 7:50 in the morning. Ten minutes later they were all dead, their lives snuffed out by the violence of a volcanic eruption. Thanks to his rocky dungeon, Auguste Ciparis was the sole survivor of the disaster. Shall we say he, the prisoner, was more " fit " than the 40,000 who perished? There is no need to add more examples. To account for educational or business success in terms of a Darwinian survival test, it should now be obvious, is a rather futile endeavor. It is also an obfuscating procedure; for it never brings to light the specific factors responsible for success or defeat as these are operative in the individual case. As a matter of fact, the Darwinian test was not intended to apply to the individual. Its field of application was an entire group or species and what may characterize a whole group need not hold true of every member. As a group, professional baseball players are ignorant of French, yet Moe Berg, the catcher, is an accomplished French student. In fact, one may think of situations in which the distinctive characteristic of the group or the whole does not apply to the separate items constituting the group. To revert to an earlier illustration: a whole pile of oranges may be arranged in the form of a square and yet squareness will not apply to any single orange in the group.[5]

The misleading application of the doctrine of biological struggle to educational affairs can thus hardly justify the evils of academic competition. The chief concern of the schools should be the welfare of the individual child rather than children taken in the abstract as a total group. Biologists are interested in group or species adjustment, but educators and mental hygienists are interested in individual adjustment. No biologist has ever had to devote his professional concern to a turtle rendered unhappy by its awkwardness and slowness, but many a teacher and clinical psychologist has had to wrestle with personal problems of human turtles: little

[4] Krout, M. H., *Introduction to Social Psychology*, New York, Harper & Brothers, 1942, pp. 1–3.
[5] We are indebted to Prof. G. F. Stout for this particular illustration.

boys and girls whose slowness and awkwardness and fatness subjects them to the humiliating jibes of more agile companions. Such human problems are private and personal. They are not solved by cavalier references to " survival of the fit," " adjustment to reality," or even " integration of personality."

PERFECTIONISM AS A MENTAL HYGIENE EVIL

One of the chief evils of unbridled competitiveness in the classroom is its possible unwholesome influence not merely on the children who fail, but also on those who succeed. This may sound paradoxical, but every mental hygienist and psychiatrist will recognize the danger immediately. It is the danger of becoming a *perfectionist*. The perfectionist is chronically dissatisfied because he expects too much of himself and of those who chance to come under his direction. We are not referring to the individual who sets himself standards of reasonable accomplishment of a relatively high order. Instead we are thinking of the individual who is afraid of making a single mistake, of falling short in a single particular, of being wrong in any respect. A clear, if somewhat extreme, instance of this was once reported to us by a school psychologist whose task it was to find out why a little second-grader was so desperately serious about his classroom assignments — so serious as to be tense, fidgety, and unsmiling. As part of his routine study of the case, the psychologist called on the mother of the child and the following dialogue approximates the decidedly revealing initial verbal skirmish:

" Good morning, I'm the school psychologist. I've come to talk to you about your little boy."

" Oh, you're the psychologist, are you? What kind are you? An educational psychologist? "

" Yes, you might consider me an educational psychologist."

" Well, then, I'd rather not discuss matters with you. I've no confidence in educational psychologists and I'll tell you why. When I was at college I once took a course in educational psychology and I made 99 on the final examination. At least that's what the professor put on my paper. But I knew I had really made a 100. When I went to see him about it, he wouldn't give me any satisfaction. He wouldn't admit his mistake. I've never had any use for educational psychologists since then."

Here was a perfectionist who permitted the disappointment of scoring 99 instead of 100 on an obscure final examination to rankle and to distort her attitude toward a group of specialists long after her Phi Beta Keppa key had worn a dent in her neck. As might be expected, her severe attitude was largely responsible for her child's maladjustment. She kept nagging the youngster to try harder and to do better. She prided herself on her high standards: the child's papers had to be flawless. Even a faint smudge meant they were " not neat." Her motto seemed to be that " if a thing is worth doing, it's worth doing *perfectly*." She applied this sort of slogan to every phase of the child's activity, such as his school work, his Sunday School lessons, his table manners, his diction, and his washing. Not only had her perfectionist striving converted her own distinguished school work into failure in her estimation, for she was genuinely aggrieved by the grade of 99, but it also threatened to mar the life of her child.

This striving after perfection elicits the mental hygienist's disapproval for a variety of reasons. In many respects perfection constitutes an impossible goal. To urge a child to struggle toward an impossible goal is the equivalent of urging a high jumper to leap over the Empire State Building or to become so expert that he can jump over *any* barrier. Of course, in the classroom very few, if any, teachers ever deliberately set such ridiculous standards. For them the concept of perfection is an outgrowth of the stereotyped rigidity of spelling and arithmetic and similar subjects. There is only one answer to six times six and only one way to spell the word *cow*. To be perfect means to master this sort of conventional curricular content in flawless fashion. It means to react with *correct* answers to routine questions pertaining to spelling, reading, punctuation, geography, and arithmetic. Not only must the answers be correct; they must also be given within a " reasonable " time. The factor of speed thus comes to be included in the concept of perfection. Current arithmetic texts often print neat little goads like: " How many of the following exercises can you complete in 20 min. ? " or " For a grade of A you must solve the following exercises in 12 minutes . . ." and then follows a table of grades for slower speeds of accomplishment. By adding the factor of speed to that of correctness one can easily make perfection as applied to school subjects a never-ending struggle. The champion in arithmetic can always be working to break his own record by cutting down his best previous time for adding a column of figures and the best silent reader can always endeavor to read still more rapidly. There can be competition among champions to set new records for speed in situations where accuracy is taken for granted. As a result even with respect to tool subjects it is possible to set impossible goals for the pupils.

To set too fast a pace for the kind of child fate did not intend to develop into a high-pressure demon of sales efficiency is not conducive to fostering the mental health of the child. It may even be doubted whether our customary idealization of the go-getting salesman, the rushing business executive, and the frantically busy housewife is a sound mental hygiene ideal to hold up before the child. Furthermore, there may be more than a chance relationship, as we shall indicate later, between our glorification of the " live wire " and our proneness to high blood pressure.

Our striving for " perfection " in school may make for the vicious extreme of the never-ending push for power and prestige. We may not think of it so much in terms of a lust for perfection as a " healthy ambition for success." But we measure the Success — with a capital S — by means of the speed with which we accumulate the dollars as well as by the number we accumulate. The competition for such Success runs through the warp and woof of our society. Our schools reflect and reenforce this strident competitiveness. And the furious tempo of our striving shows in our faces. Many of us — including our school children — have a set, tense, almost belligerently desperate expression. This is not a recent development. It has long been noticed by mental experts. Even fifty years ago Dr. Clouston, Scotland's leading psychiatrist of the period, had this to say about us after a visit to our country: [6]

You Americans wear too much expression on your faces. You are living like an army with all its reserves engaged in action. The duller countenances of the British population betoken a better scheme of life. They suggest stores of reserved nervous force to fall back upon, if any occasion should arise that requires it. This inexcitability, this presence at all times of power not used, I regard as the great safeguard of the British people. The other thing in you gives me a sense of insecurity,

[6] Quoted by William James in his famous essay on " The Gospel of Relaxation."

and you ought somehow to tone yourselves down. You really do carry too much expression, and take too intensely the trivial moments of life.

We once had to curb a college student who was so consumed by competitive ambition that he was trying to get along on about three hours of sleep in order to devote almost all of his leisure time to reading " good " books. Perfectionism as an ideal thus easily jeopardizes the psychologist's ideal of the balanced personality. Ambition can be either healthy or morbid. The perfectionist is more likely to lean toward the morbid kind of grimly bitter, self-disparaging, never relaxing struggle. Of course there is the opposite evil of indolent, self-complacent satisfaction with shoddy workmanship. Mental health calls for avoidance of these extremes in favor of a balanced mean. Smug complacency deprives us and the community of the fruits of self-improvement and better workmanship, while morbid perfectionism takes the *joy* out of both routine effort as well as creative effort.

The perfectionist is apt to kill all effort by setting an impossible ideal for himself. If our goal is perfection, fear of making a mistake is a constant inhibitor of action. There are would-be writers who never get a word written because of such perfectionist standards. They have taken the admonition to " read *everything* on your subject before you write about it " in very literal fashion. For them this means covering the entire literature of their chosen subject in all languages and may well include the history of the subject. To have to read *everything* ever written about nitrogen or Charlemagne or the Amazon River or cooking potatoes or tuberculosis or almost any other topic is enough to deter most of us from ever getting any of our ideas down on paper. Actually no expert has ever literally read *everything* in the field of his expertness. No Shakespearean scholar has read *all* that has ever appeared about the bard. No Biblical scholar can ever hope to read the tons of material having to do with Holy Writ. Even in such a new field as mental hygiene it is impossible for one man to read every book, pamphlet, monograph, and journal article that bears upon the field. In a strict sense, if this reading injunction is taken too seriously, nobody will ever be ready to write on any subject. However, only the perfectionist is likely to be so serious. His very perfectionism blocks his action. Even when external circumstances force him to some kind of action despite, as he puts it, his "inadequate preparation," his efficiency is marred by a crippling sense of inferiority as well as by fear of error or of adverse criticism. He worries about the possibility of having overlooked some important contribution to his field or about his literary style or about the possible scathing comments of his professional rivals — or worse yet — their possible refusal even to read what he has written.

Perfectionism, in other words, may make for timorousness. Fear of blundering, of not being perfect, may inhibit action. Much nervous tension could be avoided by teaching pupils to expect to meet carping criticism from some quarters no matter how excellent the achievement. The entire history of human achievement is studded with critical nose-wrinkling or downright persecution. The people of Israel demurred against Moses, the Romans crucified Christ, and the press vilified Lincoln. Joan of Arc was executed, Galileo humiliated, and Robert Fulton ridiculed. There has hardly been a single outstanding hero who did not have his detractors. There has hardly been a single eminent writer or musician or painter whose work was not disparaged in some respect at some time by some critic. It is hard to find a lengthy book review without some flaw being mentioned. When all else fails, there are always "typographical errors," incomplete bibliographic notes, or a faulty index to come to the rescue of the perfectionists among the reviewers. Popularizers are criticized for sacrificing accuracy to readability, for being superficial rather than profound, and even for being popularizers rather than experts. On the other hand, experts are verbally trounced for being too technical, too profound, and discouragingly dull.

Youngsters ought to be prepared for this kind of critical world. To the extent that perfectionism as an ideal induces them to hope for such brilliant achievement as to avoid *all* adverse criticism, it constitutes poor preparation. It would be healthier to teach them to expect some sort of criticism by some sort of people as inevitable and to reconcile themselves to this inevitability. Even in the realm of ethical achievement the exemplary citizen may be sneered at by some fellow citizens because of what may be stigmatized in various ways as being " Sunday Schoolish," " a holier-than-thou-attitude," " Puritanic virtue," or " goody-goodyness." Instead of teaching youngsters to strive to be perfect in the sense of dodging all possibility of error and expecting 100% approval of the entire public, it might be better mental hygiene pedagogy to teach them to rest content with accomplishing the best job of which they are capable under given circumstances. They ought also to be taught how to handle criticism in resolute fashion, so that exaggerated fear of criticism will not paralyze action. Fear of doing the wrong thing may be so acute that the victim protects himself by not even venturing to undertake the right thing. Volitional impulses are deadlocked and in extreme cases we may have what psychologists call *abulia,* or loss of the capacity to initiate action.

CONATION AND EDUCATIONAL VALUES

Our previous discussion of the nature of interest might well be mentioned again in the present context; for, it will be recalled, interest wanes when goals seem unrealizable. This is a chief reason justifying the substitution of attainable objectives in place of unattainable perfectionist standards. It will also be recalled that pleasure is a function of making perceptible progress toward a goal. With goals too remote and standards too high, the learner has more difficulty in detecting progress than is the case when goals and standards are brought within observable striking distance. It is easier to note progress in mastering a chapter than in mastering a whole book. One can more readily tackle the job of learning ten new Spanish words per day than the more ambitious and vaguer assignment of " learning the vocabulary of the Spanish language at your early convenience."

The psychological factors involved in these considerations have to do with such concepts as level of aspiration, conation, and closure. Although we have referred to these matters before, we shall repeat our explanation of them here. Such repetition may be boring and the relationships in question obvious to many, but the issues are of such paramount educational importance as to justify both the repetition and the risk of being tedious.

Educational goals should be so adjusted for each individual child as to make success a consequence of reasonable effort. There is no fun in reaching easy goals and no fun in struggling for futile objectives. Our earlier analogy from the realm of competitive games will clarify this. The golfing expert gets no thrill out of winning over the novice, just as the novice is apt to be painfully and hopelessly discouraged by a contest in which he is expected to trounce the champion. The level of aspiration is too low for the expert and too high for the novice. In other words, goals toward which we aspire must be such as provoke an exciting contest-attitude: they must provide us with a *fighting* chance to achieve success. Fighting or striving toward a goal is the psychologist's meaning of conation. Games which fail to arouse a minimum of *striving* are dull games. They are dull for the winner, humiliating for the loser, and a disappointment for the spectators. They lack *interest* for all concerned because the winner gets his goals with too little effort and the loser has no chance of getting any goal despite his most arduous effort. An optimal degree of conative effort on the part of both contestants characterizes exciting games.

Learning can be made an exciting game when educational tasks are so arranged as to provoke such effort on the part of the learner. To accomplish this end the task must not only come within the scope of the learner's capacity, but it must also be short enough to be accomplished within a reasonable length of time. Approaching the finish of a goal toward which we have been striving furnishes a special thrill. This closing in on our quarry, finishing a task undertaken, or achieving an objective aimed at is, in part, what the psychologist means by the *closure* phenomenon. Tasks that are too difficult or too protracted interfere with the realization of closure. This is one reason books are divided into chapters and long chapters into sections. The chapters and sections constitute sub-wholes. There is a good possibility of finishing any one of them during a single study session. They serve to remind us of the desirability of dividing vast projects and big jobs into smaller projects and littler jobs in order to achieve a satisfactory working relationship between level of aspiration, conative effort, and closure. Only in this way can interest, the joy of progress toward a goal, be introduced into the educational arena.

What we have designated as conative effort, the striving to overcome obstacles in order to reach a goal, has long been regarded as a student virtue by the traditional schoolmaster. He probably did not describe it as conative effort. Instead he talked about discipline and the value of persevering at a hard, unattractive task

until it is accomplished. Sometimes he talked as if the very unat-
tractiveness of the task gave it some special educational potency.
Even today one hears educators dividing school subjects into the
" easy " and the " hard," with the implication that the latter are
of greater educational value than the former. The so-called hard
subjects are thus surrounded by a halo of special educational merit.
Very few, if any, professors like to have their courses described as
" easy." Nor do they relish having them called dull. The ideal
seems to be the course that is both hard and fascinating. Judging
by casual student comment, very few courses approximate this
ideal.

Study may be difficult for two reasons: the amount of drudgery
entailed or the height of the intellectual barriers to be scaled. Both
call for conative effort; but the educational value of the effort is
not necessarily equal in the two kinds of situations. To appreciate
the difference it might suffice to contrast the task of adding all the
telephone numbers in the Chicago directory with the task of adding new knowledge to the theory of numbers. Both tasks would
call for hard, persevering work and both would demand endless
hours of intense application and concentration. In this sense both
would be *difficult* tasks, but the telephone job would hardly be of
educational value merely because of its painfully tedious monotony. Of course, staying with such a job would elicit punishing
self-discipline, but even this would hardly justify us in applauding
it as a pedagogic boon. It is not calculated to make for better
understanding, deepened insight, greater problem-solving ability,
more sensitive appreciation of beauty, keener reasoning, or the joy
of intellectual discovery. These are some of the genuine goals of
education. A curriculum is to be measured by the extent to which
it furthers progress toward such goals.

There is no educational magic in discipline for the sake of
discipline and drill for the sake of drill and perseverance for the
sake of perseverance. If there were, every moron could be educated by forcing him to devote one hour a day to copying the words
of the Encyclopedia Britannica, another hour to knee-bending exercises, a third to threading needles, a fourth to tracing maps, and
a fifth to memorizing the Bible. Even eight to twenty years of this
kind of hard discipline might find him with over-developed leg

muscles, a champion needle-threader and map-tracer, able to quote long passages from the Bible and the Encyclopedia in uncomprehending fashion, but nevertheless still a moron, and not an educated person.

Drudgery taken by itself does not lead to enlightenment nor does unenlightened discipline build either character or intellect. This may be obvious to the point of absurdity, but far too many teachers, parents, and army drill masters behave as if its obviousness were not manifest to them. Their attitude toward educational procedures is reminiscent of the old belief concerning medicinal herbs: a vile-tasting herb was presumed to do more therapeutic good than a pleasant-tasting one. It is almost superfluous to have to classify both the attitude and the belief as anachronistic and unworthy of endorsement.

This attack on educational drudgery should not be misinterpreted as a plea for lax standards or no standards at all. It should not be regarded as a glorification of " easy " courses at the expense of the " hard " ones. Nor should it be misconstrued as disparaging fine workmanship, rigorous thinking, accurate analyses and kindred ideals. In no sense should it be taken as a defense of the vague, the shoddy, the slipshod, the superficial, or the slovenly. It is merely a plea for the elimination of *needless* drudgery, the kind which increases the difficulty and monotony of school work and is devoid of educational significance.

For the child who already has a firm understanding of the difference between a noun and a predicate, it is needless drudgery to have to write fifty simple declarative sentences and to underline each noun with a blue pencil and every predicate with a red one. In brief, the attack is an indictment of squirrel-cage school activity: stereotyped drill involving constant movement and no progress. Part of what makes the modern progressive school progressive is its recognition of the need for endowing educational effort with significance for the learner by making such effort an intrinsic feature of the forward march toward new skills and new insights. It does not make drill or discipline an end in itself, but only an incidental means of achieving significant goals. To move from goal to goal is to make progress and to experience a sense of achievement. Sound mental hygiene calls for this kind of educational experience. The other kind, the squirrel-cage type, is a menace to healthy morale and a stumbling block in the path of intellectual development.

I.Q.'s AND MENTAL HEALTH

The recognition of the need for a sense of achievement is nothing new. Educators have developed our entire school system around this need by stressing progress from grade to grade. They have recognized increments in knowledge and ability by making each higher grade's tasks a little more difficult than those of the lower. They have also recognized the existence of individual differences in ability to cope with these progressive increases in difficulty. Youngsters are not equally bright or equally diligent. As a consequence, the top rungs of the educational ladder are theoretically reserved for the select few capable of scaling the dizzy heights. The others must rest content with lesser achievements. In other words, our educational institutions are conceived to be more or less impersonal selective agencies weeding out the incompetent all along the line as the going gets tougher and tougher with each succeeding promotion. The factor of speed plays its part here as well. Brighter pupils learn more quickly and their rate of academic progress is quicker than that of dull pupils. The latter have to repeat grades.

Taken by and large, there is thus an inverse correlation between age and class standing: the youngest child in a high school class is likely to be the brightest, and the oldest the most stupid. Then there comes a time when this most stupid member can no longer pass examinations at a given level of the high school curriculum no matter how often he repeats his courses. He is said to have reached " the limit of his educability." He slips off the educational ladder of his own accord or is pushed off by the educational authorities if he refuses to slip. At all events his education is finished. There may be some regrets and a few sighs because of blasted hopes for the accolade of a college degree; but usually no official gets very upset about it. The boy " has reached his intellectual limit " and there is no reason to hold the educational authorities responsible for his limitations. Nor should the boy or his parents be blamed. Not everybody can be a genius and not everybody can be bright. Some of us have to be mediocre just as some few of us human beings are doomed to feeblemindedness. This is the kind of world into which we have been born and we might as well make the best of it. Schools have to be realistic, too. They must not coddle the weak and the stupid and the mediocre. All they can do is to give them as much " education " as they can take and then let them find their respective niches in our vocational hierarchy. The highest levels of our educational hierarchy are not for them. Their I.Q.'s are too low to enable them to negotiate such steep grades.

We may have described conventional academic progress and failure with a little too much acerbity, but the description is substantially correct. What is more, the educators may also be entirely correct in their insistence that not all students are capable of being educated to the same level. Individual differences in mental endowment cannot be circumvented no matter how much the fact of such differences may strike us as unjust or as undemocratic. Disregarding obstetrical fees, babies are born free, but they are certainly not born equal. The only kind of equality we may eventually hope to place at their disposal is equality of opportunity. However, owing to differences in talent, temperament, and early training, their ability to profit from this opportunity will range from one end of the normal distribution curve to the other. The inevitable educational consequence is that those from the lower end of the curve will not be educable beyond a certain minimum level. Only those belonging to the upper end of the curve will be able to progress to the higher levels of educability. This accounts for the gradual weeding out of academic failures as a given crop of youngsters is subjected to academic cultivation.

Within limits the school psychologist will even venture to predict what youngsters will be able to complete the requirements for high school graduation and which ones possess enough ability to do creditable college work. More specifically, by way of example, he will regard an I.Q. of 115 as a rather dubious minimum for work at the college level.[7] Children whose I.Q.'s are below this minimum would accordingly be discouraged from dreaming dreams of campus careers. This lack of the requisite mental ability is inde-

[7] Garrett, H. E., and Schneck, M. R., *Psychological Tests, Methods, and Results*, New York, Harper & Brothers, 1933, p. 30. These authors actually say, " Unless a student's I. Q. is 115 or more it is probably unwise to advise him to go to college."

pendent of the cost of higher education. It means that even if every child could afford to attend a college, not every child could go. The vast majority — those with average and sub-average I.Q.'s — would be unable to negotiate the intellectual hurdles.

Our system of education can be thought of as a huge pyramid with the apex symbolizing post-doctorate courses and the base the work of nursery schools and kindergartens. The higher up we climb inside of this pyramid the more select and the smaller the educational company. Educationally we can never have a classless society because not all individuals can be educated to the apical level of our pyramid. This symbol furnishes a rough approximation of the conventional view of our system of education. Almost all six-year-old children can enter the broad base of the pyramid, but only a small band of hardy, intellectual survivors can emerge from the narrow apex some twenty years later. The rest will have given up the climb once they have attained their varying " levels of educability."

But what has all this to do with educating for mental hygiene? There is nothing the mental hygienist can do to jack up the I.Q. level of those who fail once they go beyond their grade of ability. And yet his professional concern centers in such failures. The tremendous prestige value of academic success makes academic failure a grievous blow to a person's self-esteem. It often constitutes the more serious kind of frustration as opposed to that of mere deprivation. To flunk out, to have to repeat courses, and to fail to climb the educational ladder is a blow to one's pride. Crushed pride or balked ambition is always a mental hygiene problem. As a result, the mental hygienist is seriously concerned about an educational system which dooms so many to the conviction of failure. Any suggestions calculated to reduce the number of failures or the adverse consequences of failure would constitute a welcome contribution to the cause of mental hygiene.

In terms of our competitive, hierarchical system of education, failure for some is inevitable at every level of the system. The very concept of a " limit of educability " suggests failure beyond this limit, as has already been pointed out. But just what does this concept mean? Does it mean that the worried sophomore whose record shows an F in college algebra, a C in English, a D in chemistry, a D in history, and a D in French, and who is known to have studied hard and long has about reached the end of his educational rope? Well, if his intelligence test score is about that of the *average* high school graduate, the usual answer to our question would be in the affirmative. His college adviser, assuming he has one, would break the news to him and suggest early departure from the academic scene before he sinks in the icy depths of junior year educational currents. The adviser recognizes the futility of expecting so weak a swimmer to keep afloat in colder and swifter academic waters. Accordingly, he " rescues " him by shifting him to the dry land of business or agriculture. Actually, this might be a dubious rescue. The boy thinks of himself as inferior and as a failure. He is apt to develop a negative attitude toward study and learning and the world of books and ideas.

WHAT KIND OF A LIMIT DO I.Q.'S IMPOSE?

What many people seem to overlook is that the concept of a " limit of educability " does not mean a limit to one's learning capacity. The pursuit of knowledge may be thought of as involving both a vertical as well as a horizontal dimension with the former pointing to the ascent to more abstruse levels and the latter to extensive exploration of a given level. A few concrete examples will clarify this distinction. The student who does average work in American history at high school and sub-average work in American history at the college level might be dissuaded from considering graduate work in this subject; he shows no promise of becoming a distinguished historian. If we like, we may say his " limit of educability " with respect to history is at the sophomore level, assuming that junior and senior levels call for more penetrating intelligence than he possesses. But does this mean that he has learned all the history that he is capable of learning? Can he not devote himself to studying the history of every other country in the world up to the more or less hypothetical level of his sophomore competence? There is the history of Spain, of Brazil, of South Africa, of Australia, of China, of each of the forty-eight states — enough history to keep one studying on and on all through the years. The subject is without limit in extensity. Contemporary events — and there are always contemporary events — prevent the establishment of permanent limits. What has been suggested with respect to history can be applied to every other subject in the curriculum. A student who bogs down at the junior level of Spanish might pursue an almost endless series of other foreign languages up to his supposititious level of " junior educability."

Very few have it in them to become Rembrandts or Oslers or Lavoisiers or Beethovens or Kants, but this does not mean we cannot look forward to countless happy hours of exploration in the fields of painting, medicine, chemistry, music, philosophy, and so on. We may not be able to climb high, but we can wander far. Not everybody can be a mountaineer, but almost everybody can take a hike into the open country and some can even negotiate an occasional foothill. Why should anybody presume to tell us our hiking days are over just because we grow faint at the seven or eight thousand foot level? There are still vast stretches of inviting forests and valleys and plateaus below our critical level. Even if we cannot keep up with the pace of our fellow-hikers, ought we to be denied the potential joy of more leisurely strolls? The laggards in our schools are not necessarily and inevitably time-wasters.

To speak of the " limit of educability " suggests that one's education can really be finished. What we are suggesting is the desirability of envisaging education as a limitless, lifelong adventure. The function of the schools should be to promote a love of learning as a positive good in its own right. A child has as much need for the acquisition of this kind of love as for the love of relaxing games, inspiring music, and ennobling friendships. Of course there are limits beyond which we cannot exhibit our devotion even in the latter spheres. We cannot all become experts at bridge, golf, billiards, or boxing. We cannot all become virtuosos and not all of us can rise to Damon-Pythias heights of loyal friendship. And yet we do not permit such limitations to deter us from learning new games, cultivating new friendships, or taking violin lessons. Even modest accomplishment can be a source of personal gratification and a means of heightening our appreciation of the expert's artistry. Everybody recognizes this as it applies to the common skills and common arts. We are content with amateur competence as dancers, cooks, swimmers, pianists, interior decorators, bridge players, and raconteurs. There is a tremendous difference between our execution of arts like these and the finished performance of the highly skilled professional. Despite this fact they are important means of relieving what might otherwise be a life of drabness. Their cultivation enriches one's inner life, lubricates social contacts, and converts us from wage-earning robots to vivid personalities. Without them our daily routine would be rendered bleaker and sadder. They serve as tonics and lend zest and variety and diversion and beauty and amusement and interest to the business of living. Even the self-taught, one-fingered pianist often seems to *enjoy* his dilettante efforts. He knows he is not and never can be a Paderewski; but this realization does not eliminate the fun he gets out of his own crude attempts to peck out a melody. And the duffer at golf, fully cognizant of his ineptitude, may nevertheless enjoy his afternoon on the links. The fact that he can never become a Walter Hagen does not humiliate him and make him despise the game. Outstanding superiority is not an indispensable prerequisite for enjoyment.

THE LOVE OF LEARNING AS A MENTAL HYGIENE VALUE

The mental hygienist is an advocate of whatever contributes to the joy of living. That is why we feel constrained to question the wisdom of educational practices which endanger the joy of getting new ideas, of widening the scope of one's understanding, or of obtaining novel insights. Why should this be restricted to the intellectually élite? From one point of view every normal child manifests the beginnings of a love of learning. The endless questions of the little child are indications of this love. He wants to know about stars and why we must die and if dogs can talk and where God lives and a myriad other problems. His is a restless, roving, persistent curiosity. He wants to know these things not in order to pass examinations, to impress others with his erudition, to get a job, to earn a degree or to win $64 questions on quiz programs, but just for the fun of finding out. For him learning is not a means to an end, but an end in itself. It is a self-justifying, spontaneous process like opening a birthday package to discover the nature of the gift. Intellectual discovery can be just as thrilling. But all too often our schools mutilate or destroy this alert, joyous curiosity of the child. What should have been nurtured into at least an avocational love of study and reflection and serious reading — the mature equivalent of childish curiosity — is crushed by the Juggernaut of the Curriculum. One can destroy a child's love for food by cramming it down his throat in excess quantity and in defiance of his appetite. Similarly, one can destroy his potential love of learning by cramming the curriculum into him irrespective of the magnitude and direction of his intellectual appetites. That is why many understanding educators are urging that the curriculum be adjusted to the child rather than have the child warped to fit the curriculum.

Curricular adjustment of this kind has been introduced at the lower educational levels in behalf of the superior child. While his less brilliant classmates are still working with traditional subjects, he is enabled to explore a wider range of topics. The value of *extensive* intellectual exploration — the so-called enriched curriculum — is thus already recognized at one level of our educational system. What we are suggesting is the transfer of this procedure to the upper, particularly the collegiate levels. This suggestion, of course, proposes to make the inferior student the beneficiary of the change at this level. It is to be his turn to explore widely while the superior student proceeds to more restricted areas of more recondite specialization. There is no need to brand him a failure at college and deny him the symbol of a successfully completed course of study in the form of an academic degree just because his course is *extensive* rather than intensive.

Once again we resort to an analogy from the realm of organized athletics to clarify the implications of this suggestion. Athletes may be trained to win championships in a single sport like sprinting. The goal of the coach is to train his star to break the world's record for a given distance. The degree of intense application required to accomplish this is such that the sprinter cannot very readily be trained to be the world's champion pole vaulter and discus thrower as well. However, the athlete who shows aptitude in several events may well be trained for five different contests and become the pentathlon champion. The competence of the latter is extensive rather than intensive.

Similarly, in the field of medicine we find the general practitioner knowing something about every specialty without possessing the expert's mastery in any one of them. And usually the specialist in medicine lacks the familiarity and certainty of touch with a wide gamut of routine problems the competent non-specialist has learned to handle as easily as a veteran shortstop scoops up a grounder. The knowledge and skill of the general practitioner is more extensive while that of the specialist is more intensive. Very often a specialist in diseases of the eye would regard the general practitioner's grasp of ophthalmology as but little better than that of a dilettante. The general practitioner on occasion might be disposed to return the compliment with respect to the ophthalmologist's grasp of medicine as a whole as it is envisaged by the experienced general practitioner. It is important to note the areas of medical territory still left for exploration for each of them. The one might climb the specialist's mountain and the other might tour the general practitioner's diversified terrain. Neither one can ever " finish " his medical education.

For the physician who loves his profession, there is *always* unfinished business on the agenda. What is more, if his love is genuine, he does not regret this state of affairs; because for him the pursuit of medical studies is tantamount to the pursuit of happiness. Even after a lifetime of practice and study, as an old man no longer able to visit patients, his most serene hours might be those spent in the quiet of his library still trying to finish the business he hopes will never be finished. The eager curiosity that was his as a child seventy years before when he started to explore his world is still driving him on and, in a way, still keeping him young as he pushes forward to the ever-receding goal of the frontiers of knowledge. His love of learning is a great stabilizing factor in his life. It helps him grow old gracefully and gives content and meaning to what would otherwise be weary days of bleak infirmity.[8]

From the viewpoint of mental hygiene, as a consequence, fostering a love of this sort is one of the chief purposes of a formal education. To tell a student that he has reached the " limit of his educability " is thus poor mental hygiene. It is apt to deprive him

[8] Adequate treatment of the mental hygiene problems associated with the onset of old age would require a separate chapter. In the present context only the role of persistent intellectual interests in facilitating these adjustment problems has been introduced. However, the very large numbers of aging men and women whose lives have been devoid of such interests cannot effect such an easy transition from decades of devotion to a regular job or vocation or routine to suddenly imposed leisure. They cannot retire from factory or roundhouse to the inspiring and absorbing haven of books and ideas. Other solutions must be found for them. For an account of some of the proposed solutions as well as an excellent outline of the mental hygiene issues involved, see Lawton, G., " After Sixty-five? ", *Mental Hygiene,* 1941, *25,* pp. 414–419.

of what has just been referred to as an important stabilizing factor by alienating him from the world of books and ideas — even " easy " books and " elementary " ideas. It is a false and distorting diagnosis if it is taken to mean that for him there can be no more learning, since he has attained or obtained his " limit."

The concept of rationing should not be applied to intellectual and esthetic commodities. Disregarding pathological extremes of feeblemindedness or dullness, there is no limit in extensity to the amount of learning of which the rank and file of human beings are capable. They may not be able to follow the abstractions of technical journals in biology or physics and yet be able to understand the more concrete exemplifications of these abstractions as presented in high school texts. The volumes of the *Proceedings of the Modern Language Association* may be too abstruse for them, but they can still derive untold pleasure and profit from the works of Dickens, Cervantes, Tolstoy, Shakespeare, Tennyson and other literary masters. It is absurd to speak of a " limit " to the learning of literature in this sense. The tragedy is that so few of our schools succeed in arousing a positive desire for this kind of attainable education. The lurid, shoddy, pulpy trash cluttering up the magazine stands of the country may constitute a silent indictment of our methods of teaching literature. It is a sad commentary on the mental hygiene efficacy of such methods when so many of our graduates drop below their " limit of literary educability " by seeking escape and excitement in the pages of the *True Obsessions* type of magazine.

MORE ABOUT I.Q.'S AND SUCCESS

As a matter of fact, contemporary experts in mental testing are by no means so confident of the predictive value of individual I.Q. scores as some of their more dogmatic colleagues were a few decades ago. They realize for one thing that for two students to achieve the same score on the same test does not signify *identity* of mental ability. It is rare for two subjects to make identical responses to all of the items of the test, even though the final score for each of them may be an I.Q. of 116. One of them may have done exceptionally well on arithmetic items and only moderately well on language items, while the relative competence may be reversed for the other subject. However, the final score obscures such differences and gives a spurious picture of identity of mental make-up because the I.Q. values are identical. In reality the personalities of the two subjects may be as different as two motion pictures both of which have been rated as Class B pictures.

In the second place mental testers are no longer quite so ready to describe the I.Q. as a measure of *native* capacity as was the fashion some twenty odd years ago. They now realize how cultural opportunity, early training, and disturbing emotional upsets may influence the outcome. The evidence in question is too vast and the issues involved too technical to be elaborated here without necessitating an unjustifiable digression. It must suffice for present purposes to give just a bare hint of this evidence. For example, many experts are persuaded that attendance at nursery schools raises the I.Q. Others call attention to the way in which a bleak home environment may depress the I.Q. by citing studies of children brought up on canal boats or of children coming from isolated mountain districts or of children living in gypsy camps. Identical twins separated in early childhood and brought up in very different environments may diverge in their mental test scores years later. There is evidence tending to show an improvement of I.Q. scores of orphanage children placed in superior foster homes. There is also evidence that slum clearance may influence mental test scores. In one study children of the slums were tested both before and after — a year to 18 months after — they moved into the better houses. As compared with a control group made up of children who continued to live in the slums, the slum-clearance group showed statistically significant gains. In other words, the drift of the evidence points to environmental and socio-economic factors as partial determiners of the level of what used to be regarded as " native intelligence." [9]

It might also be well to call attention to the fact that school achievement also depends on factors other than those measured by intelligence tests. High I.Q.'s do not inevitably guarantee high marks nor do moderate I.Q.'s preclude excellent grades. With respect to the tool subjects, the foundation of all subsequent school work, the correlation with intelligence is far from perfect.

[9] For an excellent summary of the entire problem and for references to the important source material, see Krout, M. H., *Introduction to Social Psychology*, New York, Harper & Brothers, 1942, pp. 189–220; Neff, W. S., " Socio-Economic Status and Intelligence; a Critical Survey," *Psychol. Bull.*, 1938, *35*, 727–757.

Perfect correlation, it should be realized, is symbolized by 1.00. However, on the basis of a fairly comprehensive survey [10] of relevant studies it has been concluded that success in reading correlates most highly with intelligence, the median correlation being .60; then comes arithmetic with a median correlation of .55 to be followed by spelling and writing with correlations of .50 and .10 respectively. Results such as these confirm common sense belief regarding a genuine relationship between intelligence and the mastery of school assignments. For reading to correlate .60 and penmanship .10 is in line with what the ordinary person might expect. It takes more intelligence to read with comprehension than to write legibly.

But just what does it mean to say that intelligence test scores correlate between .50 and .60 with measures of school success? These figures represent the range of coefficients obtained in many studies of the relationship between I.Q.'s and academic achievement. It is well to guard against a possible misinterpretation of the meaning of findings like these. Those not versed in statistical procedures might interpret them as showing that from 50 to 60 percent of school achievement is attributable to intelligence. But this would be an erroneous interpretation. What such findings do mean has been excellently stated by Professor Horace B. English in the following passage: [11]

Under ordinary school conditions intelligence correlates about .50 or .60 with scholastic achievement. *This means that about a third of the differences between pupils is attributable to intelligence.* But this holds only under the above mentioned " ordinary school conditions "; it is subject to very considerable change with every change in the circumstances. If all the pupils are very much alike in intelligence, the differences found will be nearly all attributable to " other factors " and the resulting correlation between intelligence and achievement will be low. If, on the other hand, the pupils tested differ very greatly in intelligence, then intelligence will account for much more of the difference in achievement; and the correlation will be high. A blanket statement about the " true " relation of intelligence to achievement is simply impossible.

[10] Louttit, C. M., *Clinical Psychology,* New York, Harper & Brothers, 1936, pp. 185–186.
[11] Guilford, J. P. (editor), *Fields of Psychology,* New York, D. Van Nostrand Company, Inc., 1940, p. 330 (Italics not in the original).

The importance for mental hygiene of the preceding passage can hardly be overstressed. It constitutes a healthy corrective to those people who have sanctified the I.Q. as a biologically fixed entity of transcendent importance not only for the child's adjustment at school, but also for his success in life.[12] Parents and pupils are often needlessly alarmed by attaching so much importance to a single mental test rating. Mediocre scores need not presage mediocre school achievement. Furthermore, the common inference from school achievement to intelligence level is also fraught with the possibility of error. Dull children can win high marks and bright children may get low marks. School achievement is based on many other factors in addition to those measured by intelligence tests. Persistent effort and longer periods of study may enable the student of average ability to obtain higher marks than some more brilliant fellow students. In many school subjects adequacy of preparation in background subjects may be more important for a distinguished record than a distinguished I.Q. Differences in strength of motivation and resolution of purpose may play as great a role in the production of differences in grades as I.Q. differences. To complicate the total picture, the grades themselves cannot be accepted as altogether reliable indices of achievement. As many investigations have demonstrated, even experienced teachers of a given subject may differ from one another with respect to the quality and quantity of work to be symbolized by a grade of " A." One teacher's " A " may be another teacher's " C." The same final examination paper may receive a high grade from one teacher and a failing grade from another. This holds true, strange as it may seem to those unfamiliar with the investigations in question, not only of such " opinion " subjects as English, public speaking, and music, but also of such " fact " subjects as geometry, chemistry, and so on.

THE IDOLATRY OF GRADES

All parties involved — teachers, pupils, and parents — are thus placing too much emphasis on the significance of academic grades. Both the elation produced by high grades as well as the humilia-

[12] Cf. Wechsler, D., " Non-intellective Factors in General Intelligence," *J. of Abnorm. and Soc. Psychol.*, 1943, *38*, pp. 101–103; Cattell, R. B., " The Measurement of Adult Intelligence," *Psychol. Bulletin*, 1943, *40*, pp. 153–193.

tion precipitated by low ones may be too extreme in view of the unreliability of the marks themselves as well as the uncertainty as to their precise implications. In some instances it is altogether possible for a student to receive an " A " in a course even though the study involved has failed to produce a change in his attitudes, to increase his body of factual knowledge, or to furnish him with new insights or new techniques. The course may involve little more than a rehash — sometimes under a different name — of material he has already absorbed in previous courses. On the other hand, another student, who completes the same course with a " C," may have made relatively more educational progress as a consequence of broadened intellectual horizons than the " A " student. Despite his " C " grade, he may thus have gotten more out of the course than many whose grades were higher.

Taken by themselves, grades tell us very little about the significance of a given course for the recipient of the grade. Sometimes a chance remark made by the instructor may be more vital for the orientation of a particular student than the entire series of planned lectures comprising the course. Freud, for example, tells us that such a chance remark by his teacher Charcot, the French neurologist, furnished him with a clue to what was subsequently elaborated into a system of psychology. Occasionally a single passage in a single book or a given fragment of a particular lecture may clarify a long-standing personal perplexity for one student and yet not be especially noticed by the others. What study and learning and reading and laboratory experience may mean to individual students cannot be compressed within the compact anonymity of letters of the alphabet. Their compactness facilitates academic bookkeeping, but fails to supply a true picture of what changes have taken place in the students themselves. Even the academic degree based on the piling up of such grades does not furnish a trustworthy picture of what the degree presumably symbolizes. The same degree may represent radically different areas and levels of accomplishment, learning, and competence on the part of numerous possessors of the same degree.

One can all too readily mislead students into regarding grades and degrees as the chief goal of formal education. The symbols become more important than that which they are supposed to symbolize. One can be tricked into accepting a pleasing label in place of serious concern about the quality of content to which the label refers. In the field of business everybody is warned not to accept signs at their face value. We are cautioned to pay more attention to what they signify than to their external allure. Significance, so we are taught, is more important than the sign. And yet in the field of education too many of us lose sight of this elementary teaching and pursue the signs of education with only incidental concern about their significance. It is this attitude which constitutes the big danger of undue preoccupation with grades and too much zeal in the pursuit of academic degrees. In running after the signs we are apt to miss their underlying significance. The fierce competition for grades may divert us from consideration of the basic purposes of schooling. The situation is roughly analogous to that of the athlete who becomes more interested in the score than in the game itself, more intent upon winning the plaudits of the crowd and adding to his collection of cups than in cultivating those values which athletic competition is supposed to promote. The purpose of cups and trophies is to develop a love for bodily skills as exemplified by tennis, golf, bowling, skiing, and so on; but when desire for the award becomes keener than love for the skills in question, then the purpose in question has been defeated. Similarly, in the case of education when marks and degrees come to mean more than does the love of learning or the joy of intellectual discovery, then the purpose of awarding such academic symbols has also been defeated.

What teachers ought to stress is the desirability of playing the game to the best of one's ability not so much in order to become a champion, but for the sheer joy of the game itself. Very few of us can become champions — in golf, in bridge, in mathematics, or in music — but even mediocre competence may be a source of wholesome pleasure and richer personal contacts all through the years. An education that makes life more pleasurable and leisure more zestfully profitable is by no means the exclusive prerogative of those few we designate as " A " students. There may be no royal road to learning, but the joy of travel is not increased by making a journey over a rough road even rougher than need be by forcing the travelers to wear tight shoes, to speed up beyond their capacity for endurance, to close their eyes to beautiful scenery, and to be nagged for falling behind the leaders. We forget that the leisurely traveler may sometimes derive more profit from his slow journey than the speeding tourist, and that some " C " students may get more out of an educational journey than some " A " students.

THE IDOLATRY OF COMPETITIVE SUCCESS

The worship of grades and the striving after honors at school may be both a cause and an effect of our general worship of prestige-enhancing competition.[13] In all phases of our life one can perceive this tendency to take it for granted that the acme of ideal mental adjustment is personified by brilliantly successful extroversion. Both as teachers and as parents we tend to hold this ideal before our children. Action and the strenuous life are glorified for them. To win, to be a leader, to climb to the top, to issue the commands, to make the wheels turn, and to make industry hum and business increase are regarded as inspiring infinitives by commencement orators. We even find educators reflecting this glorification of success in active competition. So do parents and businessmen and lawyers and college students and clergymen, and even some mental hygienists. All of us in fact at some time or other have been influenced by the Horatio Alger type of success philosophy: to fight our way through to a victorious and virtuous and decidedly dramatic finish despite hardship and adversity. The emphasis is on the ultimate reward of becoming a person of importance, a *leader* in the community, admired and envied by all. In addition, this reward is rendered still more alluring by surrounding the hero with a firm halo of dollar signs through which the daughter of the town's outstanding industrialist is permitted to poke her charming head to drive home the final moral of success in love as a kind of bonus for years of devotion to hard work, thrift, self-sacrifice, and still more work.

Most of us have been influenced by this general picture of the nature of successful living. That is why we want others to know how hard we work, how many duties we have, and how numerous are our business and social obligations. Theodore Roosevelt's ideal of the " strenuous life " is still the accepted ideal for the majority of Americans. We admire the go-getter and look down upon the

---

[13] Cf. the section dealing with competitiveness in Gillespie, R. D., *Psychological Effects of War on Citizen and Soldier*, W. W. Norton & Co., Inc., 1942, pp. 238–243.

easy-going dreamer and thinker. To go places and do things is our way of relaxing. Keeping on the move and striving to attain the next rung of the economic ladder is associated with our idea of the worthy life. High-pressure industry, driving schedules and one speedy accomplishment followed by another speedy accomplishment belong to our picture of American business success. Nor is this picture restricted to business and the accumulation of money. The lawyer likes to have the public think of his dramatically tense role in the court room. Physicians and surgeons want to be known as busy practitioners. Even college professors are annoyed when their educational work is referred to as a " life of lettered ease." They prefer to have the public know of the hours and hours of exhausting labor expended in laboratories, in libraries, and over the typewriter. Housewives, even those whose dusting, dishwashing and cooking is taken care of by servants, prefer to be known as *busy* women. They want their club work and church work and volunteer social work to be regarded as *work* and not as mere diversion or joyous service.

We are all proud of our actual and imaginary work — and a little bit apologetic about our movie-going and bridge-playing. We hate to acknowledge that some hours are devoted to loafing; we prefer to say we are " just relaxing." Relaxed contemplation is frowned upon as wasteful, and industriousness is applauded as a virtue. Somehow we feel the need for justifying our indulgence in play and recreation and contemplative leisure. We permit ourselves such indulgence only as a reward for solid work already done or as needed preparation for work about to be undertaken. The value and virtue we take for granted is work ; other pursuits have to justify themselves before we deem them right. If they help our work either directly or indirectly, they are pronounced acceptable. On the other hand, if they are judged as barriers to working efficiency, they are marked *verboten*. Even our children are taught to place a greater value on doing their home work than on participating in joyous play.

Many fathers would prefer to have their sons grow up to be engineers rather than poets. After all, an engineer accomplishes *real* things. He produces concrete highways, steel bridges, and pulsating power plants. The poet, so it is often believed, is not a genuine worker. He is a dreamer who, detached from the stream of useful action, permits his imagination to run riot. The poems he writes are catalogued as products of a *playful* imagination. One cannot do anything with a poem except enjoy it or recite it or be inspired by it; but enjoyment, recitation, and inspiration are not work. According to such a scheme of values, General Goethals, who built the Panama Canal, has done more for America than Walt Whitman who wrote *Leaves of Grass*. Goethals was a doer and Whitman a dreamer. It might be well to note that, in the jargon of contemporary psychology, the military engineer would be classified as an extrovert and the bewhiskered poet as an introvert.

Furthermore, our intense preoccupation with work, action, accomplishment and success induces us to take it for granted that the extrovert is a better man and maybe a better American than the introvert. We think of the extrovert as a leader, a realist, an aggressive, practical man who gets things done! He makes the big sales, lands the juicy contracts, organizes million-dollar corporations, dominates his industry, and has a say in the running of other industries. He gives the orders, calls the tunes, and hires and fires. He is the Big Executive lording it over the meek little introverts. At least he would be, if there were any meek little introverts. With our glorification of work and action we make it hard for potential little introverts to grow up into adult introverts. In home and school and in the Great Society we bombard the poor little fellow with success slogans. We urge him to learn to be a leader, to get to the top, to strive and strive and strive until he scores as a home-run hitter in the game of life. As a result he gets the notion that to dream dreams, to write poems, and to compose symphonies is to be a softy. Such pursuits are all right for sissies, but unworthy of he-men. He comes to believe that life is too short to waste time in quiet contemplation, the worship of beauty, the cultivation of the understanding, the nurturing of wisdom, the quiet enjoyment of good food, beautiful scenery, fine books, and the fostering of ennobling friendships. Although an occasional preacher may admonish him to " count his blessings," he rarely does; because the pattern of life around him makes a business inventory seem a much more significant kind of counting. He sees this pattern exemplified in the movies when the boss bolts a hasty lunch brought to the office on a tray so that more letters can be dictated and more orders telephoned to more places so that more wheels may turn and more orders be filled in loyalty to the insatiable gods of speed and efficiency.

Is go-getting anachronistic?

Even at the risk of digressing unduly it might be stimulating to inquire into the probable origin of this glorification of the extrovert. How has it come about that speed, an overcrowded schedule, and grim persistence in exhausting work are so commonly regarded as hall marks of the good life? Why should the ambitious, ever-pushing leader be regarded as " more successful " than his financially and socially obscure, but serenely contented follower? What has caused so many people to associate the concept of ideal mental adjustment with go-getting leadership? The answer may be found in the fact that we started our American adventure as pioneers faced with the gigantic task of converting a wilderness into a civilization. Such a task calls for the virtues of the extrovert: relentless action, indifference to hardship, and a rugged willingness to brave the dangers of a frontier existence. When there are cabins to be built, roads to be opened up, Indians to be fought off, and forests to be cleared there is no time for relaxed contemplation, for the worship of beauty, and for the pursuit of wisdom. A frontier community has so much to *do* that the doer becomes a community asset and the dreamer a liability. Only a vicious Nero will think of his music while his neighbors fight a fire.

Our pattern of the ideal life for the useful American harks back to early frontier days; hence our tacit acceptance of the glory of work for its own sake and our implicit guilt feelings when we relax and play and dream and think. The frontier is gone; but the pattern persists. It is an example of what the sociologists call the *lag* of culture. As a consequence we still feel that we ought to keep busy and not even pause long enough to evaluate the worth of our " busyness." If a play on words be permitted, we make busyness our chief business.

There are no more geographic frontiers to conquer, even though there are plenty of " social frontiers " left for conquest. A veritable wilderness of problems, and difficulties stretches ahead of those still " pioneering " in the thickets of labor controversies, national and international administration, medical research, the doldrums of institutionalized religion, the economic insecurity of millions, and all the other areas of social pathology. But ambitions to conquer such areas are not activated by the go-getter's lure of the dollar. As a group, those who are devoting themselves to conquest of our social frontiers are not seeking spectacular financial rewards for their labors. What captains of industry and corporation lawyers would regard as a pittance suffices to secure the loyal service of a settlement worker, a federal labor expert, a medical missionary, a public health investigator, a nursery school supervisor, or a highly trained research man in any of the natural or social sciences.

Not only has the disappearance of frontier life rendered some virtues of the pioneer anachronistic, but other changes have developed to transform the early American scene. For example, technological progress has surrounded us with a multiplicity of time-saving and labor-saving gadgets. Preventive medicine has added years to the span of life. Thanks to engineers, inventors, and scientists our generation can have leisure for the asking. The tragedy is that while we long for leisure, we feel frustrated when we attain it. We are afraid to use it. Our old Puritan conscience goads us to keep busy and not to fritter away the golden hours. No wonder some educators are now concerned with the problem of training young people in the wise use of leisure time. The making of money and the striving after financial success have become such ends in themselves that we now have to *educate* people in the art of wholesome enjoyment. We not only have to teach them how to practice this art but we even have to get them to divest themselves of latent feelings of sinfulness for indulging in the practice. This constitutes an important goal in the total project of educating for mental health.

Once again people have to learn the utter innocence and the positive good of simple joys: the joy of cultivating a hobby, the joy of friendly conversation, the joy of making things with our hands and watching things grow, the joy of folk dances, the joy of community singing, the joy of neighborliness, the joy of getting new ideas and novel insights, and the joy of playing in an orchestra. It is not a question of indulging in such pursuits to enhance one's prestige, to prepare for a better job, to establish *useful* business contacts or any other utilitarian objective. On the contrary it is a question of learning to accept them as desirable objectives in their own right. They are to be recognized as ends in themselves rather than as means to vocational ends. It might even be preferable to regard vocational pursuits as means of achieving such non-utilitarian ends: to make money to enable one to have the leisure to cultivate these simple joys. Maybe this is what the founding fathers meant by the pursuit of happiness.

RELIGIOUS EDUCATION AND MENTAL HEALTH

A closer approach to such mental hygiene goals might be facilitated by properly oriented religious leadership. Just what the concept of God is to connote to the child may have a bearing on personality development and mental health. In many respects religious beliefs are a reflection of one's implicit philosophy of life. In fact, as Professor Bixler, formerly of the Harvard Divinity School, has ventured to say: " Belief in God really means belief in the worthwhileness of life and this depends less on external evidence than on our own emotional attitudes." [14] The attitudes being shaped by Sunday Schools, Synagogue Schools, and Parochial Schools are consequently not devoid of mental hygiene significance. Whether the curricular content of religious schools is to be an aid or a hindrance to the child's quest for a satisfying, comforting, and helpful philosophy of life will in part depend upon what basic meanings come to cluster around his conception of God. The kind of God the child is taught to worship may make some difference in the kinds of values that child cherishes and in terms of which he disposes of his conflict situations.

Those concerned with religious education might help the cause of mental hygiene training by stressing values in line with mental hygiene principles. They might employ conventional religious symbolism to suggest that many of us, in our devotion to the gods of thrift and work, have forgotten to worship the real God. Far too many people think of worship in terms of asking favors, gaining concessions, and submitting petitions. They lose faith because prayers for wage increases do not seem to be answered with dependable regularity. They forget that such utilitarian prayers belong to primitive religion. One may even question whether such

[14] Bixler, J. S., *Religion for Free Minds,* New York, Harper & Brothers, 1939, p. 95.

selfish petitions should be dignified as worship. To worship means to admire and we admire what we deem to be excellent. When the Psalmist murmured, " The heavens declare the glory of God," he was indulging in an act of worship. There was no begging for a material boon ; just sheer esthetic joy in the beauty of the world as he experienced it. To be grateful to whatever powers there be for one's capacity to experience such joy is to be a worshipper. The man who has learned to live wisely looks for more and more opportunities for worship in this sense and the greater his success, the richer his life ; for it means he has found inner values to which he can *cling* when the outer going gets tough. These are the values that reveal the dynamics of the individual's religion. This is true in the sense that the word *religion,* according to some authorities, originally meant *to bind.* The goals and values and ideals to which we cling are the ones to which we are bound and the ones which shape our conduct and determine our choices. Religion of this sort makes a difference and that is why acts of worship may not be unimportant in the resolution of personal conflicts and the maintenance of mental health. The psychologist T. H. Howells suggests some of these broader services to be rendered by enlightened religious education when he writes : [15]

In a limited and perhaps somewhat misleading sense it may be said that the worship of God is really worship of the social organism in disguise, since God is really the symbol of society. Religion is the symbolic connection between the individual and society. The various religious symbols provide a specific point of focus and attainment of rather vague urges toward a social something of tremendous worth and significance, the exact nature of which, while they are symbolic in meaning, are nevertheless specific and concrete just as are the objects of art. In general, we must admit that these symbols lead progress in the right direction, in spite of the fact that they may occasionally be used as instruments of exploitation.

In a sense religious symbols are similar to the green flag which marks the location of the cup into which a golf ball is holed. Neither the cup nor the remote objectives of life are visible, but if the drives are directed toward the signs which symbolize them, one cannot go far wrong. It is true, of course . . . that the holing of the golf ball, or the achievement of any of the nominal objectives of play or art, is in itself

[15] Howells, T. H., *Hunger for Wholeness,* Denver, The World Press, Inc., 1940, pp. 249–250.

a subsidiary goal which is incidental to the achievement of any of the nominal objectives of play or art, is in itself a subsidiary goal which is incidental to the achievement of ultimate wholiness. In turn, the general integration which is achieved in golf is probably in some degree symbolic of the ultimate integrations of religion, and the emotion which accompanies progress in golf is undoubtedly akin to religious emotion. It is obviously true that all of the lesser integrations of life are symbolic of the universal trend toward greater integration and are therefore in some degree religious. . . . Peace, poise, and a clearer and surer foresight of the path ahead is the answer to prayer. The soul which was lost has found its way again and rejoices!

There are many ways to achieve personality integration, many ways to keep an even keel through the storms of life. To regard an extrovert's go-getting as the only way or the most ideal way is to do violence to the temperamental needs of the many whose earthly salvation calls for cultivation of less tempestuously competitive fields of endeavor. Recognition of such needs is somewhat alien to our American culture; but the professional educator, with his willingness to acknowledge individual differences, might render mental hygiene a real service by catering to the needs of the child who was never intended to fit into the pattern of the extroverted go-getter. There is much food for reflection along these lines in the following passage from a recent text by Klineberg: [16]

A person who has a desire to withdraw from the world would find it hard to fit into our American culture. Even among Catholics, escape to a monastery or a convent is not always considered a satisfactory solution. Such a person would have a relatively simple problem if he lived in a country in which Buddhism was an accepted religion, since Buddhism regards the external world as unimportant. In the psychopathic hospital in Peking the writer observed several cases in which people suffering from a mild form of schizophrenia showed simultaneously an increased interest in Buddhism and the Buddhist classics. Although this observation could not be checked by any statistical investigation, it seems to point to the possibility that an individual with the desire to withdraw from the world may find Buddhism, with its insistence upon the unimportance of external reality, particularly palatable. It is probable that many persons may actually be saved from the disease of schizophrenia because their introvert tendencies find in Buddhism a satisfactory outlet.

[16] Klineberg, O., *Social Psychology,* New York, Henry Holt and Company, 1940, pp. 509–510.

There is, of course, no intention on Klineberg's part to urge people to move to China or some other Buddhist country when they find our strenuous, keeping-up-with-the-Joneses culture uncongenial. Nor have we quoted the foregoing passage for the purpose of suggesting such a literal flight from the turmoil of American competition. We are more concerned with what educators — teachers, parents, and ministers — might do by way of changing the onesidedness of our worship of success by borrowing and inculcating some of this Buddhist understanding of the mental hygiene value of inner serenity. All of us could profit by an antidote of this sort. In other words, we are not viewing it as a type of educational therapy to be reserved for the timid, the bashful, the shy, and the meek. Even our conspicuously successful go-getters and paragons of self-assertive leadership might profit by such therapy. They may even be in greater need of it than their less ambitious, more relaxed and more introverted fellow Americans.

There may be a direct relationship between our American proneness to high blood pressure, or hypertension, and our furious lust for success and prestige. The Chinese people are seemingly immune to high blood pressure. This is not due to any unique biological factor; for clinicians have reported cases of hypertension among Chinese living among us and its loss among white people living in China. The pattern of life appears to be the decisive factor. Dr. W. R. Houston, a former professor of Medicine at Yale-in-China, regards emotional conflict as the primary cause of essential hypertension. Part of his discussion of the problem is particularly relevant in the present context and might well be introduced at this point in his own words: [17]

It has been said that Chinese living in America have arterial tension of the same level as Americans and show the same susceptibility to essential hypertension. The only case of essential hypertension that I observed of a Chinese in China was that of a nurse who had spent many years in America and brought back with her such notions of *go-getterish efficiency* that she was daily balked and ruffled in her attempts to induce Chinese nurses to live up to her western ideals. . . .

I cannot but feel that if physicians would learn to cultivate their diagnostic acumen in the direction of learning to read the human heart

[17] Houston, W. R., *The Art of Treatment*, New York, The Macmillan Company, 1936, pp. 450–451. (Italics ours.)

as evidenced by the little signs, a hesitant question, a tone of voice, a furtively inquiring glance, if they would look behind the false front of outspoken declarations as to what constitutes the care and trouble of life and learn to see more of the hidden life that lies behind, they would be better able to read the etiology of essential hypertension.

The task of educating for mental health thus goes far beyond the confines of the traditional curriculum. It involves far more than mastery of tool subjects or particular content subjects. It calls for the utilization of every agency capable of enabling the child to keep moving from ignorance to knowledge and from knowledge to understanding and from understanding to the wisdom which culminates in service to others. This is the wisdom back of the paradox of finding one's soul by losing it. Home and school and church and the Great Society have a part to play in making this kind of education a reality. Both introverts and extroverts need this kind of education. In fact, every individual needs it and, in the last analysis, as is true of all genuine education, must achieve it for himself. The educator and mental hygienist can only point the way, supply some of the travel hints, and warn of possible dangers. One big danger with which we have been dealing in this closing section is that of pursuing the tempting, but hazardous trail of the go-getter. It is a danger which James Hilton seems to have recognized and against which he warned us in his *Lost Horizon*. In our opinion, his picture of Shangri-La as the ideal retreat for the cultivation of ideal values was more than an exposition of an old Buddhist ideal. It was an indictment of exaggerated devotion to dollar-chasing as the chief virtue of daily life. It was an indictment of relentless competition and power-seeking and self-aggrandizement. It was a reminder to all of us of the need for a more wholesome perspective — a mental hygiene perspective: to look up from work bench, business ledger, and assembly line, and to " lift our eyes unto the hills " in search of steadying horizons long known to ancient seers, but lost to the myopic vision of a go-getting generation.

Glossary [1] ...

abulia, loss of the capacity to initiate action.

Addison's disease, tuberculous infection of the adrenal gland.

adrenal gland, an endocrine structure located near the kidneys; one of its hormones, *adrenin,* plays an important role in the regulation of bodily changes accompanying strong emotion.

affect hunger, D. M. Levy's term for the rejected or neglected child's craving for human affection and emotional security.

afferent, pertaining to neural impulses moving from sense organs toward the central nervous system; hence *sensory impulses.* (Contrasted with *efferent,* q.v.)

agitated depression, a type of mixed manic-depressive condition characterized by restless anxiety, self-disparaging accusations, signs of inner tension, and anticipations of personal disasters yet to come.

alcoholic psychoses, mental disorders whose etiology involves excessive indulgence in intoxicating beverages.

alienist, an outmoded designation for the specialist in mental diseases. The preferred modern term is psychiatrist. As employed at present in the field of medical jurisprudence the word *alienist* is limited to one who is presumably expert in the recognition of mental disorders or defects coming within the scope of the legal definition of insanity or mental incompetence.

ambivalent attitudes, antagonistic, incompatible, or contradictory feelings or reaction tendencies elicited by a given person or stimulus object. Examples: the boy who both loves and hates his father; the rat attracted and repelled by the same ambiguous stimulus card.

amnesia, pathological loss of memory functions.

A.N.A., abbreviation for *American Neurological Association.*

anthropomorphism, the error of interpreting animal behavior in terms of uniquely human characteristics; reading human nature into animal nature. (Contrasted with *zoomorphism.*)

apathy, morbid indifference.

audiogenic seizure, the disruptive effect produced on the neuromuscular coordination of certain animals when their hearing apparatus is exposed to the noise of an air-blast.

aura, any one of a large number of hallucinated sensory experiences — flashes of light, curious odors, sounds, etc. — by means of which the epileptic comes to recognize the onset of a seizure.

autistic, directed inward toward the self; in line with private longings or wishes. (Contrasted with realistic; hence *dereistic,* q.v.)

autonomic nervous system, the sum total of neural structures governing the action of cardiac muscle tissue, smooth muscle tissue, and glandular

---

[1] See Index for page references to a fuller discussion of the terms here defined.

structures; the system of nerves regulating circulation, digestion, respiration, and other self-governing, vital bodily functions.

avitaminoses, deficiency diseases caused by the lack of an adequate supply of vitamins in the diet. Examples: scurvy, pellagra, beriberi.

Beard's disease, synonym for *neurasthenia,* q.v.

behavior difficulty, troubles of adjustment to ethico-social standards exhibited by children and childish adults.

bel, a logarithmic unit by means of which relative differences in intensity of tones and noises can be given quantitative expression.

bimodal, a frequency distribution having two peaks at rather widely separated intervals and thus indicating a concentration of measures around two points of the scale. (The curve shown in Fig. 3 is a bimodal one.)

blacktongue, the name given to pellagra in dogs.

blue edema, a disturbance of circulation observed in some cases of hysterical paralysis in which the paralyzed limb becomes puffy and bluish. (Also called *hysterical edema.*)

cardio-renal, referring to heart and kidney.

catatonic schizophrenia, referring to a type of schizophrenic patient whose symptoms include the general clinical picture of catalepsy, spring resistance, negativism, mutism, passivity, and seclusiveness.

cerebral arteriosclerosis, a thickening of the membranes lining the walls of the arteries in the brain; popularly referred to as hardening of the arteries in the brain.

cerebral dysrhythmia, irregularity in the rhythm of the action currents recorded in the electroencephalogram and interpreted as indicative of susceptibility to epileptic attacks.

cerebral embolism, the blockage of circulation in the brain by the plugging of a blood vessel due to a clot, bubble of air, or some foreign body transmitted to the site of obstruction by the moving blood stream.

cerebrology, a term suggested by Rosanoff as a better designation for the field of psychiatry. (The term has not been adopted.)

clonic, pertaining to clonus or the series of rapid contractions and extensions of antagonistic muscles jerking spasmodically as seen in one stage of the epileptic seizure. (Contrasted with *tonic,* q.v.)

closure, the tendency to respond to a part as if the whole were present; the urge to finish partially completed tasks.

clouding of consciousness, a condition found in conjunction with delirious and stuporous states in which the patient seems confused, out of touch with his surroundings, unable to attend to and remember what is happening and as bewildered as a person *suddenly* aroused from a very heavy sleep.

C.N.S., abbreviation for *central nervous system.*

coefficient of correlation, a statistical measure which indicates the degree to which two series of measures possess factors in common; a measure of concomitant variation. Example: a coefficient of .70 between the height and weight of a group of young soldiers indicates a marked tendency for the taller men to be heavier or for the lighter men to be shorter. (Taken by itself such a correlation does not necessarily point to a cause and effect relationship.)

coma, extremely profound loss of consciousness from which the patient cannot be stirred even when vigorous forms of stimulation are used.

complex, a group of related ideas about which the individual feels very strongly because of its implications for his emotional security.

compulsion, the execution of some act, despite strong contrary inclinations, because of irresistible and usually gnawingly persistent inner goads to its performance; the motor aspect of an *obsession,* q.v.

conation, the striving aspect of mental life; having to do with the initiation of goal-directed activity or that which determines the execution of resolves, the expenditure of greater effort, or the re-enforcement of endeavor.

conditioned reflex, Pavlov's term for reaction to a substitute stimulus; *i.e.,* the result secured by presenting some indifferent stimulus like a squeak or a click while feeding an animal so that, after a series of such combined presentations of food and indifferent stimulus, the animal will respond to the latter stimulus when presented alone *as if* it were a symbol of food. In brief, CRs (q.v.) are to be viewed as reactions to signals. (The term *conditioned response* is a more suitable designation, since *reflex* suggests a fixed neural pathway.)

congenital, pertaining to that which is present at birth either as a result of germplasm inheritance or as a result of intra-uterine influences; hence not to be equated with *hereditary* in a strict sense.

conscience, the sum total of conditioned emotional reactions to situations involving moral approval or disapproval; the *superego,* q.v.

conscious content, those items of experience of which the observer is directly aware at any instant of time.

constitutional disorders, those disturbances or diseases inherent in the factors responsible for the basic physical make-up of the individual; almost but not quite synonymous with *inherited* disorders; referring to firmly ingrained disorders.

continuum, a whole or aggregate whose units of composition merge into one another by such smooth, nondiscrete transitions that no gaps or intervening spaces are left. The normal distribution curve is a graphic representation of a continuum.

conversion hysteria, a type of neurotic disturbance belonging in the category of *hysteria* (q.v.) in which symptoms of functional disability stand out most prominently.

CR, abbreviation for conditioned reflex or conditioned response.

cretinism, the condition of stunted physical growth and retarded mental development resulting from a congenital lack of adequate thyroid secretion. (Cf. *myxedema.*)

curare, a powerful drug which acts on the motor end-plates of nerves or the junction between motor nerves and muscles and thus prevents the affected muscles from contracting; used in connection with *shock therapy* (q.v.) to reduce the violence of the muscular contractions.

cyclothymic temperament, the type of constitutional organization responsible for the kind of fluctuations in mood, activity, and outlook which are manifested in extreme form by manic-depressive patients. (Cf. *schizothymic temperament.*)

delirium tremens, the state of chaotic disturbance found in some cases of alcoholic psychosis and manifested by incoherence, excitement, agitated movements, tremors, delusions, hallucinations, terror or anxiety, etc.

delusion, a false belief or conviction to which the individual clings in tenacious fashion despite its manifest absurdity.

dementia paralytica, mental deterioration and paralysis due to brain syphilis; also known as *general paresis.*

dementia praecox, the former name for a group of psychotic reactions now described in terms of the concept of *schizophrenia,* q.v.

dereistic, directed away from reality toward the direction of personal desires; synonym for *autistic,* q.v.

derived primary attention, spontaneous, effortless preoccupation with a subject or stimulus situation in which interest has been developed as a consequence of learning and training. Example: the attention baseball fans give to a tense moment at an important game. (Cf. *primary* and *secondary attention.*)

dichotomy, the result of the pigeonholing of items into *two* groups one of which is marked by a certain characteristic while the other lacks this characteristic; a twofold classification in terms of positive and negative attributes. Examples: coins *vs.* bills; lepers *vs.* non-lepers; poisonous mushrooms *vs.* edible ones; odd numbers *vs.* even numbers.

dilantin, name of a sodium compound useful in the treatment of epilepsy; since it acts as an anticonvulsant.

diplegia, bilateral paralysis; *i.e.,* involving both legs or both arms.

discontinuous, characterized by gaps or interruptions or the absence of transitional features.

dissociation, the presumed splitting-off of one group of ideas from the stream of normal conscious processes.

dizygotic twins, fraternal twins or those regarded as having developed from two fertilized ova and consequently no more alike than ordinary brothers and sisters; may be either of the same sex or not. (Contrasted with *monozygotic* or fraternal twins.)

drifting reaction, Boisen's term for ambitionless, indifferent behavior when the individual refuses to struggle against his rival impulses, ceases to be influenced by prestige motives, and is content to coast or drift along from day to day in desultory fashion; the basic attitude back of cases of *simple schizophrenia,* q.v.

dynamogenic, pertaining to the arousal of an increase in muscular action or tension, especially as a result of appropriate stimulation.

ecological, pertaining to a branch of sociology which studies the migrations of peoples from one environment to another with especial reference to the ways in which they reinstate or modify their social institutions in the new environment.

E.E.G., abbreviation for electroencephalogram.

efferent, pertaining to neural impulses moving from the central nervous system toward muscles or glands; hence *motor* impulses. (Contrasted with *afferent,* q.v.)

ego, as employed by the Freudians, refers to that aspect of the personality or self which mediates between external reality and the demands of *id* and *super-ego,* q.v.

electroencephalogram, record of changes in potential of electrical processes manifested by brain cortex under varying conditions and helpful in the differential diagnosis of epilepsy and associated symptoms.

empathy, the mental state which results when one tries to duplicate the feelings and tensions of another by vividly feeling oneself in the other's role or situation; also used to describe analogous reaction to objects of art or natural objects.

encephalitis, inflammation of the brain. The epidemic type is often called *sleeping sickness.*

endogenous, originating within the organism. (Contrasted with *exogenous.*)

end-spurt, an increase in the action of active muscles just prior to the completion of the job being done and indicated by a rather sudden rise of the curve of work toward the close of the work period.

enuresis, inadequate control of bladder functions; bed-wetting.

epilepsy, a disease of the nervous system characterized by convulsive seizures, tonic and clonic spasms, loss of sphincter control, unconsciousness, and a few other symptoms. (The etiology of epilepsy is now regarded as bound up with *cerebral dysrhythmia,* q.v.).

essential hypertension, high blood pressure not traceable to actual pathology of kidney or related functions.

etiology, pertaining to the origin or causation of disease or symptoms of disease.

eugenical sterilization, procedure of cutting the *vas deferens* (q.v.) in the male or ligating or transecting the *fallopian tubes* (q.v.) in the female. This type of operative procedure renders impregnation impossible without influencing the endocrine functions of the gonads.

exogenous, originating outside of the organism. (Contrasted with *endogenous.*)

extraversion, the general tendency to be more or less spontaneously interested in external affairs — social events, political action, dealing with people and things — to the relative neglect of thoughtful concern with underlying theories, principles and values. In terms of a popular dichotomy the *extrovert* exemplifies the man of action just as the *introvert* is regarded as the dreamer and thinker. (Cf. *introversion,* q.v.)

fallopian tube, the slender duct leading from the ovary to the womb.

filterable virus, an ultramicroscopic cause of disease so minute as to pass through the pores of a filter.

fixation, a very strong emotionalized attachment of a childishly dependent character.

flight into illness, an attempt to escape from the stress of a conflict situation by developing symptoms of illness.

flight of ideas, a rush of more or less logically irrelevant notions.

fraternal twins, the opposite of identical twins; also known as *dizygotic twins,* q.v.

fugue, a dissociated state in which the patient flees from his home surroundings and is amnesic with respect to important phases of his previous life; symptomatic of the amnesic type of hysteria.

functional autonomy of motives, Gordon Allport's designation for the dynamic factors responsible for the self-governing and perseverative characteristics of acquired interests or motives as contrasted with unlearned, biological drives and " instincts." (Cf. *derived primary attention.*)

functional psychoses, mental disorders of non-somatic etiology and seemingly due to intra-personal or inter-personal conflict; psychogenic disorders. (Opposed to organic or structural disorders.)

globus hystericus, the feeling of having a lump in the throat as a result of the spastic contraction of the smooth muscles of the gullet.

glove anesthesia, absence of normal cutaneous sensitivity in hand or forearm as a consequence of hysterical dissociation.

gonadal, pertaining to the *gonads* or the sex glands considered generically; *i.e.,* both male or female structures: testes or ovaries.

grand mal, the full-fledged epileptic attack marked by a convulsive seizure and unconsciousness.

graphic rating scale, a method for recording judgments of personality traits by having the rater locate a point on a line taken to represent varying degrees of a given trait. For example, if the line is to symbolize variations from idiocy to genius and the person being rated is judged to possess " average intelligence," then the judge or rater would check the middle of the line.

hallucination, an abnormal experience in which a memory image or centrally aroused idea is misinterpreted as a genuine perception despite the absence of relevant stimulation of the sense organs ordinarily responsible for such perception.

hebephrenic schizophrenia, pertaining to a type of schizophrenic patient whose behavior is characterized by silly mannerisms, bizarre verbal patterns, and other signs of ideational chaos.

hemiplegia, paralysis of either the right or left half of the body and often caused by influx of cerebral blood vessels.

hormone, a chemical originating in one organ and influencing another after being carried to the latter by the blood stream or by some other means of transportation. The active secretions of the ductless glands are examples of hormones; but not all hormones are of endocrine origin.

Huntington's chorea, an inherited form of St. Vitus's dance.

hygiene, the science which deals with the prevention of disease and the promotion of health.

hyperesthesia, abnormally acute sensitivity to cutaneous stimuli.

hyperhidrosis, excessive sweating.

hyperkinesis, excessive agitation of a muscle or muscle group.

hypochondria, a condition in which an individual is morbidly anxious about his health.

hysteria, a neurosis having no fixed array of symptoms but which is characterized by signs of physical disability or psychoneural dissociation in the absence of any underlying organic pathology much as if the patient were unconsciously employing symptoms of disability in order to further some selfish goal. (A wholly satisfactory definition of hysteria cannot be compressed within brief limits if one is to do justice to the varying views of different students of the subject.)

hysterical anesthesia, a manifestation of conversion hysteria in which there is functional loss of sensitivity in some region of the skin.

hysterical edema, synonym for *blue edema*, q.v.

hysterical somnambulism, pertaining to the symptom of sleep-walking found in some cases of the amnesic type of hysteria.

id, a term used by the Freudians to designate the *impersonal*, amoral, instinctive or biologically determined body cravings considered in the abstract; blindly impulsive, pleasure-seeking tendencies uninfluenced by considerations of expediency or the welfare of others; untutored drives to action which man shares with other mammals. (Cf. *ego* and *super-ego*.)

ideas of reference, the mistaken impression that the casual remarks, gestures, or writings of others are intended to refer to the personal affairs of the victim of such delusional misinterpretation. Example: the paranoid patient who believes that the strangers on the corner are talking about him is a victim of ideas of reference.

identical twins, the opposite of fraternal twins; also known as *monozygotic twins*, q.v.

inhibition, the checking or stoppage or arrest of a mental process or neural process or muscular action.

insane, a medico-legal term applied to individuals whose mental condition is so disordered as to render them incapable of differentiating " right from wrong " or of knowing the nature and consequence of their acts. (Taken strictly, insanity should not be regarded as the precise equivalent of *psychosis*.)

insight, the patient's own realization of the abnormal or distorted nature of his symptoms of mental disorder; degree of adequacy and accuracy of self-understanding. Absence of insight is not a favorable symptom and characterizes many psychotics.

insulin, the hormone produced by the endocrine portion of the pancreas and one of the drugs employed in connection with *shock therapy,* q.v.

integration, the organization of ideas, impulses, traits, habits, and other component features of the personality into a unified, harmoniously interrelated system of reaction patterns.

intelligence quotient, the quotient obtained when a child's score on a standard intelligence test is divided by his chronological age; *i.e.,* mental age divided by age in years equals I.Q., q.v.

introversion, the general tendency to be more or less spontaneously drawn to the life of thought, imagination, and kindred subjective preoccupations. (Contrasted with *extroversion,* q.v.)

involutional melancholia, a condition of more or less agitated depression whose onset in women dates from the period of the menopause and in men after the beginning of the fifth decade of life.

I.Q., abbreviation for the term *intelligence quotient,* q.v.

Jacksonian epilepsy, a form of spasm involving a circumscribed muscle group and most commonly limited to one side of the body. There is no loss of consciousness or other symptom of epilepsy. This type of epilepsy is usually regarded as due to irritation of the motor region of the brain cortex.

Jukes, the name which R. L. Dugdale gave to a so-called degenerate family whose bleak social history he traced.

Kallikak, the name by which H. H. Goddard designated a family living in New Jersey one branch of which produced exemplary citizens while the other branch spawned degenerates, criminals, prostitutes, etc.

Korsakoff's psychosis, a mental disorder following chronic alcoholism and showing disturbances of immediate memory and orientation along with a tendency to indulge in retrospective falsification.

law of emotional congruity, a principle of association to the effect that emotions and moods function as directive factors in determining the nature of aroused ideas; *i.e.,* a sad mood tends to bring sad ideas to mind; anger tends to instigate thoughts of retaliation, etc. In brief, the sequence of ideas tends to be congruous with or in harmony with the dominant emotion or prevailing mood.

lead pipe flexibility, also known as *waxy flexibility,* and referring to a cataleptic reaction in which the patient's limbs are capable of being placed in curious positions which are then held for abnormally long periods of time.

lenticular nucleus, part of the region of the brain known as the *corpus striatum.* Such disorders of muscular control as chorea and paralysis agitans are associated with damage to this brain region.

leptosome, referring to a person with a light, asthenic, slender physique which Kretschmer regarded as furnishing a constitutional background for the emergence of schizophrenic symptoms.

libido, a Freudian term referring to the dynamic aspects of the organism's sex life.

malingerer, one who feigns illness or who deliberately injures himself or who intentionally contracts a disease for the purpose of achieving some selfish goal.

manic-depressive psychosis, a mental disorder involving fluctuations in mood and action: the excited phase being accompanied by unrestrained activity, while the depressed phase usually makes for psychomotor retardation.

manic stupor, a variant of the manic-depressive reaction in which the patient seems to be seething within although stuporously unresponsive to external stimulation.

meliorative, tending to make better or to bring about improvement.

meningitis, inflammation of the meninges or membranes covering brain and spinal cord.

mental hygiene, the investigation and utilization of all factors having a bearing on the attainment and preservation of individual and group morale. The total field may be envisaged as involving both the prevention of mental disease as well as the promotion of mental health: prophylactic as well as meliorative mental hygiene.

mental set, a directive factor determining the sequence of ideas. Example: the intention to add serves as a *mental set* which causes the subject to think of " 106 " when he hears the numbers " 14 " and " 92 " instead of thinking of " 1492."

metabolic psychoses, mental disorders resulting from disturbances of body chemistry as exemplified by cases of cretinism, involutional melancholia, and some cases of pellagra, toxic goitre, etc.

metrazol, a drug employed in *shock therapy,* q.v. (Intravenous injections of metrazol in appropriate doses will result in convulsions or epileptiform seizures.)

Mongolism, pertaining to a type of congenital feeblemindedness marked by certain easily recognized physical characteristics, especially almond-shaped, oblique eye-slits; hence the name.

monoplegia, paralysis of a single limb.

monozygotic twins, identical twins or those regarded as having developed from the same fertilized ovum and consequently endowed with the same hereditary potentialities; always of the same sex and strikingly like one another in appearance. (Contrasted with *dizygotic* or fraternal twins.)

mood, the temporal aspect of emotion; a chronic, sub-acute emotion.

morale, the general state of a person's (or a group's) attitude with respect to work to be accomplished, ideals to be realized, or goals to be attained. It is shown by possession of self-confidence, enthusiasm, willingness to sacrifice, to persevere, to endure deprivation and pain in behalf of causes regarded as worthy of zealous endeavor. (As applied to a group the term is synonymous with *esprit de corps.*)

mutism, absence of speech either as a result of a pathological unwillingness as in some psychotic reactions or as a result of inability due to immaturity or deafness.

mysophobia, a morbid fear of dirt or dread of being contaminated.

myxedema, a disease caused by reduced functioning of the thyroid gland whose symptoms include dry skin, loss of hair, puffing of face and hands, listlessness, sluggish reactions in general, mental sluggishness included. Such thyroid malfunctioning dating from birth gives rise to *cretinism,* q.v.

negativism, a form of contrasuggestibility marked by resistance to comply with the requests of others and even involving a tendency to do the opposite of that which is requested.

neologisms, the often nonsensical new words coined by some psychotic patients.

neonate, the new-born baby.

nervousness, agitation prompted by a *present* or imminently threatening situation.

neurasthenia, a neurotic syndrome characterized by persistent feelings of tiredness despite the absence of exertion, feelings of inadequacy and inferiority, and a tendency to indulge in hypochondriacal brooding; also known as *Beard's disease.*

neuropathic trait, an abnormality of conduct in consequence of some disease of the nervous system.

neuropsychiatrist, one whose medical specialty is concerned with pathology of the nervous system and concomitant mental disturbances.

neurosis, a functional disturbance characterized by ambivalent emotional attitudes toward a conflict situation so that the patient feels himself trapped by these attitudes. Unlike the psychotic patient, the neurotic is well oriented with respect to his physical and social environment and appreciates the *abnormal* nature of his disturbance. In general, neuroses are minor disturbances and usually do not require hospitalization.

neurosurgeon, one who specializes in surgery of the nervous system.

normal distribution curve, a bilaterally symmetrical, bell-shaped curve constituting a graphic representation of the frequency of occurrence of individual measures of any variable whose variations are functions of a vast number of independent chance factors. (Also known as *normal probability distribution* or *Gaussian curve.*)

oblivescence of the disagreeable, a memory principle to the effect that there is a spontaneous tendency to forget the unpleasant and retain the pleasant.

obsession, a morbidly persisting or perseverating idea, impulse, emotion or other mental state which obtrudes itself in imperious and unwelcome fashion; the ideational aspect of a *compulsion,* q.v.

ophthalmoplegia, paralysis of the muscles of the eye.

organic psychoses, mental disorders attributable to damaged tissues, biochemical disturbances, infections, poisons, and kindred abnormalities; somatogenic disorders. (Opposed to functional disorders.)

paralipophobia, a morbid fear of neglecting something.

paralysis agitans, a disease of the brain centers regulating muscle tonus the symptoms of which include postural rigidity, delayed voluntary movement, and a characteristic tremor. The latter symptom is so prominent that the popular name of this disease is *shaking palsy.*

paranoia, a functional psychosis characterized by systematized, unshakable delusions of persecution.

paranoid schizophrenia, pertaining to a type of schizophrenic patient whose behavior manifests the existence of delusions of persecution. As contrasted with *paranoia* (q.v.) the schizophrenic's delusions are poorly organized, more fantastic, and consequently less plausible.

paresis, syphilitic involvement of tissues of the brain resulting in disturbances of judgment, memory, speech, writing, motor coordinations, and reflexes. (Also known as *dementia paralytica.*)

paresthesia, referring to morbidly perverse cutaneous sensations in the way of tinglings or feelings of crawling insects in the absence of correspondingly adequate stimuli.

pellagra, the disease caused by elimination of vitamin B_2 from the diet and characterized by dermal, digestive, and neural disturbances.

petit mal, Fr. for " little illness," and used to designate a mild type of epilepsy in which there is a momentary lapse of consciousness, but none of the other signs of epilepsy as seen in the *grand mal* attack; *i.e.,* there is no outcry, no falling, no convulsion, and no loss of sphincter control.

pharmacology, the science which concerns itself with the action of drugs on physiological functions.

physiotherapy, the treatment of disease and symptoms of disease by means of such physical procedures as massage, heat, X-rays, ultra-violet light, exercise, baths, etc.

pituitary gland, an endocrine gland located at the base of the brain whose hormones play important roles in the regulation of growth, sex functions, water metabolism, smooth muscle action, etc.

placebo, a harmless preparation given a patient to please him or for reasons of psychotherapy.

prefrontal leucotomy, a surgical operation consisting of the transection of the fibers connecting the front portion of the brain cortex with the *thalamus,* q.v. The operation is employed for the purpose of treating some cases of serious psychotic disorder.

primary attention, spontaneous, involuntary bodily orientation toward a stimulus situation independently of training or experience. Example: the baby's alert fixation of a brightly colored, moving object coming within its visual field. (Cf. *secondary* and *derived primary attention.*)

primary behavior disorder, a rather loose diagnostic category applied to non-psychotic and non-neurotic patients whose maladjustments are attributable to poor home training, culture conflicts, lack of discipline, etc. (Not to be confused with disorders attributable to the possession of a *psychopathic personality,* q.v.)

projection, the process of ascribing to others ideas and impulses emanating from one's own unconscious tendencies without recognizing the personal origin of the ascription. Delusions of persecution, for example, are due to the mechanism of projection.

prophylaxis, guarding against disease; the prevention of illness.

pseudo-emotion, affective or emotional change induced by reading a novel, seeing a movie, etc.

psychasthenia, Janet's name for a neurotic syndrome in which obsessive-compulsive ideas in a setting of morbid anxiety dominate the clinical picture.

psychiatrist, one who specializes in psychiatry or that branch of medicine concerned with the investigation and treatment of mental disorders.

psychic tension, Janet's term for the experienced strain of coping with the rival pulls and pressures operative in a conflict situation.

psychogenic, of psychological origin; caused by mental factors. (Contrasted with *somatogenic.*)

psychoneurosis, in contemporary usage this term has come to be practically identical in meaning with the concept of a *neurosis,* q.v.

psychopathic, pertaining to mental disease.

psychopathic personality, contemporary psychiatric designation for the kind of patient formerly classified as a victim of "moral insanity." The psychopath seems to be constitutionally unable to develop stability of character.

psychosis, a major mental disorder, either functional or organic, characterized by inadequate appraisal of reality as revealed by such symptoms as delusions, hallucinations, serious affective disturbances, distortions of memory, disorientation with respect to time, place, or personal identity, etc. Recognition of the *abnormal* nature of the foregoing symptoms is apt to be lacking in the psychotic patient. Institutional care is ordinarily required, especially during periods of acute disturbance.

pursuitmeter, a laboratory device for measuring eye-hand coordination by requiring the subject to follow a moving target by means of a concomitant manual adjustment.

pyknic, Kretschmer's term for the type of thick-set physique he regarded as constitutionally predisposed to manic-depressive psychosis.

reality principle, a Freudian term to describe the dominance of unyielding reality (in the form of inflexible social commands and taboos as well as physical barriers) over the pleasure-seeking cravings of the *id,* q.v.

redintegration, (1) a memory process by virtue of which a present reminder of a former experience tends to arouse the recall of the original experience in its totality; (2) the process of *reacting* to the reminder or stimulus as if it represented the complete situation of which it once was a part. (The first definition applies to Sir William Hamilton's concept of redintegration and the second stresses H. L. Hollingworth's elaboration of this concept.)

repression, the control over unwelcome impulses exercised by the mature self by means of appropriate *mental sets,* q.v.

retrospective falsification, a disturbance of ideation as a result of which imaginary events are regarded as having occurred in reality, the process of imagination being confused with a memory process.

riboflavin, one of the components of the vitamin B complex useful in the prevention and treatment of pellagra.

schizophrenia, Bleuler's designation for the older term *dementia praecox* and referring to psychotic reactions in which there appears to be a divorce between the world of reality and the patient's life of fantasy or a split between emotional and ideational processes.

schizothymic temperament, the kind of constitutional organization which gives rise to introvertive characteristics in the way of seclusiveness, reluctance to assume important responsibilities, diminished initiative, lack of adequate emotional moorings, marked tendencies to daydream, etc. (Cf. *cyclothymic temperament.*)

scrabbling, one of the symptoms observed in some rats when the audiogenic seizure (q.v.) results in a speeding up of running movements even though the animal's body fails to move forward at an increased pace; roughly comparable to the result of trying to walk while " running in place."

secondary attention, forced or voluntary attention or a controlled, effortful fixation upon some stimulus object or idea. Example: the kind of attention a student has to give to some tedious academic assignment. (Cf. *primary* and *derived primary attention.*)

senile psychosis, mental disorder attributable to the onset of old age.

shock therapy, a mode of treating functional psychoses by the precipitation of sudden and somewhat drastically disruptive changes in the patient's nervous system.

simple schizophrenia, referring to a type of schizophrenic patient who seems content to drift along in aimless, indifferent fashion unmindful of scornful comments provoked by his ambitionless drifting.

sinusoidal current, a type of electric current in which the potential rises from a low point to high in gradual fashion and then gradually comes back to low only to reverse the process again in alternate manner; used in the electroshock treatment of some psychotic conditions.

skewness, distortion of the symmetrical shape of the *normal distribution curve* (q.v.), as a result of the piling up of measures on one side of the median and a tail-like thinning out of the measures on the other side.

social stereotype, fixed and usually fictitious or distorted or misleading generalized concepts conventionally and uncritically accepted. Examples: typical Englishman, typical artist, typical criminal, etc.

somatogenic, of bodily origin; caused by physicochemical factors disturbing the metabolism or integrity of the organism. (Contrasted with *psychogenic.*)

sphincter control, the acquisition of mastery or control of the sphincter or ring-shaped muscles governing bladder and bowel outlets; hence control of eliminative functions.

spring-resistance, one of the motor symptoms of catatonia in which there is resistance to efforts to change the patient's postural adjustments, the limb in question resuming its original position with spring-like resiliency.

stereotypy, the repetition of seemingly senseless or meaningless gestures, phrases, movements, or postures.

stocking anesthesia, absence of normal cutaneous sensitivity in foot or leg as a consequence of hysterical dissociation.

stupor, a state of markedly reduced consciousness as evidenced by relative immobility, failure to respond to rather vigorous stimulation, and other symptoms of the kind one associates with a person under the influence of a sleep-inducing drug. Stupors may vary in degree from the blurred consciousness and momentary confusion of a groggy boxer to the extreme unconsciousness of the victim of the terminal stages of a diabetic or toxic coma.

sublimation, a Freudian term to designate the process of converting amoral or immoral impulses into socially acceptable modes of behavior.

super-ego, term introduced by the Freudians to designate the sum total of commands, positive as well as negative, assimilated by the developing personality as a result of both conscious and unconscious ethico-social indoctrination; practically synonymous with the concept of *conscience,* q.v.

syndrome, the totality of symptoms characteristic of a given disease.

thalamus, a mass of gray matter located at the base of the brain and playing an important role in the regulation of emotional changes. (Cf. *prefrontal leucotomy.*)

therapy, treatment for the purpose of restoring to health.

thyroid gland, an endocrine structure located near the base of the neck which secretes a hormone, *thyroxin,* important for the regulation of basal metabolism and the prevention of *cretinism* and *myxedema* (q.v.).

thyroxin, a chemical obtained from the thyroid gland and used in the treatment of cretinism, myxedema, and other conditions suggestive of diminished thyroid functioning.

tic, the involuntary jerking of a circumscribed group of muscles at more or less periodic intervals.

tonic, pertaining to the state of a muscle whose tonus or degree of tension is set so that the tautness is maintained over a relatively protracted interval of time as exemplified in one phase of the epileptic's convulsion. (Contrasted with *clonic,* q.v.)

tonus, the condition of reflexly maintained muscular tautness.

trauma, any wound, shock, injury or damage to the body, particularly one which produces structural impairment.

traumatic delirium, disturbance of mental functions of delirious character following injuries to the head.

trichotillomania, the morbid impulse to tear out one's own hair.

triskaidekaphobia, morbid fear of the number *13.*

unimodal, a frequency distribution having a single high point or peak. (The normal distribution curve shown in Fig. 2 is a *unimodal* curve.)

unitas multiplex, Lat. for manifold unity and employed as a description of the integrated diversity characteristic of mental organization.

unproductive mania, a condition manifested by some manic patients whose excitement is not accompanied by flight of ideas.

vascular disorders, pertaining to disturbances of the vessels involved in the blood's circulation.

vas deferens, the tube or duct connecting the male sex gland, the testicle, with adjacent structures.

verbigeration, the meaningless reiteration of the same word or phrase.

waxy flexibility, synonym for *lead pipe flexibility,* q.v.

zoomorphism, the error of interpreting human behavior in terms of uniquely animal characteristics; reading animal nature into human nature. (Contrasted with *anthropomorphism.*)

Index of Subjects . . .

Index of Names . . .